Surviving the Chronic Pain Experience:

Successfully Recover Insurance Benefits and Other Promises;

Effectively Communicate With Doctors, Lawyers,

Employers, Insurers, Friends, and Family

D1596116

Michael Werb
HEYWER

1

Surviving the Chronic Pain Experience:

Successfully Recover Insurance Benefits and Other Promises;

Effectively Communicate With Doctors, Lawyers,

Employers, Insurers, Friends, and Family

By Michael Werb, MBA, Professor & Consultant,
Advocate for Chronic Pain Recovery

Copyright © 2003
ISBN 0-9726644-1-6

Published by Heywer, LLC
11366-42nd St.
Clear Lake MN 55319

www.heywer.com
www.survivingpain.com

SURVIVING THE CHRONIC PAIN EXPERIENCE: SUCCESSFULLY RECOVER INSURANCE BENEFITS AND OTHER PROMISES

TABLE OF CONTENTS

DISCLAIMER: The information and references provided by Heywer should not take the place of advice and guidance from your own health care providers or legal counsel. Be sure to check with your doctor about changes in your treatment plan and your lawyer about legal matters.

Prelude

Every year millions of people are hurt by an accident in their car, home, or workplace, or from a disease that results in a long-term impairment and chronic pain. Today, there are more than 86 million people with chronic pain in the United States alone. Each day more newly impaired are forced to find their way through difficult social and economic circumstances into a new life for themselves and their families. Chronic pain brings suffering, along with life-altering problems, to our families and us. It brings dramatic change to our careers and financial situations, and to our friendships. Chronic pain can shatter values and beliefs. Pain, suffering, and altered abilities affect virtually all areas of a chronically ill person's life. We feel helpless as our entire lives are shaken and each part of our life falls into chaos. The losses are great. New options are very limited. There are numerous medical resources that define and describe the symptoms and treatment of chronic pain. Yet there are few resources that describe and help address the many personal losses and challenges to our lives that chronic pain brings about. We encounter a health care crisis when in need of medical care and find broken insurance promises as we struggle with our difficult new financial situation of increasing medical bills with little, if any, wage or income. Many of us lose our jobs and learn the personal implications of a national 70% unemployment rate for the disabled. The *Surviving the Chronic Pain Experience* books describe a successful approach, information, resources, and suggestions that people with chronic pain can use in their daily struggle for survival.

The *Surviving the Chronic Pain Experience* books are guides to improving the general environment of the life of a person with chronic pain. Issues of adequate medical care, alternative medicine, lost insurance and employment benefits, future insurance protection, lost jobs, future employment alternatives, legal struggles, dignity, compassion, and more are addressed. Heartfelt stories, along with detailed research, are summarized and presented. *Surviving* helps people with chronic pain address their many personal losses and challenges. It gives hope for a greater possibility for recovery and provides encouragement and sympathy for the large family of chronic pain sufferers. *Surviving* are books about self-help and social change. Complemented with numerous medical resources that define and describe the symptoms and treatments of chronic pain, *Surviving* can help an impaired individual improve his or her entire life.

People with chronic pain find their medical care and recovery restricted by the hands of their safety net providers – people and organizations that promise medical care and insurance benefits when needed but work hard to renege on their promises. This was my experience, which was not unusual. As our physical condition deteriorates and we miss time from work, medical bills accumulate and we lose our pay and wages. We turn to our safety net of employee benefits and insurance policies for help. Health care insurance, medical leave benefits, workers' compensation insurance, automobile insurance, disability insurance, and more are reviewed for benefits. But we are told we are not covered or that the fine print in our policies or other legalities excludes our situation. Later we learn that we were subjected to any number of deny and delay tactics and/or lied to by our safety net providers in order to eliminate or minimize their responsibility. *Surviving the Chronic Pain Experience: Successfully Recover Insurance Benefits and Other Promises* describes these problems and issues along with how to overcome them. Twenty-five appendixes of forms and letters in this book will help you with your survival.

While focusing on physical and emotional recovery for my injury, I confidently expected to fall into my safety net for the help that was promised to me during a life crisis. But, instead of help, my carefully layered safety net of medical care, employee benefits, insurance benefits, and social promises was all but gone. I found that only fragments of my safety net remained. The ruthlessness of this experience conveyed even greater feelings of loss and despair and further fueled the freefall of my life. I drifted toward the precipice of life and death with few options or preference for my frail existence. I fell through gaping holes in my safety net to hit bottom hard. I had no job and only limited insurance benefits to help with my recovery. In time, I learned that the holes in my safety net were caused by a chronic social illness we refer to as a "health care crisis" and other problems related to our employers' and insurance companies' deny and delay tactics. Once identified, I suggested many positive alternatives for helping and partnering with the sick or injured. My recommendations were sound, while my impairment and safety net promises were proven again and again. Yet the tactics continued. They included "hired gun" paid doctor opinions, "employer" doctors, "window dressing" business ethics policies and employee benefit promises, unenforceable insurance promises, chronic illness "psychosomatic, lazy or cheater" myths, and "constructive" firing. They also included managed health care and third-party administrator handoffs, litigation ahead of responsibility and compassion, "quick hit" small sum legal settlements, "hide and seek" discovery processes, complex statutes, rules and guidelines, prolonged and degrading depositions, limited jury awards, and much more. All along the way, the people who promised to hold the net – business leaders, insurance providers, doctors, lawyers, and others – were actually taking a part of the American safety net away from the sick and injured for their own personal gain. While this approach may appear to make good business sense, everyone needs to know the impact to the chronically ill and disabled in order for improvements to be considered.

Along my journey, many alternatives were identified to address the tactics used to minimize their impact on people with chronic pain and disability. I pushed back on my safety net and offered recommendations for system improvements to anyone who would listen. Drawing on years of business experience, my review and recommendations suggested that businesses could have productivity and profitability in an ethical manner without compromising the health and welfare of sick, injured, and disabled people. While the systems were found to be a big part of the problem, I called to account the leaders of our country's businesses, medical and legal professions, and other organizations. They were ultimately held to be responsible. Indeed, the abusive methods and tactics used to deny and delay medical care and other benefits came indirectly from the leaders who demanded certain results from the systems that were imposed on and accomplished by people working in the helping professions each day. Many big businesses, insurance companies, doctors, elected officials, and lawyers appeared to be caught up in the greed of the turn of the century – greed served on the backs of many sick and injured people.

After a prolonged struggle, I received the help I needed and found a good share of the responsibility promised from my safety net without a lengthy high-risk jury trial. Meanwhile, my quest for improvements to the American safety net continued. I had come to believe that our entire citizenry needed to be informed and encouraged to act in order for real change to occur. It is my hope that by reading *Surviving the Chronic Pain Experience* you will learn about these issues and what to do to find responsible conclusions to your situation and protect your future and the future of your families.

My story will be familiar to people like me desperately looking for help from our safety net providers in order to survive our injuries or illnesses. The process I used and describe in *Surviving the Chronic Pain Experience* will help others in this near impossible situation get the help they need while defining a new life that embraces their impairments. This assertive process of self-help and social change allows us to take control of our new destiny. We avoid the seemingly inevitable high-stakes game of trial by jury that lasts as long as ten years or more and provides limited or zero results as controlled by our safety net providers. We can take control and win our own game through hard work and tenacity.

Ironically, prior to the accident, I was a business executive and contracts expert who was known for doing business with a high degree of integrity. I was in leadership positions at work and in professional organizations where ethics and integrity were of utmost importance to my work. As a senior manager, my peers and I had to ensure efficient business processes, along with fair treatment of employees and a motivating workplace. Unexpectedly, I suffered a work-related injury in a car accident. I was now in a prime position to observe and challenge the process used by the company for injured employees. I personally felt the implications of a process that was geared almost entirely to removing responsibility from the business. I felt I had no choice but to tell people that the process was inappropriate and suggest improvements. I had to hold up a mirror to management to let them know what the process was doing to people who were injured on the job and needed the help they were promised. People hurt while working deserved the benefits they were promised as part of their employee benefit program. They were also entitled to the benefits prescribed by law through workers' compensation rules and regulations. I had to report my concerns and ask for improvements. This was what I believed and who I was. Later, I faced into these issues and others when I found similar concerns with insurance policies that I had purchased outside of the company where I worked. I also recognized and challenged other questionable parts of the system and our society on my way to recovery. Eventually this discovery part of my work as an advocate for the recovery of chronic pain was successfully completed.

As my personal story was written and researched, along with the stories of others included in *Surviving the Chronic Pain Experience*, a deeper understanding of the tangled web of the health care crisis and tattered safety nets in the United States was revealed. Also uncovered was the added suffering brought to millions of sick and injured people that occurs in such a system. Stories like these provide clear and candid examples of large holes in the American safety net. I believe these holes come from an eroding moral fiber in our society – the very fiber that holds us together as a caring and civilized people. This story is offered specifically to help those people with chronic pain as they attempt to survive the many implications of their illness each day. It is also a wakeup call to all Americans who live their lives and plan their futures and the futures of their children. Their safety nets also may not be available when and if needed. Practical suggestions and encouragement of responsibility are offered. Along with deep considerations, I present different approaches to health care with a corresponding plea to reduce suffering for people sick, injured, and impaired. With this, there is hope for the improvement and restoration of the American safety net.

This story is based on the actual events of one person's life and is complemented by interviews with many other sick and injured people with similar experiences. These personal stories are used to communicate a problem experienced by the majority of our nation's chronically ill people. Research of social and economic conditions in the United States is also included, all of which indicate there are similar stories repeated every day across our great nation. Doctors and other health care providers, along with lawyers, employers, insurance providers, government officials, other professionals and people directly involved with the systems, were also interviewed. This work was used to define and test a successful process of recovery included in *Surviving the Chronic Pain Experience*. Fictitious names are used to communicate a problem much larger than for the few people and organizations mentioned herein. This is a pervasive problem with a common theme. It is a problem of increased suffering to the sick, injured, and impaired caused indirectly by the self-indulgence and greed of a wealthy minority who set policies and control the professions and systems that are intended to heal and help. These systems also employ compassionate and caring people trained in the helping professions whom themselves become disillusioned within the structure in which they must work. These systems are in need of change.

A true story of tragedy and triumph, *Surviving the Chronic Pain Experience* is one person's difficult and successful life transition. We hope this story was told in a manner that allows the reader to experience the journey, complete with its pain and suffering, love and caring, and the hope and renewed joy for life. We hope *Surviving* will help others survive their own chronic pain. We hope it will also point the way toward social, medical, and legal reforms with all the implications and challenges implied therein which will help others survive their own chronic illness.

# # #

The Heywer organization was formed to be a voice and advocate for people with chronic pain. Heywer recognizes that surviving chronic pain is a difficult challenge. We recognize that many people who are chronically sick and injured face this challenge each day in every part of their lives. Our primary goal is to understand and communicate survival alternatives to others in our situation. We also want to identify the broader issues associated with chronic pain and bring them to the public's attention. We help each other:

- Understand our illness and loss
- Recover insurance benefits and other promises
- Find new purpose and meaning for our lives
- Encourage human compassion and responsibility
- Reawaken our beliefs and renew our spirituality
- Regain our dignity

Visit the Heywer website, www.heywer.com, and the Heywer bookstore, www.survivingpain.com. Please join us in this advocacy to help others survive the chronic pain experience.

Recovering benefits to obtain medical care, lost wages and other help is very important to the recovery and survival process for people with chronic pain. There is much more to consider. In addition to this book, *Surviving the Chronic Pain Experience: Successfully Recover Insurance Benefits and Other Promises,* those with chronic pain will want to read about the large number of medical care alternatives and other ways to manage pain and the corresponding life changes each and every day. *Surviving the Chronic Pain Experience: Understand and Manage Medical Care and Life Changes* is also available now. *Surviving the Chronic Pain Experience: The Complete Journey* will be available soon. Refer to the last page of this book for more about Heywer books and resources. We look forward to providing other information and resources in the future to help each other survive.

PART I: Rapidly Changing Times

Chapter 1

Pain and Poetry

The car accident that caused my injury happened on a beautiful sunny day at the end of April. My friend and coworker, Jack, was driving his car to the city where we planned to have dinner with two other employees of the Blaster Company where we worked. I accompanied Jack in the front seat of his car. Several miles later, in a busy construction area of the interstate, we almost hit a drifting semi-tractor/trailer at high speed. To avoid colliding with the truck, Jack turned the wheel of his car. We left the road and smashed sideways into the beams of a large road sign. The beams toppled onto the front and rear window of the car. Fortunately, the sign came to rest next to the crumbled vehicle and not on top or we would have undoubtedly been crushed. The impact of the accident was enough to break off the entire rear wheel assembly of Jack's car. Yet both Jack and I appeared fine with no apparent injury except for a scrape on Jack's hand. I was not to know until some time later the suffering I would endure from invisible injuries triggered by the accident. The invisible injuries threatened my life again and again, and I was completely changed. Numerous times I felt I neared the precipice of life and death as a permanent and near total disability took hold of and changed my entire life. My disability is hard to see, harder to understand, and was almost impossible to accept for several years.

After the accident, I reached out for medical care and insurance benefits promised to me by my safety net should I need them. Instead of help, I found an invisible social illness in the form of a torn and tattered safety net that made my journey to recovery more difficult than I could ever have imagined. The disability caused by the accident led me to an intimate understanding of what it takes to survive a chronic pain experience. I began to see with people of

15

disability and misfortune and to acknowledge and understand them rather than to see past them. This laid a foundation for me to help others survive their chronic pain. Talking to people, doing research, writing this book, maintaining a website, teaching college part time, and moving to the country to reflect on my experience and life itself were all important to my recovery. Being an advocate for others who suffered from chronic pain conditions brought meaning and purpose back into my life. I have found acceptance, a meaningful new life, the adventure of daily survival, and more. Like the sky after a summer rain, I can see my life more clearly and specifically than ever before. Indeed, sometimes my life seems to reflect the rainbow that follows the storm.

Like others in similar situations, I first had to find my way through the stormy conditions of my safety net, a journey most people face after an accident and injury or other invisible illness. The process I used, along with the eventual success I found recovering benefits from my safety net, is included in this book, *Surviving the Chronic Pain Experience: Successfully Recover Insurance Benefits and Other Promises*. Another Heywer book, *Surviving the Chronic Pain Experience: Understand and Manage Medical Care and Life Changes*, is focused on understanding and managing medical care and life changes to maximize overall recovery, living, and lifestyle. You may want to consider both for your survival.

# # #

My plan after the accident was to heal as soon as possible, which my doctors said usually happened in four to six months for an injury like mine. By October I anticipated a full recovery and return to my intense life of hard work and extreme play. Then I would make up for any missed work and other promises I missed during that time. Afterward I would go on vacation and visit my family to reenergize for more intensity of life. Over the years this was what I did with other illnesses, injuries, or setbacks in my life. But this time would be different.

For several months after my injury, I did not think much about insurance benefits and other promises. I was still working and

16

getting paid even though barely performing my job as a Senior Financial Manager at the Blaster Company. My peers and the people working for me were picking up the slack I left in my work. At first, my boss was also supportive. He asked about my medical condition and accepted many interruptions for medical care and overall less productivity from me. I was fortunate that people at Blaster were understanding and supportive. There was a lot of time spent with visits to my doctors' and therapists' offices, along with quiet time in my closed office to relax my muscles and slow the pain. The Blaster employee health care plan administered through Alto Health was paying most of my medical bills. For this, I was also appreciative. But this would soon change.

At home each day my relationship with Justine, my new girlfriend, was very compassionate and helpful. Fortunately my sons were grown and no longer needed my help as their parent. Most of my attention was on my injury, increasing pain, and the loss in my life, which I wanted so desperately to recover. Yet there were many unknown surprises coming soon. I had not yet learned that my medical condition would get worse. I had not yet learned about independent medical examinations (IMEs) performed to refute injuries and remove employee and other benefits. I had not heard of "constructive firing" or the implications for someone who had a chronic illness or injury, especially an "invisible" one like mine. There were many surprises coming, while my attention was on the pain and how to make it stop.

No matter what I did or did not do my medical condition was slowly getting worse. The muscles tightened more and earlier each day. I became self-absorbed and medically focused as the pain increased. My physiatrist, Dr. Hunt, decided to go to the next level of treatment by giving me trigger point injections on a regular basis. Using a needle and syringe, a liquid painkiller was inserted directly into the hard muscle spasms of my back in four or five different places. As soon as Dr. Hunt inserted the needle into my back and pumped the liquid painkiller into my muscles, I felt relief from the rock-hard spasms. I returned to work with less pain and felt better over the next couple of days. But the muscle tightness and pain soon returned. As a result, I called Dr. Hunt's office to make an appointment for an emergency visit for more trigger point injections.

Like a drug addict in need of another fix, I inconspicuously left work every few days and drove quickly to my doctor's office for another round of trigger point injections for pain relief. Even with this more invasive medical care, there was very little, if any, improvement to my medical condition. The doctors and therapists seemed very casual about a physical condition that I felt was robbing me of my life. I became nervous and afraid, while thinking that maybe I was not communicating well enough about my injury and its impact on my life.

I prepared an analysis of key elements of my life before and after the accident and injury (Appendix 1). The analysis showed that I had lost a lot of my life very quickly. It showed that I was also constantly making a tradeoff between medication, activities, and emotional and intellectual clarity – a tradeoff that was becoming more and more difficult. Together, the pain and drugs robbed me of my emotions and intuition. They robbed me of my life. I reviewed this life analysis with my medical practitioners in hopes of better communicating the extent of my injury. I asked for more help, including alternative medical treatment. But I did not realize that this analysis was good in that my life would continue to deteriorate. The analysis clearly showed that my condition was getting worse not better. The analysis was a tool for understanding and communicating my condition.

With the analysis considered, my doctors' prognoses soon became different. They became negative and, in some ways, incomplete and hard for me to believe. Dr. Smith, my general practitioner, told me I was "doomed" when I asked him to help me return to the active life I had enjoyed prior to the accident. He offered no medical alternatives or work suggestions beyond the medication and referral to a physiatrist for rehabilitation he had already provided. Dr. Hunt described a permanent impairment and chronic myofascial pain based on my completion of two months of physical therapy under his supervision and several weeks of trigger point injections. Yet Dr. Hunt offered little more in terms of prescribing additional medical treatment or alternative work requirements. He recommended massage therapy and a chiropractor to help with the pain.

My injury's diagnosis and prognosis now fit better with its impact on my life. My analysis for better communication had worked somewhat. Yet I did not fully understand what chronic myofascial pain was or meant to me. I hoped maybe now that I had a more realistic diagnosis I could pursue other alternatives of medical care. I hoped to find more help with my many life changes, which included an accumulation of debt I had never had before – debt in the form of medical bills for deductibles and services not covered that were piling up.

Right after the accident, I decided to cover a few hundred dollars of medical bills on my own. But I soon saw that the bills were adding up quickly and the prognosis for my recovery was not good. There would be many more medical bills. I turned to Jack's car insurance for help, as he was the driver of the car involved in the accident. One day, while at work, I called Jack on the phone and explained my problem. He had anticipated my request. He had already checked with his car insurance carrier. He had been told that the accident and my injury were workers' compensation issues. According to his auto insurance carrier, they were not his responsibility. Jack told me, "There is no coverage under my automobile insurance since legally you cannot hold a fellow employee responsible for a work-related injury. We were two coworkers driving to a business meeting over dinner."

Jack's comments made sense, but I was still surprised. I wondered why he wanted to quickly remove any responsibility that he might have for my medical bills or other harm. We had trusted each other and had shared a level of integrity in our work. Now he wanted to take no responsibility for the accident even though he had been the driver of the automobile. Jack talked assertively about his insurance company's position. He made only halfhearted inquiries about how I was feeling or healing. My immediate feeling while on the phone was sadness about my friend's response and lack of concern about my new financial situation. I felt betrayed. I felt very much alone.

With this new added concern over my finances, I thought I should hire a lawyer to help me with my medical bills and any future losses related to the accident. I contacted the local Bar Association to find a lawyer to help me. They suggested I get counsel from an attorney named Tom Young. I called Attorney Young for an appointment and a few days later drove to his office in downtown Dayton. He explained the laws and rules related to my situation and quickly agreed that my injury was work related. But workers' compensation insurance was not my only source of benefits. His views and conclusions made sense to me. In time with the help of attorneys and others, I discovered several sources of insurance benefits including Blaster's employee benefits, my own and Jack's automobile insurance, my personal umbrella policy, workers' compensation insurance, and more. Over the years I had purchased a safety net of insurance to help me in a time of need like this. Eventually my insurers all paid something. But first they would repeatedly say no with various tactics and even fraud to deny and delay payment of benefits. There was a long and difficult path to recover insurance benefits and other promises.

In September of that year, I turned to Blaster for reimbursement of my medical bills under workers' compensation insurance for my work-related injury. I learned that Blaster was self-insured for workers' compensation insurance, as many big companies were at the time. I talked directly with my boss, Mr. Blair, and the human resources director, Mr. Seabert, about my claim. This was the first time I approached Blaster and formally asked for help with my medical bills as a workers' compensation claim. I explained Jack's position about his car insurance, while more assertively emphasizing that my injury was not healing as everyone had hoped. In fact, according to Dr. Hunt, I was looking at a permanent impairment.

The discussion with my boss was a surprise in that, after I explained my situation, he appeared angry that I was filing a workers' compensation claim. And he appeared angry that I had hired legal counsel to help me process the paperwork. Mr. Blair commented to me while in my office one day, "You realize that Corporate Headquarters will hear about this?" I shook my head in agreement and told Mr. Blair, "Yes, but I do not want medical bills and paperwork to be a further distraction to my work. I am having a hard enough time just making it to work each day and trying to deal with the daily pain and the effects of medication. It takes time to do the stretching and exercises prescribed by my doctor. My life has changed dramatically." But Mr. Blair, in what was to become a fairly common aggressive response to my medical situation, smiled slightly and said, "I can't blame you for wanting to make a little money." I was shocked and disappointed that he suggested I would try to gain financially from my injury. I told him, "I just want to have my medical bills paid and do my job." Without even acknowledging my comment, Mr. Blair turned toward the door and walked away.

Once I filed a workers' compensation claim, I found that my supervisor, along with some of my other management peers and coworkers, was suspicious of my injury and motives. In the halls of my office building, comments and whispers could be heard about my injury and workers' compensation claim. People looked away or changed the subject when I tried to explain my medical condition and asked for their understanding. The disbelief from people around me, on top of my constant struggle with pain, saddened and sometimes outraged me. How could they question my integrity? They knew me better than that! I deserved better!

Although I had only been working in Troy for five months prior to the accident, Blaster's senior and executive management around the world had known me for years and encouraged me to move to Troy. I had worked hard and supported the growing Blaster businesses in many different locations. They knew my hard work, integrity, and business accomplishments. Many of them knew me personally and were considered my friends. The people at Troy had seen my talent and successful hard work even in the short time since I started working with them. How could they be so uncaring now after helping me so much with my work since the accident? Slowly I began to understand. They wanted no responsibility for my injury, however that would be accomplished.

To review my workers' compensation claim, Mr. Blair directed me to Mr. Seabert, Blaster's Director of Human Resources. I called Mr. Seabert and scheduled an appointment in his office. It was the largest and nicest office in the Blaster plant in Troy where over 700 people worked. His large polished wood desk sat toward the back of his office facing the door in front of a matching credenza. He had a large high-back leather chair on wheels and another matching credenza along the wall perpendicular to his desk. A number of pictures and plaques of recognition for him and Blaster covered the walls. There was a round table with four chairs in the large space between the doorway and his desk. There were two comfortable chairs sitting directly in front of his desk facing his chair behind the desk.

When I arrived for our appointment, Mr. Seabert invited me into his office to sit in one of the chairs directly in front of his desk. Our personal small talk was unusually brief, after which Mr. Seabert looked sternly across his desk at me. He raised my workers' compensation application form into the air and waved it toward me with his right hand. As he waved the form slowly in the air, he questioned the classification of the accident as work related and told me that it was now an Occupational Safety and Health Act (OSHA) recordable. He told me that my medical bills should be covered by car insurance. In response, I explained the discussion that I had recently had with Jack about his car insurance.

Mr. Seabert set the form down on his desk and replied, "Even if you prove the work relationship and extent of your injuries, Blaster will subrogate any bills paid by other insurance companies." I told him, "That makes sense to me. I only want to get my bills paid once." Mr. Seabert became more upset and said, "If you want us to pay the bills, you're going to have to get a lawyer and he is going to take a third of everything." He paused and smiled smugly as he explained, "You will be treated no differently by this company than anyone else."

Mr. Seabert's comment and demeanor suggested that Blaster would fight to avoid their responsibility. I was surprised that they did not want to accept responsibility for their injured employees. Obviously, the company did not want my injury to be a workers' compensation issue either. But it was. I was hurt in a work-related accident and I felt a responsibility to report my injury as work related. Yet, before I even filled out the paperwork, I had a feeling that Blaster would not want me to file a workers' compensation claim.

The formal government statistics that measure the health and safety of Blaster's workplace would be affected. Yet, had I not filed a workers' compensation claim, I would not be following the rules regarding work-related injuries. That is the way it had to be recorded and viewed even if there were other more beneficial approaches to having my medical bills paid. I had shared responsibility with other senior managers for ethics at Blaster. This, along with my personal integrity, said I certainly did not want to begin lying to Blaster, OSHA, or the insurance companies to get my bills paid!

I became anxious when I saw that my injury was significant. It seemed to me everyone else was indifferent or upset and did not want to help me. I needed their help. Through my attorney, I learned that my doctors had minimized the extent of my injury in their reports, contrary to the fact that they verbally told me the injury was significant. Dr. Hunt told me of chronic myofascial pain and a permanent impairment. Yet he had not documented his prognosis or formally prescribed more medical care or any work restrictions. Dr. Smith told me I was doomed but formally reported nothing permanent or significant. Something did not make sense. I was surprised, disappointed, and concerned. Did they not believe me? Was my life so unimportant to them that they were disinterested and felt my concern was a waste of their time? Or did they think I was trying to build a case? Were they so afraid of their own responsibility regarding my injury?

I called my attorney for help, but he also responded in a casual and nonchalant manner. I could not believe the response I was getting from my attorney and the doctors I was seeing. I was paying these people to help me, but they were so unsupportive. I felt frustrated and thought I was not communicating. Once again I turned to formal communication in a letter I sent to my attorney (Appendix 2) with the life analysis attached. My goal was to communicate the significance of my situation and ask for his help. Yet, once again, he provided no response to my concerns nor did he advise me relative to the appropriate workers' compensation paperwork. Further, he did not advise me about what to do when a few weeks later Blaster formally denied my claim with the State Bureau of Workers' Compensation by saying that the injury was not work related.

Was my attorney, Tom Young, consciously allowing the conflict to build? Was this his way of telling me that I was not only doomed medically but legally and financially as well? I was afraid. I felt confused in that my suffering was growing and my life was changing dramatically. Yet there appeared to be very little help for my situation. But I had to assume Attorney Young would handle the issue with Blaster so I could continue to concentrate on healing while working as much as possible. I wanted to live with as much quality of life as possible at this time. At least this was my plan.

Eventually, with increasing concern for my deteriorating condition, I felt it necessary to consider another doctor's medical opinion and suggested alternatives. It also made sense for me to see a doctor not tied to Blaster's employee health care plan like Drs. Smith and Hunt. I asked my attorney to suggest other doctors who were known to be effective with this type of injury. He suggested Dr. Lee, an osteopath, and Dr. Masters, a psychologist.

Chapter 2

The Diagnosis

As the new year began, I tried to do everything in my life as low key as possible to minimize the pain reaction. I also continued trying to resolve my medical issues by using medication, along with physical therapy and massage therapy. Since November of last year, my medical care was shared between two doctors. Dr. Hunt's office was close to Blaster, where I could quickly go for trigger point injections. Dr. Lee provided "chiropractic" adjustments and more aggressive physical therapy. Yet, even with all of this medical care, my condition continued to deteriorate. The really bad days of intense pain were coming more often with pain sessions so significant that Justine would say my eyes would sink into my head. I would almost pass out. Sometimes it felt like the muscle tension was going to ball up and break in some way. Other times I thought I would explode from the intense pain. Each time I tried to do even simple, less intense activities at work, my muscles got tighter and tighter. More normal activities of pulling together a short presentation or working a little overtime, as we did during the budgeting and year-end closing cycles, caused the corresponding pain to intensify. I knew that I needed to cut back on my work activities even more, including travel. Shortly after I returned to work after the holidays, I went to see Mr. Blair to further explain my medical condition and ask for his help.

"Mr. Blair," I said as I knocked on the open door of his office, "do you have a minute?" Mr. Blair turned to look at me and replied, "Come in." I walked quickly into his office, stood next to his desk and nervously said, "I am concerned about two consecutive business trips that are coming up soon. One trip is to the west coast and the other trip is to the east coast. Travel increases the tension in my muscles and the corresponding pain, and I am not sure if I will physically be able to do two trips like that back to back." Mr. Blair looked at me with surprise and disbelief. I became more anxious about my medical problem and its impact on my work and quickly added, "I also need to find a position that better fits my reduced physical capability. My doctor has confirmed that my high-intensity job and the cold weather tighten my muscles and make my pain much worse." Mr. Blair looked shocked as I continued to tell him about my medical situation. I hoped for his support. To my surprise, Mr. Blair firmly responded, "This is not acceptable."

Mr. Blair was obviously disappointed as he told me, "You have to do your job. We will have to meet with Mr. Seabert to discuss this." Mr. Blair picked up the phone and called Mr. Seabert to see if he was available. He was, so Mr. Blair and I walked quietly to Mr. Seabert's office and sat in the two chairs directly in front of his large wood desk to discuss my injury and its implications for my work. We talked about finding a position that I could handle with fewer responsibilities somewhere within The Blaster Company, preferably in a warmer climate. Mr. Seabert looked at me directly and explained, "You realize that your pay will be much less than it is now." "Yes," I replied, "that makes sense. I just want to keep working for Blaster." I imagined there would be a job I could do somewhere at this large global company. After we discussed my situation, Mr. Seabert promised to ask around the company for a less demanding position for me. I felt relieved that I would get help from my employer in terms of a less demanding job. Yet I was sad that I had to give in to my impairment and step down from my wonderful job as a Senior Finance Manager. My future was now on hold as I hoped that a good job alternative would soon be found.

Fortunately, one of the business trips was canceled. In pain and on drugs, I went on the other business trip to the east coast for the annual management review meeting. While there, I went through the motions of each day as best I could even as my back pain intensified during the day and through the week. Not surprisingly, I felt that my attendance at the meeting was a waste of time and company resources. When I returned from the trip to Troy and my daily responsibilities, each day seemed more like a painful waste of time for everyone. I struggled for a few more weeks after returning from the business trip. Then I stopped by Mr. Seabert's office and reminded him of my request for a less stressful job. As I stood in the middle of his office, he replied, "The other Blaster businesses are not interested. They do not know what to expect from you with your condition." He looked me directly in the eye without emotion. I was surprised and felt let down. I quietly replied, "Thanks for checking," and walked slowly out of his office. Sadly I knew in my heart that my problem would only get worse if I stayed in the same job.

When I asked Mr. Blair for help, it was the worst possible time. My annual performance review was in process. But I knew that it really did not make any difference. I needed help badly and could only hope to further communicate my need during the review. In the documentation for my performance review, Mr. Blair wrote that my job performance prior to the accident was better than my current performance. He wrote that he believed my work before the accident was more in line with my true abilities. He also noted my request for a less stressful position with a Blaster business located in a warmer climate due to my physical limitations. After we went over his review of my performance, I asked Mr. Blair to add a letter from me as an attachment to the performance review. This was the first time in my over twenty-year career that I had provided an attachment letter to a performance review. I knew this was considered politically unwise, but I wanted to clearly communicate to the management of Blaster the extent of my injury and its impact on my ability to do my job.

In the letter, I wrote about the intense levels of pain I experienced and the prescription medications I was taking each day. I wrote that the medication not only killed the pain but also substantially reduced my personal drive and business intuition. I noted that I had replaced some of the medication during the day with more physical means of addressing the injury, including a reduction in the number of hours I worked in a day to eight or less. I wanted to be sure Blaster was on notice that I could no longer work even an eight-hour day because of my physical impairment. I also told them I appreciated their patience and understanding.

In the letter, I wanted to be very candid and forthright with Blaster by indicating what my abilities were now. I needed to let them know I would like to find something that would better fit both my personal needs and the needs of the business. After all, the company needed someone in the job who could be more engaged than I in the high-level responsibilities and intensity of work my position required. For the first time, I formally told my employer that I could no longer perform my job. This was one of the hardest things I had ever done in my life. I felt I had failed in my career. Yet, at the same time, I felt good about being honest and forthright with Blaster. I felt relieved that I was asking for help. I hoped I would find help and relief from my pain. It seemed only fair and, with this positive gesture, I naively imagined help would come from my employer.

Now my injury was causing me to lose a lot of my physical capability and more. I was going to have to live with limitations that I had never known before. My situation deteriorated as the medication became less effective and the physical therapy did not work. I was unable to perform my job even to minimum standards. I was not sleeping much, but was awake in anguish most of the time in the early hours of the morning. Many times I cried over the pain and my situation. Depression and despair grew deeper and deeper. The constant daily pain was thick with a cloudy nauseous drug stupor. The despair and hopelessness increased until I felt I could no longer live.

On February 18, ten months after the accident, I went to see Dr. Lee with a desperate plea for help. In one of his small examining rooms, I sat in a chair in the corner. Dr. Lee sat in a chair across from me while leaning on the examining table to write. He listened to my symptoms, saw my suffering, and decided to put me on an eight-month medical leave for more aggressive physical therapy and recovery. His decision was made after I had tried ten months of medication, physical and massage therapy, and trigger point injections prescribed by Drs. Smith and Hunt. I also had used meditation, prayer, and other alternative approaches to manage the daily pain. Yet my condition had not improved and seemed worse in some ways even with the increasing medical treatment. Now that I had a medical leave from work, I was relieved of any work stress and could concentrate on the healing process while defining a new balance in life.

Surprising to me, and I think to almost everybody else, was the length of the medical leave. Later I learned that Blaster was also concerned that a doctor outside of their health plan and outside of their control had prescribed a medical leave. I had first put my life in the hands of Drs. Smith and Hunt, who were both part of Blaster's health plan. Neither suggested a medical leave even though I knew that it was absolutely needed. Had I continued, I probably would have collapsed or worse. I was suffering with incredible physical pain, along with hopelessness and depression. I needed to disconnect and find a way to get well. I did not know at the time if an eight-month leave, a two-month leave, or a twenty-month leave was necessary. I simply knew that I could no longer work with such pain and despair while taking so much medication. Later, after I had been out of work well in excess of eight months, I realized that of all the doctors I went to see about my injury and chronic pain, Dr. Lee was the most medically accurate. I was glad I had added Dr. Lee as a third doctor to my medical team. He was someone primarily interested in my recovery. He had an independence from the company's goals to minimize medical costs and other benefits.

I called Mr. Blair the next day and explained the eight-month medical leave prescription from Dr. Lee. Once again, Mr. Blair scheduled a meeting with Mr. Seabert so the three of us could discuss my medical leave. At the scheduled time, I arrived at work. Mr. Blair and I walked quietly together to Mr. Seabert's office on the other side of the building. We once again sat in the two chairs in front of Mr. Seabert's large wood desk. Messrs. Blair and Seabert asked me to describe my condition in detail, while they busily took notes and affirmatively shook their heads. I repeated the details of my medical condition that I had already explained to them in the ten months since the accident. I also told them my plan for my medical leave. I hoped to dedicate myself full time to healing and recovery so I could return to work as soon as possible. I also explained how important my career and my job at Blaster were to me and said, "I hope you will understand and support me."

Instead of the support and compassion that I had hoped for, their questions about my condition and medical leave became very direct and pointed. They busily took notes without even looking at me. I became suspicious of the meeting and their intent toward me. I became afraid of the ramifications to my career. While a General Manager and a Director of Human Resources were interrogating me, an emotional feeling of overwhelming sadness and despair built up inside of me. This was probably the result of ten months of daily pain and suffering while few people believed the seriousness of my condition. Soon I broke down, crying uncontrollably. I had never cried at work, no matter how difficult the situation. I quickly got up from my chair and retreated to the corner of the room to try to collect myself. I sobbed in the corner for a few minutes until I could stop. Then I dried my eyes and wiped my runny nose with my handkerchief and returned to the chair next to Mr. Blair.

Mr. Blair looked over at me and asked, "Do you have enough drugs?" I paused to appreciate his compassion, realizing however that he did not really understand my situation. "I have plenty of drugs, but they rob me of my emotions, intuition, and desire to work and live," I explained. Then I paused to look at Mr. Blair seriously and chose stronger words to help him understand. "I might as well be dead." He looked at me directly and shook his head in agreement. Still the probing questions continued from Messrs. Blair and Seabert. I felt defensive from the many questions and asked one of my own. "Why have I been asked to see a company-hired doctor next week? His name is Dr. Blunder. He is supposed to perform what is called an independent medical examination. I've asked other doctors and my lawyer about Dr. Blunder. They told me that he is a bleed-on-your-shoe doctor, the kind of doctor usually hired by companies to refute the claims of injured employees." Mr. Seabert looked directly at me and assured me that the doctor's evaluation was a formality. Yet his smug grin suggested something else. Mr. Blair smiled and shook his head in agreement with Mr. Seabert. He said to me, "We are compassionate people." My reaction was dubious. I remembered Mr. Seabert's promise at an earlier meeting, "You will be treated no different than anyone else." Surprised and disappointed about the meeting in general, I said nothing more except goodbye when they decided the meeting was over.

Mr. Blair offered to walk me to the front door of the plant. I appreciated this gesture since I was somewhat embarrassed to leave work with red eyes and a flushed face. But the greater embarrassment that day was the reaction of these business leaders to my medical leave – interrogation of an injured employee, along with defensiveness over their own perception of their compassion and understanding. I was concerned for the purpose of the meeting. However, I needed to put it behind me and focus on healing while I was on my medical leave.

One week after my medical leave started, I drove to Dr. Blunder's office to attend the IME scheduled by Blaster. I was anxious about the examination. People had told me that IME doctors like Dr. Blunder were hired by companies to render opinions that refuted injuries in order to eliminate or at least minimize the company's responsibility for injured employees. How would he do this? My pain was so intense that you could see it on my face, you could feel the spasms in the muscles across my back, and you could observe my protective body language. I changed into a hospital gown as instructed and waited for Dr. Blunder in his office for what seemed like an eternity.

I soon found the answer to my question. Dr. Blunder entered the examining room where I was waiting. He quickly instructed me on what to do. Dr. Blunder frequently interrupted my responses to his questions. He ignored any questions I asked. This added confusion to my anxiousness. His physical examination of my back was accomplished with a light brushing of my skin with the fingertips of his right hand. He made no attempt to feel into the muscles of my back to understand the knots and spasms that were now a part of my life and had given me so much pain every day since the accident. As I stood in my underwear and the flimsy hospital gown, I felt I was being touched physically for a purpose other than what had been told to me by Blaster. I felt violated by his examination. He was obviously not interested in a true medical evaluation. His exam lasted less than fifteen minutes and was supposed to have included a complete review of my medical history, a neurological examination, and a physical examination. It was supposed to have included a review of my present symptoms and approach to medical recovery. It did not fairly or reasonably accomplish any of these. I was surprised and disappointed that my employer sent me to this IME. It appeared that Blaster was preparing to dispute my injury to remove their responsibility for my medical care and other employee benefits. I was unsure of what to think or do other than wait as I continued to try to recover from my injury.

In time, I realized that my business philosophy had been shaken by Blaster's response to my medical problem. When I first learned of the process Blaster used for injured employees, I wondered if I had maybe lost touch with the hard reality and necessity of the business world. After reflecting on the above, I decided instead that an aggressive business approach toward impaired people was not right for me. It certainly was not right for anyone sick, injured, or otherwise impaired. Indeed, it did not support the common good as responsible businesses did.

For quite some time, I believed that people were at their best when helping each other be their best by holding an abundance mentality in their hearts and minds, leveraging diversity, and creating synergy. I remembered how enjoyable and rewarding many of my experiences in the business world had been when I mentored and coached people at work and outside of work to help them grow in their professions and careers. I felt good when they succeeded. It seemed that life rewarded me with my own career success. We worked together across many businesses around the world in contracts, engineering, finance, manufacturing, and other functions. Male or female, young or old, we helped each other and shared many rewards. Sometimes there were only richly intrinsic rewards, but great rewards nonetheless. From my reflection, I knew I needed to trust in life even more with my injury and pain. I knew there was a responsibility to be found even while suffering. A book I was reading, *Essential Zen*, reinforced to me that "… the understanding of deep ecology reminds us that we cannot fully experience each moment with positive emptiness unless we participate in changing the social situations that are harming living beings and the environment."[1] I now believed that there would be something to learn from my chronic pain experience, some purpose that was not yet clear. No matter how disappointing the situation, I decided to assertively respond to Blaster and others when their business practices or approach did not make sense to me.

After the accident and prior to my medical leave, I had coasted at work and reduced or stopped most personal activities in my life. But even that was not enough. I had to dramatically cut back in all parts of my life to see if I could heal the injury and reduce the pain. I had to reduce activities more and more as the medication was becoming less and less effective in masking the pain. My life appeared to be in a freefall with no bottom in sight. There were limitations and pain even while on medical leave and not working. Several weeks of my medical leave had now passed where the reality of a freefall seemed to be the order of the day. Yet, with my medical leave and full-time schedule of recovery, there was at least a glimmer of hope of healing. Eight months on medical leave was a long time to focus on recovery. Maybe in this amount of time I would begin to see possibilities for my future. I knew I had to respect this time for recovery and keep the glimmer of hope for my future alive. This was the most difficult transition of my life. I had to believe in and realize the possibility of a greater plan and purpose from my life. This hope was all I had left of my now fragile existence.

Chapter 3

Disposable Resources

A few weeks into my medical leave, Blaster sent me a letter to explain the employee benefits I would receive while on a medical leave of absence. This was in accordance with company policy and the Family Medical Leave Act (FMLA). I would receive full pay for two months, followed by partial pay for a few more months that would be increased if my injury was determined to be work related. When I read the letter, I was relieved of my financial concerns and felt very fortunate to have medical leave benefits. My employer was going to continue to help me as they promised. Perhaps the IME was just a scare. Yet I also hoped and prayed that I could return to work within a shorter time period than the eight-month medical leave Dr. Lee had prescribed. Later, to my horror, I learned that at the same time I received the letter, Blaster was preparing to take away my benefits through the use of Dr. Blunder's IME report that they had sent to me a few weeks earlier. The letter was an empty promise sent to me to "prove" for legal reference that the company had provided medical benefits and followed the rules of the FMLA.

Shortly after receiving the letter, I called Mr. Blair to discuss the status of my medical condition and the aggressive therapy I was receiving. I also discussed the improvement I felt in the early mornings on most days. Mr. Blair quickly asked me what the probability and timing was of my return to work. I agreed to have lunch with him as soon as I could meet with my doctors and ask their opinions and advice on returning to work. I recorded my doctors' opinions for review with Mr. Blair. At the end of March, Mr. Blair and I met over lunch to discuss my condition and possible return to work. I felt good about the day as I hoped for a meaningful discussion with Mr. Blair about my job and physical limitations. I parked my car and walked into the restaurant where I greeted my boss who was already sitting at a table by the entrance. We shook hands and talked briefly about the weather, our families, Blaster, and how people at work were doing. I told him how much I appreciated the people at Blaster who were covering my job while I was gone. Then I explained my doctor's recent opinions about my return to work, which included limitations on the time and intensity of work I could perform. Surprisingly, Mr. Blair's response was to ask me to consider the medical suggestions as unnecessary, "look into wearing a copper bracelet like some of the professional golfers ... I'm sure you've seen them on TV ... you know diet can be a factor ... (my wife) has been serving a more balanced diet and we both feel much better." I was surprised at his minimizing, almost dismissing my medical condition. I quickly and defensively explained, "I've done a considerable amount of research of Western and Eastern medicine and I'm trying everything possible. I've tailored my diet, exercise, and medication to my condition. I'm trying herbs, oils, meditation, a magnetic mattress, spiritual prayer, physical and massage therapy, and more. There are no limits to what a person will try when facing this level of pain every day." While I talked, Mr. Blair ate his lunch with his usual healthy appetite and controlled business-like mannerisms. When I finished talking, he barely paused eating and only briefly looked up from his plate to respond. He gave an analogy of my condition to a wolf pack. "The leader of the pack will go to the back of the pack and check on the injured. If the injured can't keep up, they are left behind."

My heart sank and we were both quiet as he continued eating his lunch while I thought about how his story carried an important message for me to consider. When our conversation continued about the many demands at work, I kept thinking about the wolf pack analogy and became nervous. I could barely eat my salad. I frequently stopped to respond to his brief comments as if defending my job and myself. Soon my appetite was gone and lunch was ignored as my stomach felt tied up and nauseous. It was clear the company was not going to help me as I had hoped and they had promised.

In the next several days after my lunch with Mr. Blair, I thought about his story of being left behind and how important and enjoyable my work and career were in my life. I also thought about the improvement I felt in such a short time with more aggressive therapy while on medical leave. I started to question my doctor's prognosis and even my intuitive sense of the extent of my injury and impairment. After I completed my medical leave, my doctors suggested a slow increase in the number of hours I worked or what they called ramping up to full-time work. I decided not to wait for the end of my medical leave. To protect my job and career, and stay connected to the business, I decided to take a risk with my injury and return to work part time. I thought I could slowly increase the number of hours I worked until I was again working full time.

While on leave, I had achieved some recovery from the pain and clarity of my mind and heart a few hours each morning. Now I wanted to return to work as soon as possible and work as much as physically possible. The next day I called my boss and the Director of Human Resources to ask if I could return to work part time and ramp up over time. Mr. Blair was not available so I talked to Mr. Seabert about my suggestion. "I would like to return to work part time and ramp up to a full-time work schedule over time," I explained. But Mr. Seabert not only quickly turned me down, he also explained, "According to Dr. Blunder's IME report, you are well enough to return to work full time now. Your sick leave pay benefits have been stopped. You can use your earned vacation to receive your salary or you can return to work full time in your job as the senior finance manager."

I was shocked at his response and how different Blaster and I viewed my situation. The next day Blaster formally notified me by registered mail that I was not impaired and should return to work immediately. Their conclusion was based on Dr. Blunder's IME that they sent me to in February, just one week after my doctor had put me on an eight-month medical leave. The IME report concluded that while I was injured in the accident, I was already completely healed and fit for full-time work. When I read the IME report, I saw that my doctors' opinions, along with my answers to Dr. Blunder's questions, were misquoted. Important facts were misstated or omitted and situations were minimized or exaggerated. Dr. Blunder's IME report contained more than thirty errors, omissions, and misstatements in an effort to support a conclusion that there was no continuing injury, impairment, or additional medical improvement possible. Therefore, I should return to full-time work.

I remembered how less than two months earlier Mr. Seabert had told me that the IME was a mere formality. Yet during the IME, I felt there was something wrong. Now I knew there was something wrong. The examination was obviously a ruthless approach to provide a medical report with the power to force me back to work or out of work. Indeed, Blaster, as the leader of the wolf pack, was prepared to leave me behind and planned to do so without taking responsibility for the work-related injury that caused my inability to do my job. They would not even honor the promises of employee benefits that were made to me when I accepted the position of Senior Finance Manager in Troy. This was a job that I had left my hometown area for and worked hard at during the time before the accident – a job that I had struggled hard over and suffered to keep after the accident.

The registered letter signed by Mr. Seabert explained that I needed to return to work immediately or my employment and its benefits would be terminated. Further, if I returned to work, I was expected to fulfill all the responsibilities of my job. I was shocked and afraid as I read through the letter that also informed me there were no other jobs at the company that fit my capability. I felt there must be a misunderstanding or some other alternatives that the company and I could explore. Toward the end of the letter, there were other legal positioning statements, along with an option for another IME. This was the only realistic alternative for me in the letter.

I felt betrayed. I wondered if a second IME would be any better. As soon as I finished reading the letter, I called Mr. Seabert to explore other possible alternatives. I was at home alternating between sitting on the edge of the couch and pacing the floor while I talked to Mr. Seabert about my IME experience and the inaccuracy of Dr. Blunder's report. The stress further tightened my muscles and increased my pain until I could barely think. Regardless of my plea,

Mr. Seabert re-asserted, "You should return to work. Based on Dr. Blunder's IME report, your medical leave pay and benefits have been stopped." I nervously reminded him, "I have experienced some improvement during my medical leave as a result of the more aggressive therapy, but if I return to work full time now, I will probably fall flat on my face. This does not make sense for me or the business." He replied, "My decision is not personal." I thought to myself that of course this is personal and said, "This is my career and my life we're talking about!" I paused, as did Mr. Seabert. Then I asked Mr. Seabert about the option identified in the letter to see another doctor for another IME if I felt the Dr. Blunder report was in error. Mr. Seabert said, "I will provide you with a list of doctors to choose from. Blaster will pay for and manage this second IME."

I was suspicious of another Blaster-paid medical opinion but agreed to another IME. I felt I had no other option except to leave my job with no pay or benefits. I knew returning to work full time was both impossible and irresponsible at this point. I was upset and angry. I had lost my medical leave pay and benefits through the use of an obviously erroneous medical opinion that Blaster paid for. I felt betrayed by my employer whom I had worked so hard for over the years. Despite the formal letter and Mr. Seabert's response, I still wanted to resolve the issues. I wanted to continue trying to heal my medical condition and return to work as soon as possible and work as much as possible. Hoping for another alternative, I called Mr. Blair as soon as he was available to discuss my concerns. His response was the same as Mr. Seabert's. My only realistic choice was to have another IME.

Later, I tried to make sense out of my situation by talking with my lawyer and Justine since both had years of workers' compensation experience. I was told that after an IME most people either returned to work injured and unable to perform their jobs whereupon they would be fired for not performing their job, or they quit and found a less-demanding job with another employer. People familiar with the system referred to this as "constructive firing." In the end, this eliminated the employer's responsibility for the work injury at the expense of the injured employee. While I was not comfortable with either of these options, I felt bad for the people who lived from paycheck to paycheck to support their families and had to accept such an injustice. Indeed, maybe there were a few people who reported false medical claims and were looking for money without having to work. It was hard for me to believe people would struggle so much with the system when it would be much easier to go to work. But this also made me think that maybe the system had shifted over time from protecting business to actually hurting people who believed in an honest day's work for an honest day's pay. There were honest people who needed help from time to time from their employers. They had worked hard for years and were promised benefits if they became sick or were injured. They were people like me. I began to understand their position more and more.

At this same time, my medical bills were accumulating and no payments from workers' compensation insurance were being received. I called the company nurse, Ms. Jones, who handled the workers' compensation claims. I asked her for a payment status. Nurse Jones replied that the paperwork was not completed properly and that my attorney was impossible to work with so I called Attorney Young and asked him to help Nurse Jones with the paperwork. He assured me that he had tried to process the paperwork. He also said, "You should be aware of Blaster's deny tactics for workers' compensation. I have 150 to 200 workers' compensation cases that I am working on and Blaster is one of the most difficult employers to work with. It takes too much time. You should consider a lump sum settlement." Since Attorney Young seemed anxious to settle early with minimal effort on his part, I wasn't sure if there really was a problem working with Nurse Jones or if Attorney Young had other motives.

A few days later, Attorney Young invited me to his office downtown to discuss my case further. On the morning I was scheduled to meet him, I got up very early before the workday started, drove downtown, and quickly felt the intense pain from the drive come into my back. I parked my car and went to his office where he asked me to sit down. He said to me, "Your case is too difficult to support because of Blaster's tactics. You need to find new counsel if you want to pursue your claim." I immediately wished he had told me this over the phone so I would not have had to make the painful drive downtown. Then I became anxious. Now I had to hire another attorney to help me sort through the existing paperwork issues and represent me at an upcoming workers' compensation hearing. I felt even more suspicious of Nurse Jones and Blaster over their workers' compensation process. My suspicions were proven true when later I learned that Blaster had a long list of deny tactics for workers' compensation. Nurse Jones would not work with any of my counsel or with me directly. I also wondered why Attorney Young had not filled out any paperwork. He had not, to my knowledge, worked through any of the details of the workers' compensation system.

Later I learned that there were many "quick hit" lawyers who did very little work while waiting for small lump sum settlements. This minimized their effort and maximized their return on a large number of cases. Eventually I also understood that the workers' compensation rules were difficult and time consuming. Maybe "quick hits" were one way of making a good living while working in a difficult legal area. Indeed, I also heard from my attorneys that soft tissue injuries were difficult to prove and were tainted by fraudulent claims filed in the past. Soft tissue injuries usually became low value cases. But I knew I had large losses and a lot of integrity. Eventually, with Justine's help, I found other lawyers who shared my hard work and challenge perspective and also followed their integrity.

Justine talked to the lawyers in her office about other lawyers who might help me with my workers' compensation claim. They referred me to Jim Severs who seemed as interested in helping me with my medical condition as he was with having my medical bills paid. After our first meeting, I wrote the following letter to him:

> A couple of thoughts came to mind after our discussion Monday. First, I have enclosed a copy of the rationale for the business purpose and job relationship of the business dinner meeting we were traveling to on the evening of the accident. I understand this is needed for the worker's compensation determination. I also reviewed this with the driver of the car, who reminded me that we

had scheduled a specific business topic for that evening in addition to those listed in the enclosed.

Finally, I neglected to ask you about the alternative medical solutions you are aware of. You mentioned the possibility of the Mayo Clinic providing help to me. I need anyone's help I can get to pursue my primary goal, which is to heal my back as much as possible, as soon as possible.

This was the last time Attorney Severs and I discussed any medical alternatives. It appeared that his interest in my medical care was used to convince me to be his client – an interest that was gone with my signature to hire him. Fortunately though, Attorney Severs was available to represent me at the workers' compensation hearing to decide the work relationship of my injury.

Earlier in the year, Blaster denied my workers' compensation claim as not being work related. The formal workers' compensation hearing that I attended a few weeks after I had lunch with Mr. Blair was relatively brief and straightforward. Even Blaster's lawyers did not dispute the work relationship of my injury. As a result, Blaster was instructed to pay my medical bills. Apparently Blaster had decided there was no issue over this being a work-related injury so they went to the next level of tactics by submitting Dr. Blunder's IME report into the Bureau of Workers' Compensation (BWC) files. In this way, the BWC, along with future IME doctors and the state doctor for medical evaluations and determinations of benefits, could use his report to refute my injury. This would also facilitate Blaster's removing their responsibility for payment of specific medical bills and lost wages at future BWC hearings. Between hearings, Blaster did not pay any lost wages or medical bills except for deductibles for prescriptions. I had to fight for every other penny.

Blaster introduced the grossly erroneous IME report into the records even though I had shown Mr. Seabert and others at Blaster how bad the IME by Dr. Blunder was and, as a result, we agreed to a second IME. Not only this, Blaster also helped to minimize the medical conditions that were allowed by the hearing officer. Only cervical and thoracic sprain/strain were recorded as allowed conditions. Chronic myofascial pain was excluded even though it was in Dr. Hunt's medical reports and workers' compensation forms. My new attorney missed it, I didn't understand, and the Blaster attorney and nurse were silent about it at the hearing. At the conclusion of the hearing, they walked away smiling and once again I felt betrayed.

Blaster had turned up the heat to force me back to work so that I would fail or be forced to quit with none of the benefits promised to me as their employee. Because of this, they lost my trust and respect. I wondered if even they believed their IMEs. Maybe Blaster was simply focusing on reducing benefit costs while protecting their system of denying employee benefits and workers' compensation responsibility for work-related injuries. From the people I talked to about my situation, I learned that many people who became ill or were injured experienced the same or comparable harsh tactics that organizations use in order to protect company profits. In protecting company rights, they protect their own livelihoods. Safety and health statistics, as well as recordable OSHA reports, were also understated and benefited the company. These companies reported safer workplaces than existed while putting employees at risk. Anger built up inside me and called forth a need to respond to such unfair treatment with a sense of responsibility to myself and other people who become ill or were injured at work. As a part of my senior management position with Blaster, it was my responsibility to protect other employees and respond to such unfair treatment.

I wrote Blaster a letter addressed to Mr. Seabert that documented my thoughts and concerns. For the first time, I wrote a formal letter to my employer about the benefits that I was promised when I was hired and how I was being treated as an employee. The letter I wrote was an attempt to find a fair and responsible handling of my work injury by my employer while protecting any interests in case the issues escalated in the future. In the letter, I explained that I was looking forward to another IME from a doctor jointly selected by Blaster and me. I also formally asked Mr. Seabert or anyone else at Blaster to review Dr. Blunder's IME report with me. I referred to the Blunder report as "grossly erroneous with a large number of errors, omissions, and misstatements." I chose these words very carefully to clearly and accurately describe the IME report.

In the letter, I also mentioned that I would be sure Blaster received a copy of an updated physical therapy plan for me by Dr. Lee. Mr. Seabert had told me this was requested by Blaster but had not been received. When I followed up with Dr. Lee's office about Blaster's request, I learned that there was no record of a request from Blaster for a physical therapy plan. This was another indication to me that the tactics were heating up and becoming deceitful, perhaps even fraudulent. I wondered more and more if, with the use of whatever tactics worked, Blaster's ultimate goal was to remove me as an injured employee from the company. I concluded my letter to Mr. Seabert by reiterating that I wanted to return to work as soon as possible and fulfill the duties and responsibilities of my position. A few days later Mr. Seabert sent me a list of doctors from which to choose a second IME doctor. He did not reply at all to my concern over medical benefits. As far as I knew, I was no longer on a paid medical leave from work and there would be no additional reimbursement of my medical bills. My concerns about my job and career increased, as well as the potential financial impact of my medical condition. My concern for medical bills and lost wages continued to grow while the issues over my medical leave went unanswered.

Chapter 4

Safety Net

If my medical bills and lost wages were not covered by employee benefits and/or workers' compensation, I wondered if one of the many other insurance options I had would provide benefits. I called my insurance agent for Country Garden Insurance, explained my situation, and asked if I had any insurance coverage for my injury. She quickly said, "No, you don't." I paused with surprise considering all the automobile, homeowners, and umbrella insurance policies that I had purchased from Country Garden over the years. I asked her again, "Aren't there any benefits for medical bills, lost wages, house payments, or anything?" Again she said, "No." I replied, "Please review my policies in detail to see if I can get any help." Then I reiterated, " I am no longer working and it appears all of my employee benefits have been lost." She researched my question and called me back a few days later and said, "No, there are no benefits in your policies. But the driver of the automobile should have coverage for you." I again explained that the driver's policy did not apply since the accident was a work-related workers' compensation issue. Again she replied, "There is no coverage under any of your policies."

Later I found out that my Ohio automobile insurance policy had a medical payments insurance provision that paid medical bills related to a car accident regardless of who was driving the car or who was at fault. I also learned that there was a Minnesota Country Garden no-fault automobile insurance policy in effect at the time of the accident that had not yet transitioned to Ohio. Either of these policies should have covered my injury. Yet, when I learned of my insurance coverage, the agents in Ohio and Minnesota each argued that the other was responsible even though both policies were with the same company. This was clearly another delay of insurance benefits. The agent also did not mention coverage for uninsured and/or underinsured coverage for a "phantom vehicle" from either of my policies or Jack's automobile policy. The semi-tractor/trailer that helped cause the accident by drifting towards us was referred to as an unidentified "phantom vehicle" with potential liability similar to a hit-and-run vehicle. In these cases, insurance coverage is included in the uninsured and underinsured provisions of most automobile insurance policies. When I eventually learned about the medical payments, no-fault insurance, and the phantom vehicle liability, I wondered whether the agent had lied to me or was incompetent. The next time I was in my agent's office I looked into her eyes and said, "I understand I was covered by an insurance policy for the accident in April 1997. Why did you tell me there was no coverage?" She looked directly into my eyes and replied, "Do you want to file a claim?" Her quick and unemotional response suggested that I had once again been told a lie. Years later, I also learned of an umbrella policy in effect at the time of the accident that should have paid benefits. This took quite some time and effort to uncover, but when it was uncovered, the dishonesty involved was obvious.

# # #

My experience with the Blunder IME was so bad that I decided to carefully prepare for my second IME that was scheduled in a few weeks. I knew that companies gave their hired IME doctors a list of questions to answer in order to direct the evaluation and conclusions in their favor. I thought I should try to do the same. I asked Blaster to allow me to provide medical reports to this IME doctor and they agreed. Then I asked Attorney Severs to help me develop a questionnaire so my doctors could focus their evaluation of my medical condition and prognosis. I drafted the questions for Attorney Severs' review, but I was surprised that I had to wrestle with him to get his legal counsel for this sensible new approach to IMEs. He seemed more interested in trying to force an employment severance package from Blaster than continuing to work through my medical issues and workers' compensation claim. I told Attorney Severs that

I was not ready to leave my job at Blaster. Nor were they ready to accept any responsibility, let alone pay a severance package. But he continued to push for the higher dollar severance package. It appeared to me that he wanted to take one-third for himself with a much better payday and less work than a workers' compensation claim.

After finally obtaining Attorney Severs' review, I completed the questionnaires for my doctors (Appendix 3) and carried them to their offices to ask for their help. Both Drs. Hunt and Lee were supportive of my approach for the second IME. They also provided me with suggestions of which doctor to choose for the second IME from the list provided by Blaster. As I sat with my doctors in their offices, they answered the questions in writing so I could submit their medical opinions in a package that I was preparing for the second IME doctor. In addition to the questionnaires with their medical opinions, the package included copies of medical reports from my doctors, therapists, and psychologist, along with an updated life analysis (Appendix 4) and a summary of time spent on therapy, exercise, stretching, and meditation (Appendix 5). It also included a description of my job for the IME doctor's evaluation and return-to-work conclusion. The package turned out to be a fairly comprehensive review of my medical condition and situation since the accident of one year earlier. The updated life analysis also helped me see how much my condition had continued to deteriorate.

Early in May, I attended a second IME that was held at Valley Hospital. To perform the second IME, I chose Dr. Waits from the list of doctors provided by Blaster based on my review with my doctors. Both Drs. Hunt and Lee thought Dr. Waits was knowledgeable about my type of injury and would be as fair as possible considering Blaster was paying for the IME. At the start of this examination, I provided Dr. Waits with the package of medical reports and analysis that documented the treatment I had received and was continuing for my injury. The diagnosis of a permanent impairment caused by my injury, with its spasms, strains, and chronic myofascial pain, was well documented, along with my doctor's suggestion to continue with therapy before returning to my job as a senior financial manager. Dr. Waits' examination seemed fairly credible so toward the end of the exam I asked, "Could you please provide me with some insight into what is going on with my body and some suggestions on how I can address my injury and chronic pain?" He replied, almost apologetically, "I am not in a position to do that. Medical help is not the purpose of this evaluation. I am required to only answer specific questions provided by Blaster. I cannot help you."

The purpose of the second IME was confirmed when I received a copy of his report. Dr. Waits concluded his report with words that I was sure were chosen carefully. He said that I could return to work for "no more than forty hours a week for several months at least." Dr. Waits knew, as did everyone else, that the job I had was not a forty-hour-a-week job and "for several months at least" would be too long to continue to limp along with the level and type of responsibilities included in my job. Nonetheless, as a result of the second IME, I was required to either return to work after three months of the eight-month medical leave prescribed by Dr. Lee or lose my job.

While I felt better about the accuracy of Dr. Waits' IME report compared to Dr. Blunder's IME report, there were still a number of errors. Among these was a note that I was both walking between four and ten miles each day, and running three miles per day. During the exam at the hospital, I told Dr. Waits that I was walking two or two and a half miles once or twice a day when I could and that I was not running at all anymore. This error and other comments in his report made it sound like I was very healthy and maybe even enjoying my medical leave. Further, he said my medical history included a "diagnosis of left C5 radiculopathy in 1978." After some research, I learned that C5 is the fifth cervical vertebra, while radiculopathy is a diseased condition of the roots of spinal nerves. Dr. Waits' comment inappropriately referred to an inflamed fifth cranial nerve problem that I had in 1978 as a cervical spine issue. At the IME, I explained this inflamed nerve on my brain problem from almost twenty years earlier, but he instead reported a prior medical problem in my neck and back. This error suggested that I had a history of chronic back problems, but I certainly did not. When I re-read this error in the second IME report, I felt even more disrespected by the system and my safety net. Betrayal as a human being seemed to be becoming a chronic condition with me!

Even though I was concerned that I had not healed enough to return to work, I at least wanted to give it my best shot considering my only alternative was losing my job and career. Yet I also felt a need to prove myself, almost like holding up a mirror to the people responsible for forcing me back to work so they would see the impact of their actions. Indeed, my choice was either to return to work and risk my health or accept a jobless and impaired life of chronic pain with no insurance or other benefits. Blaster had already cut off my employee benefits, including sick pay and workers' compensation benefits, based on Dr. Blunder's IME report. One day I was walking down the street with Justine and said, "If I'm not getting paid and I have no employee benefits, then I don't have a job ... I'm unemployed ... I'm fired!"

I was appalled that Blaster could take such action with no apparent consequence. I had to go back to work regardless of the pain and suffering in order to fight for what was right even though I had little idea of what that might be. I thoughtfully considered their impaired employee process as being ruthless with its paid doctor opinions and other tactics, while I continued to struggle to find a resolution to my injury and chronic pain. Under my doctor's care, I spent half my day stretching, exercising, walking, and meditating just to have a few clear and relatively pain free hours in the morning with no complete medical solution found. Nevertheless, there were doctors for hire willing to refute my injury and remove Blaster's responsibility. As I saw my life beginning to unravel, there seemed to be too many pieces inappropriately falling to the ground. Somewhere within me grew a need to fight back, an ever stronger need to fight for my life.

At the same time, Blaster was preparing to simply fire me. They would probably first determine their legal exposure over my situation with the support of a cadre of corporate lawyers, the IMEs, the medical leave letters they sent to me, and other legal posturing. I was concerned and wondered if there was any legal protection or recourse for me as an injured employee. I called Attorney Severs and asked for legal counsel as soon as possible. "What about employment law or benefits that were promised when I was hired? I am afraid for my livelihood and ever-increasing unpaid medical bills" was the message I left with his paralegal. But Attorney Severs did not respond even after several phone calls to follow-up.

With no legal help, I decided to try to work directly with Blaster and the insurance companies, while fighting back on my own as much as necessary. Then I asked Attorney Severs to bill me what I owed him so I could let him go. Surprising to me was that both Attorneys Young and Severs were uninterested in working the details of the workers' compensation system to help me pay my bills and cover some of my lost wages. Instead, they talked about handling 150 to 200 cases at a time, which led me to conclude that the lawyers' approach was not lack of interest but probably lack of time. Instead of working through a very difficult system, they could delay the time-consuming detail work, request a small lump sum settlement for their injured client, and still collect their one-third. The long delay would make the injured person anxious and willing to have any amount covered.

Later, when I discussed this situation with another attorney, he smiled at me and said, "A quick hit." These attorneys knew what they were doing when they asked the injured to settle for small amounts with little effort. Yet, for me, this was a process and system that I was not willing to accept. Instead, I felt a need to find a reasonable solution that fit my situation.

Before returning to work, I called Nurse Jones at Blaster and asked her to help me process the paperwork for workers' compensation reimbursement of my medical bills. I also told her I no longer had legal help and would need her support with the very technical requirements of the workers' compensation system. She agreed to help me and talked compassionately about my medical condition. At the end of our phone call, we also shared friendly stories about our families. Her response was encouraging to me. I later learned not only the emptiness of her promise but also how far she would go to ensure benefits would <u>not</u> be paid.

I also contacted Jack's car insurance company to let them know that I no longer had legal representation. My goal was to work directly with them to have them pay any medical bills and lost wages over and above anything covered by workers' compensation insurance. I provided them the life analysis that showed the impact to my life from the car accident in which I was a passenger in a car driven by their insured. I also gave them my doctors' reports and medical records to support my claim. I soon learned that they were not interested in helping me without the benefit of lawyers and the long legal process. Indeed, I was disappointed but not surprised that they too wanted the luxury of long delays and forced responsibility. The many broken promises of employee benefits and insurance coverage added despair to my injury. Despair set in as the medical bills and lost wages accumulated, while the many medical alternatives I tried did not provide the complete recovery I had hoped for. Soon the impact of both the ongoing pain from the injury and the ruthless delay and denial of employee and insurance benefits became more than I could handle. I had to do something more.

To try to better understand what was happening, I wrote a long letter to myself (Appendix 6) that described the difficulty I was facing in my life. The letter was complete with descriptions of my physical problem and the implications to my work and personal life. I wrote about the circumstances of the accident, my physical impairment and life limitations, the medical care I had received, and the improvement and relief I had found while on medical leave from work. Then I described Blaster's response to my situation, including my first experience with a company-paid doctor opinion. The letter was another attempt to make sense out of a tragic injury and the senseless response from the people I worked with and others whom I had asked for help. While praying and meditating after reading the letter, I was reminded of the incredible amount of pain I had already suffered and how my fear and concern grew during this time. I was also reminded of the indignity I felt, especially at the hands of the independent medical examiner, when I felt physically and emotionally violated for the first time in my adult life. While I hoped to find answers and recovery from this letter, I felt only despair as I more clearly saw that so many important pieces of my life were falling down around me. I was shocked and angry when I found my health care and employee benefits, along with insurance benefits, were being delayed and denied.

My health insurance and employee benefits were supposed to be a safety net during a medical tragedy. Instead, the safety net I had earned and was promised to me as an employee or paid for by me was all but gone. By writing and seeing the situation in black and white, I hoped I would understand why this was happening to me. In a childlike way, I hoped maybe the letter would make it seem less real and it would go away. But, of course, it did not. Instead, I could not believe what was happening to me as frustration was growing on top of my pain and suffering. This letter was never sent. Whenever I thought someone might listen, I talked about its ramifications for me and other people. Many people listened and some agreed with my general observations about the ruthlessness of the system used for injured people that brought added harm for most people. It was true that I was probably being treated no differently than anyone else, not only at Blaster but in many organizations across the country. As I talked to people, including those who were responsible for the systems, there were few, if any, responsible actions that came about as a result of these many conversations. Instead, people accepted the situation as "that's just the way it is," while they implied or directly encouraged me to do the same. But I could not.

A safety net was as much a part of the American Dream as a family, home, automobile, and meaningful work. My expectation was that my safety net would include respectful and trusting medical professionals. They were to provide reasonably good medical care, to help me heal, and to minimize my physical pain and suffering if I became sick or injured. Employee benefits from Blaster, along with various other insurance benefits, were promised to my family and me so we would not suffer financially, as well as physically, from injury or illness. My employer promised that sick leave and health insurance benefits, workers' compensation benefits, and/or disability insurance benefits would help pay medical bills and lost wages. I assumed that my employer would reward my hard work and loyalty of the past with an alternative work assignment if one were needed. Blaster and I even discussed that the probability of any alternative work for me would pay less. I replied that less pay for less work was acceptable to me as long as I could continue to work. I wanted to be self-supportive, however much any one job paid. Over the years, I had seen companies help people in this way many times. Maybe now times had changed or maybe an invisible illness was too suspicious or risky to support. Whatever the reason, Blaster denied me another job. I had assumed there would be adequate support from my company's safety net during times of great need, especially when a permanent impairment or disability was realized. There was not.

Apart from work, I had also purchased automobile and homeowner's insurance with an umbrella policy and paid into Social Security to further broaden and strengthen my safety net. If absolutely needed, I imagined a fair and impartial judicial system, complete with attorneys acting on my behalf, would represent me and help me recover any losses. Yet, when my injury and situation deteriorated, I reached out for these many promises and, instead of help, I found betrayal and indignity from broken safety net promises. Not only benefit promises, but also important medical care was delayed or limited from my doctors because they were tied into a health care system controlled by big companies. The corporate priority was profit and shareholder wealth.

I knew there were some doctors who simply did not trust their patients because they did not really understand chronic pain and the full impact of taking so much medication. Or maybe they distrusted because of their experience with fraud in the past or what big business and others told them. Many times, instead of expensive medical care, drugs were prescribed quickly and easily to quiet the pain. They also quieted the desire to properly heal. The necessary therapies were delayed or not offered at all. I tried to be careful as I watched Drs. Smith and Hunt, my "employer doctors," prioritize reduced medical care and cost over healing until I insisted on healing and paid for some of the medical care myself. When my medical care providers suggested alternative medicines where benefits were not available, I tried them anyway and paid for them myself.

In time, I was very glad that I had turned to Dr. Lee, an "employee doctor" outside of the company's health plan network. His medical care cost me extra money because he was outside of the network. Indeed, if not for the medical leave from work that was prescribed by Dr. Lee, I would have failed at work earlier. I could only assume that I would probably have been fired with an explanation that I had not performed my job properly rather than because of medical issues from the accident. Dr. Lee was also willing to prescribe narcotic muscle relaxers and painkillers strong enough to kill the pain without the many bad side effects of other medications. The thin blanket of narcotic medication became my security blanket and safety net of last resort when all else failed. Then, with so much suspicion and inconsistency over my medical care and prognosis, I stockpiled Dr. Lee's prescription medications like a squirrel preparing for winter. Instinctively, I somehow knew there was a long, hard, painful season coming, especially after returning to work.

The persons, my employer, lawyers, and others involved with the accident and my claim began what to me was a grotesque dance. My employer used deny tactics and fraudulent practices to limit their responsibility to me for medical leave pay and workers' compensation benefits. Workers' compensation insurance and automobile insurance companies employed corporate lawyers to push their responsibility away from them to others. My automobile insurance and Jack's pointed to each other as responsible and to the workers' compensation insurance that was denied by my employer. Disability insurance details and fine print limited benefits to extreme disabilities that rendered the sick or injured completely unable to work because of injuries that could be x-rayed. The disability had to be approved by the company and its hired IME doctors who were good at denying responsibility.

The dance continued and my unpaid medical bills and lost wages quickly ran into the thousands of dollars. I covered those from my personal savings and retirement investments. While I knew I was very fortunate to have these monies to fall back on, I was concerned that the money would not last. Even more important than the money was the feeling of betrayal and anger when people broke the safety net promises and sometimes even acknowledged their ruthless practices with smug attitudes. Even the lawyers I hired to represent me were a disappointment as twice I had hired counsel with goals different than mine. People told me that I would eventually need to find a lawyer who would take a hard-working, detailed legal approach to help me recover benefits. First I had to return to work to see what I could handle and what additional help my employer would provide, if any.

For three months I had concentrated on healing my injury while on a medical leave. Now my options to find more time to heal were gone and it was time to return to work. Even with the pain, I wanted to return to the job and work that I loved. I was not ready to give up my successful career of over twenty-one years. My company benefits and employment were stopped. They would resume only if I returned to work. As I anticipated and planned my return to work, I became excited despite all I had been through. While on medical leave, my medical approach included aggressive physical therapy, massage therapy, meditation, and other alternative medicine that took six to eight hours per day. This time would have to be cut back in order to return to work. When I returned to work, I would find out if the gradual improvement in my medical condition while on medical leave would enable me to do my job. Maybe I would continue to improve. In the mornings, there was now relief from the pain. There was clarity of my mind and heart that I had not enjoyed in almost a year. A few pain-free hours in the morning on these good days brought such excitement and hope that I wanted to live fully again. In order to do so, I had learned to pace myself. Part of my plan for returning to work included doing my most important and demanding work in the mornings and slowing down in the afternoons. I hoped there would be other benefits from my medical leave that would help me successfully return to work.

Chapter 5

Return to Work

At the end of May, I returned to work after only three months of the prescribed eight-month medical leave given to me by Dr. Lee. The choice I had was to return to work immediately or I would be unemployed with no pay or benefits. I would have preferred to continue with my medical leave to try to completely heal while using the benefits that Blaster had promised to me when I was hired. If I did not heal completely by the end of my medical leave, I would have been very grateful if Blaster found me another job to fit my abilities so I could continue as their employee. However, this was not an option. I was not ready to give up my job or career as I enjoyed my work and its many rewards, including the people I worked with and had befriended over the years. There was no way I wanted to lose this very important part of my life if I could help it.

There was also a part of me that wanted to believe the IMEs, as well as a few people at work who thought that I was well enough to return to work full time. Maybe if I tried again I would find a way to succeed. I knew Blaster was disappointed that I had filed a workers' compensation claim and hired a lawyer to help me. I knew they were angry when I went on the medical leave prescribed by Dr. Lee, a doctor outside of their health care plan and control. Because of this, I was concerned about how Blaster management would treat me when I returned to work. Rather than let fear build up inside me, I prayed about the situation and decided to trust Blaster once again. When I returned to work, I would be putting my recovery and job responsibilities in their hands to see if a reasonable alternative could be found for both my injury and career. I hoped Blaster would help me find a way to succeed.

When I did return to work, I reported to Nurse Jones for a formal approval of my physical fitness for work. She asked me how I was doing, read me the second independent medical examiner's opinion, and scheduled appointments with the company doctor while suggesting I see her for more frequent medical care. From that day on, I met with Nurse Jones almost every day and the Blaster company doctor every week or two for a medical review. Each day over lunch, I went to the company gym to continue my tailored exercise and stretching program that Dr. Lee and his therapist had developed for me. After I showered and dressed in the company locker room, I stopped by the infirmary to apply hot packs to my back while meditating to relieve the pain. Nurse Jones was usually in her office and frequently stopped by for a status report of my condition, along with a little small talk about our work or families. Each day I charted my exercise, therapy, level of work and home activity, level of pain, and the medication I took. I used this chart to describe the impact of my return to work so I could further understand my impairment. Also, I needed to communicate my condition to others involved, including the company doctor, Nurse Jones, Mr. Blair, and Mr. Seabert.

After I saw Nurse Jones the first day, I met with Mr. Blair in his large general manager's office to discuss my return to work. His office was nicely decorated with beautifully polished hardwood furniture and comfortable cloth-covered chairs. There were nicely framed pictures on the wall and a shaded lamp in the corner. The lamp suggested a warm, comfortable visit. I knocked on the door. Mr. Blair, without looking up from his computer, motioned with his hand for me to come in and sit down in the chair in front of his desk. I sat down and looked at him. I blurted out, "I will do everything the company asks me to now that I am back at work. I am glad to be back." Mr. Blair looked up at me and responded, "People at Blaster are very disappointed that you were not more direct and specific about your condition before your medical leave." I was surprised at his comment, given the communication I had provided to him, Mr. Seabert, and others before I went on medical leave. I said to him, "Help me understand what you mean." He replied, "You did not allow Nurse Jones and the company doctor to examine you and be a part of your medical treatment." I told Mr. Blair, "I was not aware of that option. I have always been open to any help I can get. Before I went on medical leave, I tried to address my problem without creating too much trouble for you and others at Blaster."

I paused to recall informing Mr. Blair and others from time to time about the status of my medical condition, including when I was no longer able to work forty plus hours a week and later when I was unable to work even forty hours a week. Earlier in the year, I had also told him and Mr. Seabert that I could no longer handle my job. I had formally asked for a position with less responsibility in a warmer climate, if at all possible. I told them what was going on in my life as best as I could while frequently reminding Mr. Blair that I wasn't performing my job at the levels expected or required of me. They had all seen me in the middle of the day run out to my doctor's office to get trigger point injections for the pain relief that I needed in order to continue working for the rest of the day. The disappointment Mr. Blair now expressed was difficult for me to hear since I had tried hard to keep him and others informed about what was going on and had asked for their help.

It was my first day back at work. I felt the old sense of distrust and suspicion coming from my supervisor and the company. I told Mr. Blair, "I will get as much help from Nurse Jones and the company doctor as possible. I have also let go of my legal counsel and will work with the company directly on any issues." He smiled confidently and seemed pleased about the control over my situation that I had returned to him. Then he looked at me closer with a frown and asked, "Why did you put your house up for sale?" I paused thoughtfully and replied, "When I learned in the letter from Mr. Seabert that my benefits and pay were cut off, I felt like I was out of a job. Justine and I cannot afford the house we live in if I am not working. I could not return to work at the one hundred percent you required so I thought I had no job. Now that I'm back to work, we thought we would continue to try to sell the house until we're sure of our future, maybe move closer to Dayton where Justine works. Under the circumstances, it seemed a prudent thing to do."

I felt a bit uncomfortable stretching the truth as I looked directly at Mr. Blair for his response. After all, how could I tell him that I did not trust him or the company and wanted to get rid of the responsibility for the house in case I was unfairly fired? His manner softened as he asked me, "Is there anything we can do to help you?" I quickly replied, "I could use a different chair, a flat-backed, shoulder-height chair, nothing fancy or expensive. The one I have in my office is curved and brings my shoulders forward causing the muscles to tense up which increases the pain I feel. The intensity of pain comes more quickly to me each day while sitting in that chair." He said, "No problem. We can do that. Just check with Mr. Seabert." I said, "Thank you." However, I did not get up to leave.

The most important concern to me had not yet been discussed. I moved forward slightly in my chair and explained my biggest concern about returning to work. "It will be a real challenge for me to do my job with the forty-hour-a-week limitation the IME doctor prescribed and we agreed to. I will try to work the forty hours, but my job usually requires more than a forty-hour week." Mr. Blair paused to look me directly in the eye as he cautioned me, "We will be watching your work. You have an important job at Blaster and you will be expected to meet all of your responsibilities." Then he turned his chair to face his computer, which signaled the end of our meeting. I left feeling the threat in his comments.

I soon found that the agreement Blaster and I had for me to work a maximum forty-hour week was not respected by the company. Meetings and work assignments went well beyond an eight-hour day. I constantly had to remind people, including Mr. Blair, that I needed to limit the number of hours I worked. Yet, whenever I mentioned my concern or the agreement, people usually looked away, changed the subject, or walked away. Of course, every time there was a delay in the length of my workday, there was substantial pain for me to suffer that day and usually carried into the next. I suspected that the company's approach was a conscious strategy to wear me down and force me to quit. I remembered Mr. Blair's words, "We will be watching your work … you will be expected to meet all of your responsibilities."

While on my medical leave, I talked about my situation with other injured people and with people who worked in workers' compensation legal practices or for the Ohio BWC in an effort to understand what was happening. They warned me that it was common practice for companies to force employees back to work before their injuries were adequately healed. Even though the individual was in pain, he or she found little or no compassion and eventually either quit or was fired for lack of adequate job performance, which he or she was incapable of giving. Mr. Blair told me that Blaster would be watching my work. In other words, if I did not perform to expectations, I would be fired. I remembered the wolf pack analogy Mr. Blair shared with me one day while I was on medical leave. The lead wolf checks on the injured and leaves them behind if they cannot keep up with the pack. This implied threat, on top of the daily challenge to do my job while taking medication to overcome the ever-increasing pain, added to my stress. The stage was set for failure and Blaster's goal seemed to me to be to dispose of an impaired asset (impaired asset was an accounting term for assets that were no longer productive or of value to a company). This time the impaired asset was me!

As I struggled to do my job, I became increasingly concerned about jeopardizing the healing that I had achieved prior to returning to work. My medical leave was cut short – by five months – as I was seeing improvements in my condition from my tailored physical therapy program. After returning to work, my injury regressed until the chronic pain was once again unbearable, beyond that which it had been in the past.

Why would I subject myself to such torture? Why didn't I just quit? Because I had bills to pay, as most people do, and I did not want to lose my career. Although I had wanted to believe my medical problem would improve once I returned to work, it was becoming obvious that this was becoming more and more unlikely. When the intense pain returned, I at least wanted to know how much I could do at my job. There were probably other reasons, but more important than any was that I wanted to regain my dignity and fulfill my responsibility to my job and my own life commitments. As a compassionate human being and Blaster senior manager, I felt a responsibility to other injured people subjected to a process that unfairly denied the benefits that they were promised. This responsibility became the impetus of a challenge to myself to study the process I was undergoing and not to be another helpless victim.

My senior management peers and I had to ensure efficient and ethical business processes, along with fair treatment of employees and a motivating workplace. It was part of my responsibility as a senior manager to challenge inappropriate business processes, including those related to injured employees. When I considered Blaster's injured employee process, the fair and motivating treatment of employees and my own values of ethics and integrity were put to the test.

I was disappointed over the medical benefits promised to me when I started work at Blaster. The company pushed hard on me with tactics like paid doctor opinions and unreasonable work expectations to cut these benefits. I was incredulous and dismayed. When I imagined how difficult this was for other injured people who did not have the ability to push back or the financial resources to obtain medical care and live on as I did, I became sad for them and disappointed with Blaster. These injured people were unable to demand the medical care and benefits they were promised. My blue-collar background helped me to empathize with others in my circumstances. By using my own experience, I became a mirror for Blaster management to see what their system was doing to injured employees in pain. In this way, I could challenge the process and suggest recommendations for improvements. I wondered if others in Blaster's senior management really understood what the impact of their actions on another human being was. Maybe if I helped them understand, they would agree with me that there was a need for change. Of course, at the time, I did not realize that Blaster's injured employee process was only one part of a larger system that denied benefits for the sick or injured. Had I known, I probably would have felt and responded in the same way.

Before I went on medical leave, people at Blaster and elsewhere implied that I was a cheat, a dishonorable person lacking integrity, and/or someone who was trying to take advantage of the system. I was subjected to my management peers' glancing, sneering eyes, comments in the hallway about workers' compensation cases, and jokes about my condition that were whispered to other people as

60

they walked by my office. Their unkindness only increased my suffering since respect and integrity were very important values in my life. I felt I was losing both. Their comments and jokes made me sad even though I understood that they were probably reacting out of bad stereotypes for injured people trying to collect workers' compensation benefits.

I had learned first hand that these stereotypes were not always correct. I wanted other people to understand this and at least have some compassion for those people injured or sick and unable to work like they had in the past. I believed I had to address Blaster's process, and the only way I could do that was to return to work and hang in there even while subjecting myself to the daily torture of increasing chronic pain.

After I returned to work, I stared each day at an ethics policy in my mailbox with a one-page letter I was required to sign that certified I was following the policy. From time to time, all employees had to recertify compliance with the company's ethics policy. Coincidentally, that time had come once again. I could not sign it this time. I could not lie to the company or to myself by signing the ethics statement without raising my concerns. The more I thought about the timing of this recertification, the more I felt this was more than a coincidence.

During my own suffering and despair, maybe this was a message for me to assertively challenge the approach Blaster used for injured employees. I knew I could not just turn my head away from this disagreeable business practice no matter what the effect would be on me. Maybe it also felt right since I had already lost so much and had so little left to lose. My dignity had already declined and my integrity was questioned. I had an obligation to myself as well as others.

There were other feelings I did not fully understand at the time that encouraged me to do something, anything. I was upset with Blaster for taking away my benefits the way they did. I was also very sad and sometimes depressed about becoming injured and impaired and losing so much. Since I did not want anger to be the force behind my actions, I reviewed my concerns and suggestions with Justine. She helped me quiet my anger and focus on the issues with her voice of reason that was seasoned by her insight into workers' compensation practices. This came from her many years of experience supporting workers' compensation lawyers. The practice of forcing injured people back to work to be fired for nonperformance rather than pay workers' compensation benefits was so wide spread that it was commonly known as "constructive firing." Nonetheless, I knew that the only way I could sign the ethics statement and be in compliance with the policy was to file an ethics violation over the injured employee process. Ironically, compliance with good business ethics policies was part of what I was hired to do. All told, I knew in my heart that I had to do something and so I began.

I submitted a letter to Mr. Blair about my medical experience and the injured employee process used by Blaster. In the letter, I explained how Blaster had canceled my medical benefits and changed my FMLA status based on an erroneous IME. I explained Blaster's claim to request medical reports that my doctors did not receive and trust issues between the company and me. I agreed with him but felt it was my trust with the company that had been broken. After all, they had taken away my employee benefits using an IME and other tactics to empty my safety net at work. From an emptied safety net to hallway comments and looks of suspicion, their betrayal had broken my trust with them. The trust issue was mine. "Trust" in regard to my employer had become a ludicrous word to me.

In the letter, I described how I had asked to return to work to ramp up to full time before I was informed of any change in my medical benefits, but Messrs. Blair and Seabert told me to return to work at one hundred percent or nothing. This demand was made even after I explained to them that I would quickly fail if I returned at one hundred percent. It seemed an irresponsible action for both Blaster and myself. I also made reference in the letter to the second IME as being more credible in spite of significant errors, along with carefully chosen words, to send me back to work with a forty-hour-week limitation "for several months at least." I explained that this limited work schedule would be worth a try, even though the demands of my position required much more time.

In the letter, I also asked that my medical benefits be returned to the levels that were promised when I was hired by Blaster, including the higher pay and longer medical leave for work-related injuries that was included in our employee benefits policy. Instead, Blaster required that I exhaust my vacation benefits rather than pay at the higher work injury benefit level. I wrote about a few other people at Blaster who told me that they had directly or indirectly experienced many of the same underlying issues and concerns I had. I concluded my letter by simply asking Blaster to review Dr. Blunder's IME report with me and to help me better understand the overall medical leave and injured employee process at the company. I referenced the requirement in the ethics policy for prompt reporting of potential ethics violations like this. About a week and a half later, I formally reported an ethics violation since I had not received a response from Mr. Blair, Mr. Seabert, or anyone at Blaster.

In my ethics letter, I repeated the issues that I had written about in the earlier letter, along with other concerns about the injured employee process. I also referenced the Blaster ethics policy in that it goes beyond following the laws, rules, and regulations by requiring that the business be conducted at a higher level that embraced the spirit and intent of the rules. From my years of finance, accounting, and ethics compliance experience, I knew that "spirit and intent" was a phrase sometimes used by companies and other organizations for show when, in fact, the ethics policies were used primarily to protect organizations and their management from legal consequences for their actions, including criminal prosecution. Later, when the company is accused of any wrongdoing, management points to the policies and statements signed by each employee in order to blame the individual for not following the policy rather than have the company or management take responsibility. Since the Blaster ethics policy clearly said this, I felt I had to hold the company to this higher standard of spirit and intent, a standard that clearly would not allow me to sign a piece of paper certifying that I followed the policy unless I reported on the injured employee process. Once I reported my ethics concern, I signed the certification with a calm heart, a clear mind, and a good sense of my own integrity.

In the letter, I also indicated that now, three weeks after I had returned to work, the company doctor, who I had been seeing on a regular basis at Blaster's request, recognized regression with my injury and chronic pain, and suggested that I cut my hours to thirty per week. Neither my supervisor nor Mr. Seabert were willing to adjust my hours at work or my job responsibilities according to the company doctor's suggestion. Further, I noted in the letter that there was still no high, flat-backed chair provided for my use as I had requested a number of times. Even though the Americans With Disabilities Act (ADA) required that special provisions be made for people who have disabilities and medical needs, Mr. Seabert explained to me, "We cannot afford to give everybody a special chair. If we provide you with one, then everybody might want a similar chair." Later, Blaster's response to my comment about the ADA was that I had not achieved a qualified disability rating. I had explained that I was diagnosed as "permanently impaired" and that, with my doctor's approval, I had already purchased a new car, a new couch, a new bed, and other items at home to help with my daily pain. I simply asked Blaster to provide me with a comfortable chair, a request that I believed was in line with the spirit and intent of the ADA. Indeed, following the "spirit" of the ADA suggested these accommodations would be provided, whether as a special chair for me or other special equipment to any employee with medical needs.

There is still sadness in my heart when I remember a broken chair that was offered to me to accommodate my request for a comfortable chair – sadness that there could be such meanness in people I had trusted. Several days after I sent the letter, I was in the restroom and saw Mr. Seabert. He smiled at me and asked me to stop by his office to look at a chair he had found for me to use to help my back problem. We washed and dried our hands and walked to his office to look at the chair. But the chair was designed for low back problems and was old with a small broken back support. I stood back from the chair while looking over at Mr. Seabert and reiterated, "I need a high, flat-backed chair for upper back support. This chair will not work." My voice was low as sadness carried my words. I remembered I had requested and described the type of chair I needed a number of times. There was no question that he knew what kind of chair I needed. Yet here he was with smug and arrogant demeanor looking over at me and pushing the broken chair back and forth as it squeaked. He smiled and said, "But this was used by an employee after a back operation," as if a back operation was the badge of a real back problem. I felt hurt and sad for his betrayal of my trust in him. Even though I knew he was probably upset about my letters, I thought we had achieved a more professional and dignified relationship than this suggested. We were peers in senior management positions who had worked hard together many hours on business projects and employee activities. Still I felt the pinnacle of his disrespect and betrayal with this incident, along with a deep sadness in my soul as I watched a human being purposely hurt and humiliate another human being. I softly told Mr. Seabert, "That chair will not work. I'm sorry," and slowly left his office carrying the weight of his betrayal.

My ethics letter also included a suggestion that it would be more beneficial to have Blaster's doctors and the injured employee's doctors working together on behalf of the injured worker. This would avoid an adversarial situation with a handoff to Blaster's third-party administrator for workers' compensation who was shown to be ineffective with my claim, at least in terms of helping the injured. Trusting the employee and everyone involved in the process to work together, including the company doctor, the company nurse, and other employees, would be beneficial in helping the injured. I became more personal in the letter when I noted that compassion was an issue in a situation where all the doctors, even the IME doctors, agreed that I had a permanent impairment that placed limitations on my life.

The struggle with Blaster over medical benefits added to the physical and emotional challenge that comes with a significant physical impairment and the dramatic changes to an individual's life. Employee benefits were explained one day and within a couple of weeks the benefits were taken away by using inaccurate IME reports. Phone calls I made to people at work about the process and my benefits were not returned or were returned several days later. Then, when I asked to come back to work part time, Blaster cut my benefits and I wondered whether or not I was still employed. All this, even though I had kept people at Blaster informed all along of my pain and the medical treatment that I received. When I returned to work, I gave my medical care and insurance trust over to Blaster. I found more difficulty with my employer instead of alternatives and support to help me succeed at work. It was now thirteen months since the accident and injury. Various medications had adversely impacted my judgment and ability to perform my job. Five months earlier I had asked for a lesser position in a warmer climate per my doctor's advice. I suggested that a large company like Blaster could help injured employees find alternative work so the business could retain some of the talent and experience of their employees, even those impaired. But none was found or offered to me.

The ethics letter continued on about trust issues, hallway conversations, and jokes that I heard from other members of management that referred to people like me with workers' compensation claims. My personal example supported what other employees voluntarily confided to me. Blaster did whatever they wanted to do regardless of rules or policies and what was right. They believed that the company did whatever they wanted whether on the job, in the community, or related to health and other benefits promised to employees. In the ethics letter I described other trust issues that people told me about and mentioned that my neighbors had observed people sitting in a car watching my house around the time of the workers' compensation hearing. I wrote that I hoped Blaster was not spying on injured employees, but I found out they were. Within a short time after returning to work to fulfill my responsibilities as a senior finance manager, I was personally signing fairly large checks to suppliers and executing other significant responsibilities. Certainly, there was trust associated with these responsibilities. But there was very little, if any, trust associated with the medical condition that I had and the injured employee process that I was subjected to.

Soon after I returned to work full time, Mr. Blair explained to me that legal obstacles got in the way of whether or not I could do some work at home, or whether or not I could come into the office a couple of hours a day. I asked Mr. Blair about the legal obstacles, but he had no comment. I thought to myself, what are the legal obstacles? Could we have overcome the obstacles so I could return to work part time or were "legal obstacles" a way of referring to their strategy to rid the business of an injured employee? Communication and general trust certainly would have helped Blaster and me throughout the process. Was Blaster working a plan to conclude the employment of an injured employee – "an impaired company asset?" Was this simply a routine plan carried out from time to time by the company's management with the support of a cadre of high-paid corporate and outside lawyers in order to minimize the ongoing costs of employees injured at work? Indeed, I would never know the answers to these questions or who made the decisions. I found troubling suspicions and conclusions as my situation unfolded, while I researched and learned about other people in similar situations in the Blaster corporation. I suggested in my ethics letter that the current process used for injured employees did not seem to be in the spirit of the employee benefit policies, workers' compensation insurance, or the ADA. Instead, the process was geared toward denying claims. This was most likely a result of the need for companies to meet their aggressive cost reduction goals and safety statistics. Finally, I simply commented, "I just wanted the benefits I was promised in order to complete my medical care. I was on a medical leave that my doctor had prescribed."

When he received my ethics letter, Mr. Blair responded quickly by asking me to work directly with Mr. Seabert. I called Mr. Seabert and told him that I would hold off reporting to Corporate so we would have an opportunity to clear up any misunderstandings even though reporting was required promptly per the policy. He declined my offer. About a week later, as promised, I forwarded the ethics letter to Corporate Headquarters. Then Mr. Seabert sent me a letter in response to my concerns.

Mr. Seabert eventually agreed to schedule a meeting with me to review his letter and my response to his letter. Even though I knew the review was probably going to happen only because of my formal ethics report to Corporate, I was pleased to finally be able to review the many issues, concerns, and recommendations that I had made about the injured employee process. Even if changes did not occur within my Blaster lifetime, I believed that my thoughts had to be heard and recorded if there was to ever be a possibility of change in the future. Indeed, I knew that sometimes the seeds of change lay dormant for a long time waiting for the right circumstances to bring them to life.

Mr. Seabert confirmed that there indeed were people spying on me outside my home, but he added, "It was not done at Blaster's direction. Our third-party administrator went outside of his authority when he had people sit outside your house." I responded, "Maybe the third-party administrator was also responsible for obtaining reports from my doctors that were never requested. Perhaps he hadn't done his job in that situation either." Mr. Seabert sat quietly with no comment or reaction. After a short pause, I mentioned Dr. Blunder's IME report. Once again I asked Mr. Seabert to review this report with me. He responded to my request by stating, "We would have to have medical training in order to recognize this report as a problem. The medical evaluation and conclusions are outside of our capability as businessmen." I was very disappointed in his excuse. I knew as senior managers that we had always questioned anything and everything about the business. I also knew that the errors were obvious and numerous. I told him, "I don't think medical training is necessary to see the deception. My doctors and I were misquoted. The magnitude of the errors, omissions, and misstatements are grossly erroneous … they all support a conclusion that I am medically okay and should return to work. This evaluation occurred within one week of my doctor prescribing a long medical leave for my injury." Mr. Seabert's response was to look at me with a blank expression and no further comment.

The entire time I talked about the process for injured employees and my experience, Mr. Seabert usually sat calmly and listened. He did not suggest any shared concerns or possible improvements to the process, other than commenting on the spying by their third-party administrator. It appeared to me that Blaster wanted to continue to use erroneous IMEs and other tactics to minimize their responsibility for injured employees. And Mr. Seabert seemed content that their strategy worked. While he looked at me and pretended to listen to my plea for improvements to the injured employee process, he did not seem seriously engaged in the topic of the meeting.

I made one last attempt at meaningful dialogue with Mr. Seabert by asking an open-ended question. "What do you think?" Mr. Seabert looked at me thoughtfully and carefully replied, "I think you were hurt in the accident ... but I think you are doing this for the money."

Stunned, I thought what money? They had actually cut off all of my benefits at one point. Did he mean that they never intended to pay the benefits that I had been promised as an employee and wouldn't have paid any had it not been for my formal reporting that demanded their responsibility? Or maybe he did not understand the extent of my injury or possibly viewed this as simply another profitability game for the business. But he was partially right, so I replied, "All along I have told people I want to have my medical bills and some lost wages covered as promised by my employee benefits and workers' compensation insurance."

I paused and looked Mr. Seabert directly in the eye, saying, "I sincerely think that we can do better for people injured at work." Then we looked at each other with what felt like a great distance in our hearts and minds as I also thought that we had probably not been completely honest with each other. Indeed, I was not emotionally honest at our meeting as I held back my anger over his and the company's morality.

I knew Mr. Seabert could not talk about the high profit and management bonus stakes of this employee benefit and workers' compensation issue across the company. I wondered if he was indirectly telling me that had I not spoken out about the injured employee process, they would have been able to fire me for performance issues when I returned to work. Or would I have quit under the increasing pressure to do my job fully like so many other people in similar situations? By formally reporting my concerns, I had recorded my medical condition and created a potential legal liability for the company. Blaster would now have to find a way to address this legal exposure. The possibility that I might publicly explain and pursue remedies for their treatment of injured employees became a concern to them.

I suspected that this was the last time Mr. Seabert and I would discuss the injured employee process, and I was correct. But there was still the independent evaluation of the process by Corporate to look forward to, even though I wondered whether or not the review was going to be a truly independent evaluation.

Struggling with Blaster over my benefits and the injured employee process was very hard at a time when I also suffered deeply with my impairment and medical condition. But I needed medical care and had to pay my bills, so I started thinking of other financial alternatives, including filing a disability insurance claim. At the time of the accident, I was covered by disability insurance that I had purchased through Blaster during the nine years I worked for the company. I assumed that, in the event I became disabled and could not work, I would receive a portion of my earnings from this insurance policy to help pay my house payment and other living expenses. When I looked at the details of the disability insurance, I found that I was only covered if I could not work at all. Further, a physician chosen by the plan, i.e., Blaster, would decide my medical condition.

I now knew that doctors could be hired to render opinions the company was looking for, and I knew that my doctors were tied into a system of returning employees to work regardless of their pain and suffering. Requesting disability payments was probably a waste of my time and already depleted energy. Disappointed once again, I decided to not file a claim for disability payments in order to avoid another struggle with my safety net where so many of the rules of the game were unwritten and far too complex for a reasonable conclusion. Requesting employee benefits and workers' compensation insurance benefits would prove to be a great challenge to my painfully fragile life for quite some time. This, and my struggle to survive my painful chronic illness, would claim all of my time and energy for months to come.

Chapter 6

Near the End

After I returned to work from my medical leave, I drove to work at the last minute each day and quietly slipped into my office hoping to avoid my boss in his office next door and my peers down the hall. We were responsible for running the business and setting the strategy for most of its direction. This took time and energy, along with talent and business intuition, all of which seemed to be almost gone from my life. Instead of engaging in conversation about the company's strategy and operations, I went directly to my office and looked at the in-box on my desk for urgent and important items to delegate to others. I was concerned about the mistakes I was making. I knew that my mistakes could hurt people, as well as the business itself. I wanted to be responsible even with my pain and drug stupor. If I delegated, I had a better chance of getting by one more day at work. After all, most of my work was delegated to others when I was on medical leave and the business did not suffer too much. I decided to continue to delegate and ask others for help until an alternative was found for my situation. Maybe my medical condition would slowly get better and I could keep more work for myself. Or maybe my medical condition would get worse until the company eventually helped me with an alternative work assignment. My list of maybes seemed to be getting shorter as my condition did not improve and soon became much worse.

The intense chronic pain and suffering was extremely bad and hard to accept or justify. It was more than any other struggle in my past and more than enough challenge for my life today. The added struggle with the people around me who either did not believe what I was experiencing and/or suggested that I was trying to get away with something was more than I could tolerate. Even more troubling was realizing that their behavior was either ignorance or, worse, motivated by material greed for the personal financial rewards that came from lower costs for injured employees in order to increase company profitability and management bonuses. The better business results looked good on paper, but there was an incredible sense of indignity served on top of physical and emotional suffering for the injured employees. This was certainly my opportunity to hold a mirror up to management, other leaders, and professionals who probably would not get a chance to see this experience. While they would probably continue to hurt injured people for what they called "the good of the business," maybe they would better see that this was not for the good of other human beings or humanity. I understood that it was sometimes hard to see business practices that went unquestioned and evolved in ways that did not make sense from a moral perspective. So I held a mirror up to people at Blaster, to people working in systems like workers' compensation, medical, and automobile insurance, and to doctors and lawyers who were all part of the system that made up our safety net. Unfortunately, these people and organizations, consciously or unconsciously, stole many of these promises of a safety net at the expense of the individual who was injured and experiencing intense chronic pain and other losses. This safety net issue troubled me, yet I knew, at least for the time being, that I needed to put these issues aside and once again concentrate on healing.

Blaster was heading into a business cycle of strategic planning, budgeting, year-end closing, and other things that would require more intense workdays, along with a lot of overtime. It was highly unlikely that I would be able to meet these greater responsibilities given that I was not doing well with my day-to-day tasks. I also suspected that Blaster had lost patience with my situation. I feared that I would be fired without any benefits. Mr. Seabert may have taken my reporting on the injured employee process personally since it was a process that his department was directly responsible for. He had probably never experienced a thoughtful, intellectual, and assertive response to Blaster's strategy to rid itself of their responsibility for impaired employees. Quite possibly, the politics of my situation were not good for Mr. Seabert,

Mr. Blair, or other executives since I was a senior manager who had filed an ethics violation. I felt I was sure to get an aggressive response from the company when it was time to take another month off of work to attend the pain program.

I made a decision to meet with Mr. Blair and ask for his help once again. I stopped by his office, knocked on the door, and asked if he had a few minutes. He motioned for me to enter his office and sit in the chair in front of his desk. I sat down on the edge of the chair and explained to him how physically I had regressed. I told him how a pain program was now the only alternative for me. I told him I had worked directly with the company as he requested when I returned to work and that I could not continue trying to do my job anymore. I told him that I needed to return to intense therapy, including a pain program. I told him I knew I would probably need to find work that was a better fit with my physical limitations. I needed his help to do this. For the first time in my life, I explained to my boss that I could not do my job and that I had failed, while I also asked Blaster to see their way to helping me somehow. I, in effect, placed myself even more at the mercy of Blaster than when I returned to work less than two months earlier.

From my discussion with Mr. Blair, I realized that it would be best if I left Blaster even though I really wanted to use the medical benefits they promised to me when I was hired. I wanted Blaster to stand behind me when I returned from another medical leave to attend a pain program by providing me a job at the company that fit with my impairment. After all, my impairment was caused by a work-related injury, and I had tried very hard to recover and meet their demands. But, at this point, I hoped for anything that I could get from Blaster to help me pay for the medical care that I needed to heal my injury. Mr. Blair asked me to document our discussion and promised to look into my request. My documentation included the same request for benefits that I had made earlier, along with an alternative of me leaving the company with severance pay. This request for severance pay probably would have not been possible had I not written letters to formally and assertively question the injured employee process and how I was "processed" by Blaster after my injury. Perhaps this was the meaning of Mr. Seabert's comment "I think you are doing this for the money." While the money was not my primary goal, it is interesting how often money will follow the principle of doing what you feel is right. They promised me benefits and had to pay something.

Over the next few weeks, the company worked behind the scenes, probably with Corporate human resources and legal counsel, until one day in the last week of July 1998, Mr. Seabert called me on the phone and invited me to stop by his office. Once again I walked the hallway to his large office on the other side of the building and knocked on the door. Mr. Seabert invited me into his office and motioned for me to sit in one of the chairs in front of his desk, the same chair in which I had sat a few times before to discuss my injury and its many implications. With a slight grin, Mr. Seabert leaned forward in his chair and looked across his large wood desk into my eyes as he said, "You are involuntarily terminated."

My heart dropped to the floor as he paused and looked at me with a smile and a twinkle in his eyes. I was overwhelmed by his comment. I'm sure my eyes were staring at him in disbelief, while my mouth hung open to breathe with fear. I felt a deep sense of failure and loss as I realized that I was fired. I had never in my life been fired from a job. For many agonizing seconds, I looked directly at Mr. Seabert, while he grinned with delighted satisfaction as if the victory was his. I thought that somehow I had been fired with no benefits or severance pay. I became very anxious.

After a long pause, Mr. Seabert explained, "There will be severance pay under certain conditions. You will have to sign an agreement to remove any claims you have with Blaster and our employees." With the thought of some help, I was quickly relieved that I could now focus on healing my injury and chronic pain. I would accept whatever they gave me.

Since I was involuntarily terminated, Blaster gave me short-term financial help provided for in the company's employee benefits policy that included several months of salary and health insurance coverage for another year. That day, and others, I thanked Messrs. Seabert and Blair repeatedly and sincerely for the help. I knew that they probably could have denied this benefit by using IMEs and other tactics and legalities as they had with so many other benefits. I thanked them for throwing me a lifeline. But I knew even this amount of monetary help was trivial when compared to the benefits that I gave up by leaving the company. I also knew my unpaid medical bills and loss of earnings potential in the future was enormous. But I knew Blaster was not interested in the benefits that were promised or even the levels of pain that I had experienced and probably would experience for the rest of my life. I understood and accepted that I was hurt in an accident and would have to shoulder the pain and many life changes. All I ever wanted from Blaster was the benefits that were promised to me when I started my job and a little compassion at the end. Yet the benefits were few and no compassion was ever expressed by any of my management peers at Blaster over the losses in the life that was to be my future. Instead, I was fired and received severance pay with an agreement that was legally postured to stop the company's responsibility for me, including my future workers' compensation benefits.

Probably to be sure I would not come back later to say that I was under duress when I signed the agreement, Mr. Seabert insisted that I review the agreement with my attorney. Asserting duress to get out of the agreement was a real possibility since everyone knew how much pain I was in, as well as the level of medications I was taking to get by while working. But I no longer had legal counsel once I returned to work. I took the agreement to a local attorney for a quick review. At my request, the severance agreement was revised to say that I could continue to pursue my claims for workers' compensation benefits.

While this agreement allowed for my workers' compensation claims, Blaster would fight hard with other lawyers, third-party administrators, and IME doctors who were good at overcoming these types of claims. There was also an unstated legality about giving up claims to lost wages if you take money as part of a severance agreement. But I did not know about their success disputing workers' compensation claims and this legality, nor did the attorney that I hired to review the agreement on my behalf. No wonder Blaster so readily accepted this change to the severance agreement.

Once again, Blaster and their cadre of high-paid company lawyers minimized the expense of disposing of another impaired resource by using legal tactics to reduce Blaster's responsibilities and costs on the back of an injured employee. Unlike Blaster, I did not have such legal expertise at my disposal or proven business practices with a list of tactics tested and refined over the years in a number of businesses throughout the United States. But I did have my own sense of responsibility and intuitive guidance, along with a few alternatives for pursuing and prosecuting my workers' compensation claim with Blaster.

Over time my alternatives for prosecuting my workers' compensation claim, while hopefully helping other injured people pursue their claims, would include filing a complaint, appeal, and report of fraud to the state BWC. I would also write this book, set up an organization called Heywer to help other people survive chronic pain, create a website for Heywer as a resource for information and shared stories about chronic pain survival, and other activities for helping people survive chronic pain, including personal one-on-one discussions and encouragement. As the possibility to help others became real to me, this work became meaningful and worthwhile. A ruthless side to humanity was highlighted in a magnitude that I had never before seen in my life and I felt my developing work as an advocate for others in similar situations to mine was truly needed.

Blaster knew they had responsibility for my medical bills and lost wages under workers' compensation insurance guidelines. They had to have some responsibility or they would not have used so many deny tactics and legal posturing along the way. Justine told me one day, "They will never really believe you unless they have to pay." My hope was that the severance pay, in addition to being helpful to me and very much appreciated, also meant that I was heard and the system had been dented as a result of Blaster seeing at least part of the mirrored reflection I had been holding up to them. They probably could have continued with their process of IMEs to again say I was fit to work, deny my need for a pain program, and then fire me when I left work to attend the pain program. But they did not, maybe because of my ethics reporting, other employees watching my situation, or their need to move ahead with the business. However decided, the severance pay felt to me like a positive gesture from Blaster. It was also like cashing in the last chip I had from my career

– a chip that was polished by holding up a mirror as an injured employee and documenting my concerns in a formal ethics report before they had a chance to fire me.

Over the next few days after my termination, I went to work a few hours each day to finish up some of my open projects and help out as much as possible. I was also having a hard time leaving and letting go of the people who were my friends and colleagues at work, along with the job and career I loved. After a few days of slowly finishing up my open projects, I sadly told Mr. Blair, "My last day will be tomorrow. I am ready to go."

On my last day at the plant, as I was packing my personal belongings in a box, Mr. Blair stopped by my office and handed me an envelope. It was a letter from Corporate that said their investigation of the potential ethics violation I reported was complete. They concluded that there was no ethics violation with the injured employee process or my situation. I stood in quiet contemplation behind my desk for the last time and read the letter twice. I put it back in its envelope and tossed it into my box.

After I finished packing the pictures of my boys, some personal papers, and a few inspirational posters I carried with me over the years, I told Mr. Blair that I was ready to leave. He escorted me through the hallways, down the steps, and outside to the security desk so the guards could examine my box of personal belongings. As we walked, Mr. Blair suggested we get together in the future to visit over beers. I agreed but suspected that it would never happen. A few people that I knew walked by and looked away or looked down when I smiled at them. They recognized the security routine for terminated employees and were uncomfortable. All I wanted to do was say goodbye to my former friends and coworkers, but I was never given that simple opportunity for closure.

Even though for the first time in my life I had been fired, my emotions changed quickly from despair and disbelief to a calm acceptance. The acceptance of more loss of my previous life and its capability was encouraged by a sense of relief that the work decision had been made, the termination event had occurred. This was an event that I had come to believe was inevitable. Acceptance came in part from my intuitive sense that Blaster wished to see me gone so they could continue to move forward aggressively in the business world. After over a year of trying to heal while at work, then being out on medical leave for more aggressive therapy, followed by returning to work and experiencing tortuous pain while under-performing my job, I was finally terminated. Indeed, I had suspected that I would be terminated at some point, especially after being forced to return to work at the request of the company doctor and the IME doctors. I knew I had returned to work in order to hang on to my job and the intense and challenging career that I had known for most of my life. And, if necessary, I wanted to demonstrate the extent of my injury to the skeptics. After all, I could not just walk away from so many trust, integrity, and benefits issues. By hanging in there at work, I was able to request changes and improvements to the systems that the company used for handling injured employees. This was part of my job. I was also able to make one more request of the company for help in the context of the benefits promised to me as an employee of Blaster for over nine years. Unfortunately, the return to work came at the expense of much pain and a cloudy, medicated mental and emotional state that almost let my life pass over the precipice. Fortunately I had survived again, at least for the present time.

# # #

Fifteen months after the accident and now unemployed, the pain had become so incredible that my despair was probably as much as it could be while still hanging on to life. There was only one hope left and it had nothing to do with my family, my work, or even my love of life. Even the most important parts of my life were no longer felt. They had disappeared in my pained drug stupor. The only option left was to find some medical relief that would allow me to experience hope once again in my life. This possibility, this last hope, was the pain program at Valley Hospital in Dayton, only thirty minutes from my home in Troy.

For many months, I had heard from a number of doctors and others that the pain program was the last resort for chronic pain sufferers. Indeed, I had tried everything I could possibly think of.

Western medicine, alternative medicine, reading medical, spiritual and self-help books, prayer and spiritually, reviewing my past, stopping all my personal activities, and more were tried. Now I finally had concluded my employment. Even though the adverse financial impact of my injury continued to deepen, along with my fear of future earnings potential and questionable insurance benefits, I decided to attend the pain program at an estimated cost of more than $12,000. Hopefully the health insurance included in my severance agreement would pay for most of this expense. I had to reach for this last hope no matter what the financial consequences would be. The feeling of being alone with so much pain and loss in my life was more than I could bear. I felt stripped to the bone physically and empty emotionally and spiritually. I had reached the precipice of life and death. There was nothing left – nothing left but screeching pain in my life and a dim flickering green light of hope from the pain program at Valley Hospital.

Sixteen months after my injury, I was admitted into the pain clinic at Valley Hospital to learn a pain management program. While I was hopeful, I really had very little idea of what was going to happen during this one-month, full-time program. There would be a second month of therapy, aftercare, and follow-up. Once at the hospital, I soon found that the pain program taught a broad collection of techniques to manage pain. Pain management was complemented with physical therapy and other Western medicine to accomplish the most healing for each patient's injuries. The program was designed with new patients starting each week so that there were always patients from the four different stages of the program attending at the same time. The idea was that patients new to the program could learn and be inspired by the patients who were starting their fourth and final week of the full-time portion of the program. Later I also learned that the pain program was a place to transition – to transition to a life of chronic pain with the possibility of finding acceptance of a very different new life for each patient.

When most people started the pain program, they believed the only possible solution to their hopelessly painful life was a medical fix, a drug, an operation, or something that would turn off the switch of pain that was there every day. This was my belief as well until, at the end of the program, I realized that there was no switch and there was no cure. The physical manipulations, therapy, and adjustments at the hospital most days for six weeks all reduced the level of pain. The tailored home exercise program and constant stretching I learned to practice each day of my life also helped. A new physical approach to daily activities using sound body mechanics also provided some relief. The relaxation techniques that provided a way of going inside of myself, focusing on the pain, and relaxing my muscles also helped turn down the pain level. Yet, at the end of the program, the other patients and I were still left with a lot of the pain and discomfort we started with. Fortunately, we also left the program with new tools, renewed hope to carry us forward, and a newfound confidence in redefining our lives. My current daily pain management program is included as Appendix 18.

Indeed, the pain program experience provided some physical recovery and hope for a future. From the last few conversations I had with the medical practitioners at Valley Hospital, I knew I had been given all the treatment that was available from Western medicine, along with some alternative medicine. For me, the pain program was a fresh start to an eighteen-month-old problem. From here on, it was up to me to make the best of life that I could with the tools I now had for pain management. Indeed, I needed to put a new life together for myself. Unfortunately, my new life would include an ongoing struggle over insurance and other benefits promised by my safety net providers. For a complete review of a pain management program, read *Surviving the Chronic Pain Experience: Understand and Manage Medical Care and Life Changes.*

Chapter 7

Mirrors

The year and a half I spent living with chronic pain before gaining acceptance into the pain program was a year and a half too long for me. Learning and using a tailored pain management program was very important to my daily survival of chronic pain. I had a hard time imagining what it was like for the people who had to wait three, four, five, or even seven years or more to find relief for their chronic pain condition. Yet they had little choice but to wait for a better way of understanding their physical limitations and how to manage the chronic pain in their lives. These people had to wait because they were told to wait. Instead of providing medical care and compassion, the systems pushed back on the patient with a delay and deny response to a pain program prescription. They were forced to wait while their prescription to a pain program was delayed. Sometimes the medical system provided cheaper alternatives such as different drugs or operations for people to try. Or people were told to try different approaches on their own, which many times were trivial in comparison to their pain condition. Erroneous doctors' opinions, impossible paperwork, and other tactics were also used to avoid the high expense of the pain program. Many injured people could not handle the pain, along with the delay response, so they exited the system. They simply went away to find their own pain management through a life of drugs, alcohol, and unemployment. Some people simply chose to conclude their painful and hopeless lives of endless suffering and inadequate medical care. Chronic pain is cited as the cause for as much as half of all suicides in our country.

Toward the end of my attendance at the pain program, I came to believe strongly in the promise and possibility of the program with its renewed hope for people with chronic pain. I wrote a positive letter of recommendation to the Administrator (director) of the BWC for the State of Ohio (Appendix 7). I also sent a copy to one of the State's elected United States Senators. I wrote to the BWC since most of the people I knew had come to the pain program with work-related injuries. All of them experienced long delays from their workers' compensation insurance. They encountered a very difficult approval and funding process, along with other BWC and employer tactics, to delay their benefits. These people had suffered every day from an injury that occurred while they were performing their work responsibilities. They were also subjected to a difficult and onerous process for recovering insurance benefits. They needed medical care and some help with lost wages. Their medical conditions deteriorated from inadequate medical care, along with the stress of the denials for the much-needed benefits. Their lives were now physically and financially challenged.

My letter to the BWC documented my concerns with the health care system, workers' compensation insurance, and various administrators that supported the tactics to deny or delay desperately needed pain programs. People injured at work were covered by workers' compensation insurance but could not get the benefits they needed. I asked the BWC Administrator for his help to improve the workers' compensation system. I also volunteered to further discuss the issues, along with my concerns.

Just in case this first letter was too much of a generalization, I wrote another letter the following week to the BWC Administrator. I asked for his review of my specific situation and requested changes to Blaster's workers' compensation process (Appendix 8). To make my point and encourage his review, I detailed the issues, along with the significant effort I put into my claim. Yet I had very little success, even though the validity of my work injury had been tested and confirmed at a BWC hearing.

A few weeks later, I received a phone call from an individual in the BWC Administrator's office. He explained, "We are pleased that the pain program was a success for you. We support its use as medical treatment where appropriate." Then he paused, as if he had made his only important point. I reiterated, "Part of my letter explained that there are many times when people are not provided

82

this medical treatment in a timely manner even when prescribed by their doctors." He replied, "The proper documentation and prescription from the individual's physician of record is very important." I explained, "But many times the program was denied or delayed even with the proper documentation and prescription. The medical care was delayed for various reasons like those I noted in my second letter that covers my specific experience." He then explained, "The workers' compensation system is moving to a managed care concept similar to that in place for regular employee health insurance. We believe this new development will help with your concern."

The Administrator did not seem to be very familiar with my situation with Blaster. Instead, it sounded like the BWC believed a new system was supposed to solve all the current problems. The BWC usually directly administered workers' compensation insurance only for smaller companies. The managed care system he mentioned was simply another handoff to a third party similar to the third-party administrators that were used by many large companies self-insured for workers' compensation insurance – companies like Blaster. This handoff would be an opportunity for smaller organizations to say "no" to their injured employees. Later I learned that the managed care concept did just that – deny and delay where the third-party handoffs are the gatekeepers to medical care. These gatekeepers who are interested in cost reduction ahead of adequate medical care have become an integral part of the health care crisis in our country. The theory of a helpful administrator or third party was good. But when they were directed and controlled by a business or other organization, then the goals of the business or organization were served. These goals include reducing the cost of health care. Even though my personal issues were well documented in my second letter, I decided not to argue any more with this man. I thanked him for his phone call, he thanked me for my letters, and we said goodbye. I wondered if he really understood the details behind the broader issues with workers' compensation and health care insurance that we call a health care crisis.

The United States Senator that I sent a copy of the letter to did not respond to my pain program recommendation or concerns. Was he too busy to respond? Was the issue too politically charged? Or was he unconcerned for the years of additional pain and suffering that injured employees experience at the hands of the State's workers' compensation system? I would never know the answers to these questions. I did know that our elected officials certainly understood the issues making up the health care crisis. They had read or been briefed about deny tactics and third-party handoffs. Maybe the politics of the health care crisis did not yet support its resolution.

#

When Justine came home from her job each day, we usually went for a two-mile walk around the neighborhood. Many times she listened to my anger and frustration about my safety net and usually offered to help me even more than she already had. With her support, I decided to continue to ask for improvements from my safety net providers as I searched for closure to my situation.

Early in the day, I drafted letters to people and organizations requesting improvements to the system. Later in the day, I dictated and edited this book. At night and on weekends, Justine typed my work and helped me sort through my thoughts and emotions while she encouraged my recovery. Over time, I saw Justine's support, my restlessness, and the free time I had as a spiritual message for me to continue to push back on the systems and to finish this book. At times, I even felt a calm and peaceful labor of love while I wrote my story and the many letters. Maybe this was where some difference could be made.

The letters I wrote after my time in the pain program would help people understand the implications of the many inter-related systems making up the health care crisis. People would understand the emptied safety nets of people sick or injured. Indeed, sending the letters also helped satisfy my spiritual desire for closure to the many safety net issues in my life. I hoped a few people would use the letters as templates to write for help with their own issues. Or maybe some people would be encouraged enough by my work to hold a mirror up to other people in order to make a difference. More and more people would add pebbles to the pond to effect some worthwhile change for the better care and compassion of the sick, injured, and impaired. This was certainly a worthwhile cause to support.

Eighteen months after my car accident, workers' compensation insurance had paid less than $200 of my $9,000 of medical bills. More bills were accumulating for the pain program and other medical care. My financial concerns and frustration over my safety net were increasing. I turned to a third law firm for help with my workers' compensation claim. Dr. Lee, whom I trusted and was also independent of Blaster's health care plan and its influence, recommended this law firm. After the law firm reviewed my situation and agreed to help, Attorney Cliff was assigned to my case. Attorney Cliff's workers' compensation expertise included many years as an experienced lawyer, as well as a respected teacher at a local university.

In a letter, I asked Attorney Cliff for guidance about the additional harm caused to me by the erroneous medical opinions given by Blaster's IME doctors and its company doctor. The letter summarized my situation and medical care since the accident. The visits with the IME doctors and the impact of their evaluations on my job and medical benefits were also explained. Their medical opinions were used to force me back to work before I had sufficiently recovered. I was unsure if I would be able to do my job adequately. A few days later, Attorney Cliff called and told me there was no legal help possible. The only recourse I had was to file a complaint with the State Medical Review Board, so I did.

In the complaint (Appendix 9), I explained that the IME opinions included erroneous and false information to support medical conclusions that were used to force me back to work before I was adequately recovered.   Once at work, I failed because of the inadequate medical care and intense pain from my injury.   The Medical Review Board completed their investigation and concluded:

> After thorough review, the Board's Secretary
> and Supervising Member decided that the situation
> outlined in your complaint does not support initiation
> of disciplinary action under the State's Medical
> Practices Act. Even though your complaint has been

closed, it will be kept on file. Thank you for bringing your concerns to the Board's attention.

After I read the Medical Review Board's response a few times, I concluded that apparently doctors could render medical opinions without any consequence, regardless of the accuracy of the opinion and its impact on injured people. The medical opinions rendered by Blaster's IME doctors were "paid opinions" purchased to refute my injury, reduce or eliminate Blaster's responsibility, and force me back to work. Ironically, the time spent and money paid by Blaster for these hired guns could have been used to support my medical recovery and increase the probability that I could have returned to work as a productive employee. But this must not have been their goal. Instead, other systems were soon called on to help Blaster dispose of an impaired human resource.

One month after my discharge from the pain program, Blaster sent me to yet another IME. Since I no longer worked for Blaster, I wondered what the purpose was for a third IME at a time when I now had tools for managing chronic pain and improving my condition. I was suspicious of its purpose and distrustful of its conclusions so I did not ask for a copy of the report. Eventually Attorney Cliff sent me a copy to read anyway. I quickly learned that the third IME report was written to dispute Blaster's responsibility for my pain program medical bills from Valley Hospital. Blaster used the first IME with more than thirty errors, omissions, and misstatements to cut my employee medical benefits and workers' compensation benefits while at work. This was not enough; Blaster used a second IME to force me back to work before I had completed my medical leave and sufficiently healed. This too was not enough; forced back to work, intense suffering, and being fired was not enough. Blaster had hired the third IME to be sure that they did not have to pay workers' compensation benefits for the $16,000 of medical bills I incurred for the pain program.

Fortunately, the healing I experienced from therapists, fellow patients, and others at the pain program gave me enough strength to continue a forward momentum in my life. This help from hard-working people of integrity had guided me away from life's precipice, refreshed my spirit, and strengthened my emotions and self-confidence. I realized I would need this strength and more to face the many disappointments in my safety net, especially since I also wanted to push back on the system and my safety net providers in a meaningful way.

When I read the third IME report, I remembered the day of the exam. I drove to the IME doctor's office and waited uncomfortably for over an hour in the lobby of the doctor's office. Even though discouraged and in pain, I promised myself that I would answer the doctor's questions honestly and with integrity. Eventually I was escorted to an examining room. After a shorter wait, the doctor came in, smiled pleasantly, shook my hand, and said, "Hello, I'm Dr. Topaz." I said, "Hi, I have a package of doctors' reports and journals for your review." I handed him a package similar to the one I had provided the second IME doctor in order to explain my condition as accurately as possible. Dr. Topaz sensed my concern as he tried to assure me, "I will do the best I can to provide an accurate medical evaluation."

Later, while reading Dr. Topaz's IME report in detail, I found that the report had more credibility and fewer errors, omissions, and misstatements compared to the first and second IME reports. Nonetheless, with all the medical history provided by my doctors and the reports written by Blaster's other two IME doctors and its company doctor, he chose words and phrases that would once again minimize the extent of my injury to reduce or eliminate Blaster's responsibility for the pain program. Dr. Topaz also took the opportunity to omit certain medical opinions and facts from my treating physicians. Dr. Topaz indicated that I had pain over the shoulder blade that radiated into my right arm, but he did not even mention the constant pain in my back or the occasional neck pain. He indicated that I had tingling in my right arm, which was present off and on, yet he did not say it was an unpleasant tingling or a pain referral from my shoulder and back. He indicated that I denied any prior significant injury, while the file indicated a car had struck me in 1966 when I was eleven years old and also had had several motorcycle spills in the 1970s. I explained to Dr. Topaz that there was no aftereffect from the car accident more than thirty years ago.

The motorcycle spills came from riding at slow speeds in the grassy hills and occasionally losing control and laying the bike down. I simply got up, brushed myself off, got back on the motorcycle, and drove away with my buddies. This happened when I was fifteen years old. Neither incident was significant for any long-term pain or impairment. I denied any prior significant injuries since there were none.

Dr. Topaz's report also had a section called Psychiatric History where he indicated that a psychologist saw me in 1987 due to personal problems and in 1998 by Dr. Martin through the pain management program. I had explained to him that in 1987 I was going through a divorce. I had custody of my sons as a single parent and had moved to another state for work. My boys and I went to see a psychologist to help work through some of the issues related to the significant changes we were going through in our lives. I simply wanted to be sure I was approaching our challenging family situation as best as possible. Referring to this as "personal problems" seemed to place it in a different light. Later in his report, he also provided a one-paragraph summary of his review of the files provided by other doctors. Here, he picked out certain facts and omitted many, many others to support his conclusions and opinions. While his medical opinion was better crafted than the first two IMEs, his report was definitely slanted to support the company's goal to reduce or eliminate their responsibility for the pain program.

In his report, Dr. Topaz did not mention who had referred me to the pain program. Nor did he report the impact to me from being forced to return to work. He did not mention that once I returned to work, my condition quickly regressed, the pain intensified, and more medication was needed earlier in the day. My decision-making ability and job performance declined from the increasing pain and drug stupor until I was involuntarily terminated because of my medical condition. While back at work, I was seeing the company nurse almost daily and the company doctor weekly or every other week in the company's medical office. I repeatedly asked them what I should do. Nurse Jones suggested a TENS unit, different medications, and attending a pain program. The company doctor said there was nothing more he could do and suggested I return to

Dr. Hunt, the doctor of physical medicine who had treated me. When I saw Dr. Hunt, he also prescribed the pain program.

It was the pain program for which Dr. Topaz was hired to write a third IME report to refute Blaster's responsibility. There was no reference made in his report that both Nurse Jones and my doctor had suggested the pain program. I was sent by the company doctor to see my doctor for help with my deteriorating condition. My doctor had cared for my injury and chronic pain from the work-related car accident eighteen months earlier. But this was not mentioned. After all, this medical history would not have supported another comment in the third IME report that I was found maximally medically improved as early as six months before starting the pain program. This reference was made by Dr. Topaz to Dr. Blunder's IME, thereby inferring I was okay and did not need to attend the pain program because of my injury from the car accident.

Dr. Topaz concluded that the pain program was required due to conditions not recognized on my claim. At the BWC hearing eight months earlier, my injury was decided to be work related as a thoracic and cervical sprain/strain. My chronic pain condition was not included as an allowed condition. At the hearing, my lawyer, Attorney Severs, should have argued that my chronic pain diagnosis was a medical condition for my claim. But he did not, possibly because of my last-minute change in counsel. The Blaster lawyer and Nurse Jones did not mention the chronic pain diagnosis at the hearing either. Yet we all had the doctor's reports in our files with the chronic pain diagnosis. In the end, my chronic pain diagnosis was not entered into the Record of Proceedings for the hearing. I wished I would have known the importance of reporting the full diagnosis on all the BWC forms and at formal hearings. I assumed others would report the full diagnosis and facts. I should not have trusted people, including my own doctors, lawyers, and employer, to file or fully acknowledge the reported diagnosis or treatment, including the chronic pain diagnosis that was so important. Indeed, this diagnosis would eventually have to be allowed in my claim at another BWC hearing if I would ever have my claim fully supported and accurately decided.

Even though the chronic pain diagnosis was included in many of the BWC forms and doctors' reports that Dr. Topaz was given for his review and use in his IME, my chronic pain condition was not recognized in the third IME. In the end, nitpicking the BWC paperwork was the support behind the third IME opinion rather than an appropriate medical evaluation and comprehensive diagnosis that was well supported in the file. The difficult forms and requirements for recovering workers' compensation insurance was certainly an opportunity for nitpicking paperwork to deny claims. The IME opinions with many errors, omissions, and misstatements were another opportunity to support the denial of medical treatment and responsibility. Yet very few, if any, mistakes or errors supported my condition and medical treatment. A fellow coworker of mine used to refer to situations like this as "mighty funny rubber that doesn't stretch both ways."

I was disappointed that Blaster would go to such lengths to avoid their employer responsibility for a work injury and the medical treatment I needed. I was beginning to see a pattern of deceit that was unbelievable to me. I was disappointed that there was a large group of IME doctors who would perform limited medical examinations to render adverse medical opinions that provided a tool for employers to get out of their responsibility to injured employees. The third IME provided another round of despair and sadness for me over what seemed like an endless system of employers, IME doctors, and lawyers that pushed their responsibility onto the backs of the injured. These high-paid professionals did this until they got away with whatever it was they could. Surprisingly, I did not feel a sense of violation of my person when I saw this third IME doctor like I did while attending the first IME. Instead, this time I felt numb – numb to the doctor's touch, numb to the whole system and its process, numb to more and more violation of my person, and numb to the dishonesty I saw in this practice.

After I read the third IME report a few times, I put it aside and once again tried to put the entire experience into a reasonable perspective. As I reflected more thoughtfully, I began to see a discrepancy between my physical impairment and how my safety net providers responded to it. They did not respond to the reality of the many implications of the injury in my life. They responded to their own needs of self-protection. My impairment with its physical limitations and ongoing need for medical treatment and pain management was a part of me. I wanted to accept and care for this part of me like I did my entire physical, emotional, intellectual, and spiritual being. Maybe acceptance was the key.

Even after my meditation, I was still very uncomfortable with my safety net. I felt a need to follow my spirit that was encouraging me to request responsibility from my safety net providers. I had to respond to an ugliness of humankind that was repeatedly shown to the injured. Self-serving businesses, organizations, and many medical and legal professionals did these things in the interest of shareholder wealth, bottom-line profitability, and individual greed. At first I did not understand Blaster's Director of Human Resources when he told me that I was going to be treated no differently than anybody else. I eventually learned firsthand what he meant and that he was right. My disappointment and disbelief over the loss of safety net benefits for me and others who shared his promise was so thick that acceptance could not cut through to a new life. An equitable mistreatment did not make it right, no matter how many matter-of-fact comments of acceptance I heard from the medical and legal professionals and others working every day with our safety nets. They repeatedly said, "That's just the way it is."

Even the doctors I had chosen during my course of treatment told me that IME doctors would give companies the kind of reports they wanted in order to help the company avoid financial responsibility. They did this regardless of the injured's medical condition or the consequence of the benefits the sick or injured lost from an erroneous IME. Comments I received from so many other people working in the system each day verified that these tactics and more were readily available, acceptable, and used by companies to refute all of their injured employees' medical care and claims. The work on my safety net became meaningful for me at a time when their obvious deceit did not seem possible and was difficult for me to believe. And no other work was found to satisfy my yearning to work during these many long days of pain and grieving.

#

While meditating one day, the thought came to me to contact the local BWC about my concerns with their workers' compensation system. I telephoned the BWC. They agreed with my observation and encouraged me to file a formal complaint. The woman I talked to at the BWC was surprisingly helpful and understanding of my situation as she encouraged me to pursue my claim. Later during the phone call, she also explained that the tactics to deny responsibility were commonly used by many self-insured employers. She and others were aware of the impact of financial problems added to the physical pain and suffering of injured employees. She accepted the system, just as so many other people did. Rather than getting more upset, I tried hard this time to understand why there was so much acceptance for the system. Some people had tried and were still trying to make positive changes to the system. Did other people think the system was too big and/or difficult to change? There were also many people who simply needed the jobs the system provided them. Those paid indirectly by the BWC included the IME doctors that were paid for their opinions and the lawyers who took one-third of the injured's benefits that had to be fought for legally. Maybe the BWC woman's compassionate listening to my concerns was all she felt she could do since she was also employed by the system. Either way, I appreciated her encouragement to continue my quest for responsibility and safety net improvements.

The next day I wrote a letter asking my attorney to help me recover medical bills and request system improvements. I suggested a strategy of filing a complaint with the BWC with copies to government officials and others to show how blatantly irresponsible Blaster used the system. After a few weeks went by with no response from Attorney Cliff, I decided to once again handle the reporting and request for improvements on my own, starting with my BWC complaint.

The woman at the BWC had mailed me a complaint form to complete that included boxes to check for areas of complaint, along with an area for comments. I checked the following boxes on my form:

- Initial compensation not timely paid in allowed claim
- Compensation not paid biweekly
- Compensation payment refused/delayed in allowed claim
- Compensation not paid for entire period of disability
- Employer not responding timely to request for treatment
- Employer forces use of vacation/sick leave before paying compensation
- Medical bills not timely paid in allowed claim (attach copies of bills)
- Employer refuses to acknowledge change in attending physician
- Employer refuses to pay travel expenses (attach copy of request)
- Employer does not explain or assist injured worker with workers' compensation

While five other boxes were not checked on the form since they did not relate to my situation, I checked the "other" box and commented:

- Other: Employer lied about involvement of BWC and third-party administrator receipt of documentation, etc.; injured worker's representative unable to work with employer's "tactics;" employer suggests employee ask new attorney to start over as forms and rules are too difficult; completed C-161 forms were not forwarded to the third-party administrator (twice faxed to employer) for the two physicians of record; third-party administrator and employer would not assist or explain requirements as promised; no formal response to 07/20/1998 pain program request, verbal approval provided by employer, while third-party administrator indicated not approved (verbal); employer and third-party administrator claim no receipt of documentation they claim to have provided to each other, unable to confirm receipts of duplicate documentation; and blatantly irresponsible process to deny claims (detail attached)

In order to demonstrate the sincere effort on my part, along with the deny tactics used by Blaster and the third-party administrator, I attached a letter that explained my complaint in greater detail (Appendix 10). I detailed some of the numerous conversations I had relative to my workers' compensation claim. Much of this information was an update of my activities to those already detailed in an earlier letter to the BWC (Appendix 8). There had been no response to this letter by anyone at the BWC or Blaster.

The details of my conversations over the phone or in person with Blaster and others about my claim demonstrated inconsistencies and tactics that seemed obvious to me. I wanted others to read the history and draw their own conclusions about Blaster's BWC process. Regardless of all the detailed conversations and activities, I felt the numbers spoke for themselves. Blaster had only reimbursed $200 of over $9,000 of medical bills I had submitted to date, which was before receipt of the pain program bills that alone totaled more than $16,000. And my lost wages had not even been considered.

After submitting the BWC complaint, I thought that if my medical bills were not reimbursable under workers' compensation insurance, then Blaster's employee health plan was another insurance source to cover my medical bills. I could ask for reimbursement, at least until the workers' compensation issues were resolved. Not surprisingly, though, my employee health insurance company, Alto Health, had already adopted a similar, although less aggressive, "deny, deny, deny" approach. For example, prior to my interviews for the pain program, my primary care physician for Alto Health, Dr. Smith, submitted the necessary referral for the pain program at Valley Hospital. Both the hospital administrator for the program and I called

Alto Health to ensure the necessary paperwork was submitted. We were told that Alto Health covered me for the pain program. Later, after I completed the pain program and the medical bills were sent out by the hospital, Alto Health twice claimed they did not receive the referral paperwork. I called Alto Health repeatedly with the dates of the paperwork until they agreed that the referral had been received. Next, the hospital sent a bill in excess of $10,000 to Alto Health. They first claimed it was never received and then was lost. When additional copies of these bills were sent twice by the hospital to Alto Health at my request, the insurance company still told me that the bills had not been received in their system. Yet, when Valley Hospital contacted Alto Health directly, they were told that all the bills had been received. When the bills were still not paid, I called Alto Health again. This time they told me that the bills had not been received, probably because they had a limited capacity for the electronic submission of bills. Without pause, I made numerous phone calls over the next several weeks and waited on hold for long periods to challenge Alto Health's personnel until they recognized that all the billings were at least received and would be considered for payment. Then Alto Health lumped the occupational therapy and physical therapy under "hospital incidentals" and denied payment once again by claiming the pain program referral did not cover these charges. After many phone calls, they agreed to match the referral to these mislabeled bills.

During my review of medical bills with Alto Health, I learned that the psychology portion of the pain program bill was forwarded to another insurance company. Psychology Insurance handled mental health care separately, according to my employee health plan. Psychology Insurance needed a separate referral and pre-certification that was not explained to the hospital administrator or me before I attended the pain program. Since we did not get the pre-certification for the psychological care, it appeared that $1,000 or more would not be considered for payment. The $2,100 for psychological treatment was now considered "out of network" and would be paid after a larger deductible.

The two insurance companies, Alto Health and Psychology Insurance, also disagreed over who should be responsible for some of the bills, so they both denied responsibility and payment. Then Psychology Insurance told me that they had requested medical reports from Valley Hospital but had only received an itemized billing. Once again, I called the hospital to ask the hospital administrator for the reports. She again requested the medical reports and this time personally copied and mailed them to Psychology Insurance. Psychology Insurance met even this effort with another delay. Over the next few weeks, I left three voice mail messages with Psychology Insurance to verify that they had received the medical reports from Valley Hospital, but no one ever returned my phone calls.

Alto Health's employee health plan's deny and delay tactics were similar to those used by Blaster and their third-party administrator for my workers' compensation claim. They were similar yet less aggressive in that Alto Health eventually accepted most of their responsibility for my medical bills. While I understood the need for companies to reduce medical costs, I felt more and more that using deny tactics to support broken safety net promises was very harmful to the sick and injured. These people needed the medical care and financial help they had been promised. The denials and tactics to not pay benefits to the sick and injured exacerbated their condition as a result of inadequate medical care. There was added despair and depression over a difficult financial situation for the injured and their families. Blaster, like most big companies, was self-insured for employee health insurance and workers' compensation insurance. They benefited directly by denying or delaying medical benefits and reducing medical insurance costs, regardless of how it was accomplished. My resolve to push back to require fulfillment of the promises of the insurance companies and others responsible for my safety net and the safety nets of others increased.

Whenever I requested the payment of medical bills from my employee health plan and workers' compensation processes, I also explained to the people that I talked to the impact of the system to an injured person's life. I explained about the added financial difficulties that greatly increased the emotional stress and suffering to an injured person and their family during their health crisis. Most people listened to my plea for responsibility and compassion. Many suggested that it was simply "the way it was." A few encouraged my advocacy for the sick and injured. But no one agreed to take up the cause with me in any significant manner. Yet I felt good about my efforts. The insurance people and others were left to choose what difference this awareness would make in their lives as safety net providers and administrators of the systems.

Chapter 8

Acceptance

About the time I found a part-time job teaching at the local vocational school, Valley Hospital started to push me to pay my medical bills for the pain program I had attended six months earlier. They hired a debt collector to force me to pay the bills. I realized I needed to continue to work my safety net issues, albeit much slower now that I was teaching. At the time of the letter from Valley Hospital about the debt collector, I had outstanding medical bills that exceeded $18,000. There were no lost wage benefits from any insurance provider and minimal earnings from my part-time job to help me pay my bills. The debt collector situation was scary. I quickly called the hospital and explained my concern for lost medical benefits as a result of deny tactics by my insurance providers. I told the hospital bill collector, "I have worked to get my bills paid by workers' compensation insurance and my employee health insurance. I paid thousands of dollars of medical bills from my savings to avoid credit problems and to try to put this part of my life behind me. You need to understand that part of the insurance problem is related to hospital billing statements and other paperwork that has not been received by my employee health insurance company, Alto Health. Part of my insurance problem is caused by the hospital not providing the necessary paperwork. My insurance will not pay if you did not submit the appropriate paperwork." I wanted the hospital to help me with my problem. Yet, regardless of my explanation and plea, the hospital bill collector responded, "The hospital embraces a strategy of aggressive patient collections. You need to take responsibility and accountability for your medical bills. You should pay your bills immediately or the debt collector will take action."

The hospital was taking an aggressive approach with me to pay my bills even though I had made phone calls almost daily to insurance administrators until some action was decided. Then I followed up on their promise date for the action or at the next billing cycle, whichever came first. Usually only a small amount was paid at each billing cycle. I continued to assertively call for more responsibility from my insurance providers until my bills were paid as promised in my employee health insurance policy. Then I paid the difference, even though Blaster's workers' compensation insurance should have paid the entire amount. Indeed, even with this assertive approach on my part, insurance benefits were not paid to the hospital primarily because of the many tactics and excuses of my insurance providers. Yet part of the problem was because of paperwork the insurance company had not received from the hospital. The large outstanding balance at the hospital was not overcome. I was very concerned. I felt I had been very responsible and did not appreciate the hospital bill collector's lecture. Now I felt alone with the responsibility for my medical bills and financial loss. I understood the hospital's need to get paid. Yet I was also angry over their aggressive collection strategy and lack of compassion. I became even more frustrated over the many broken promises of my safety net providers.

As a last resort, I sent a letter to the hospital's billing and collections department to request their help (Appendix 11). In the letter, I listed my concerns and promised that the balance would be paid once the insurance company and hospital had fully resolved the propriety and responsibility of my medical bills. I promised I would pay the balance even though my employer's workers' compensation insurance should have paid all of the bills. In the letter, I also decided to share some of my anger over the hospital's lack of compassion and my safety net issues during this difficult time. I wrote, "I will not be bullied into paying outstanding balances I do not understand. I do not understand why the hospital has not addressed outstanding issues."

Two weeks later, I called the hospital to discuss the issues identified in my letter. I asked for their bill collections area and this time a different woman answered the phone. She found my letter on their system and quickly agreed to help. Something had changed. I wondered if this was a result of my letter. A week later, Valley Hospital's Director of Collections sent me a letter of explanation and apology. She must have also assigned a new priority for her staff to help me. The people in the collections area of the hospital stopped using debt collectors for my unpaid bills and took the lead in the collection process with my employee health insurance plan. The hospital found much greater success getting bills paid by Alto Health than I did. They obviously had a greater influence with Alto Health than I as a single individual. Within a few months, Alto Health addressed most of the bills for the pain program. Only the deductibles and psychology bills remained in the outstanding balance. The psychology portion of the hospital bill was not paid at all by insurance because of a separate pre-certification that was not obtained. I remembered how diligently I had worked with the hospital and insurance company to obtain all the pre-approvals and other paperwork needed before I even started the pain program. But we missed the pre-certification for the psychology bill. Surprising to me, without being asked, Valley Hospital took full responsibility for this error and wrote off the entire $2,100 psychology bill. Now all of my medical bills had been appropriately addressed. I called Valley Hospital's collection department to thank them and tell them that I appreciated their help very much. After all, they had succeeded with insurance providers when I could not.

When the balance of the hospital bills for the pain program came in the mail, I quickly sent the final payment of $849 to the hospital, as I had promised. I felt a great relief about my medical bills and was hopeful for other patients at Valley Hospital. Maybe the hospital would help other patients with their bills as they had successfully helped me. I knew I would have to continue to pursue reimbursement from Blaster's workers' compensation insurance for the $849 I had paid and the rest of the more than $12,000 that had been paid by Alto Health. It would only be a matter of time before Alto Health, my employee health insurance plan, would want reimbursement for all of the medical bills they had paid. These were supposed to be paid by workers' compensation insurance.

#

With most of my medical bills under control, I returned to work on my safety net issues with a refreshed perspective. It was now four months after I had filed a formal complaint with the BWC about Blaster. I called the auditor assigned to my complaint to check on the status of their review. She returned my phone call and left a message. She said, "I have reviewed the files of Blaster and their third-party administrator for your workers' compensation claim. I have found that there is no basis for your complaint. I have concluded that you took medical actions too early." This did not make sense to me, so I called her back. I wanted to ask her about Blaster's irresponsibility in the process, the obvious delay and deny tactics, the potential fraud related to instructions by Nurse Jones to Dr. Hunt's office to not fill out the workers' compensation forms for the pain program, and more. She did not return my phone call, so I called her again several days later. This time I was told that she was too busy to take my call so I left a message for her to call me. Several more days went by and she had not returned my phone call. I called her again and left a voice mail message. "I want to understand your conclusions better, along with the scope of your audit." After all, she only checked Blaster's and the third-party administrator's records. She had made no attempt to verify or review my records. I was sure their records were in order.

As a former Internal Audit Manager, I knew that auditors generally viewed fraud as outside of the scope of their audits. At the end of my voice mail message to her, I said, "I am very concerned about the scope of your audit. Please return my call and advise me with respect to filing a fraud report with the BWC." Again, she did not return my call. Within a few weeks, she sent me a letter detailing the same audit findings she had left earlier as a message on my answering machine. She concluded that I had taken medical actions too early, prior to obtaining approval. There was no basis for my complaint. From her conclusion and other details in her letter, I concluded that the company had probably provided her with "facts" different from those that I had in my files.

The auditor's letter also informed me that I could appeal her findings, so a few weeks later I filed an appeal (Appendix 12). As I wrote the appeal letter, I wondered about the ongoing relationships and possible influence Nurse Jones had with the people at the BWC, where she had worked for many years. After my first BWC hearing, Nurse Jones had proudly explained to me her knowledge of the system and whom she knew at the BWC. Maybe this mix of relationships and politics was accepted as how things really worked.

There was a similar theme to the letters I sent and the response I received from the State Medical Review Board about the IMEs, the State BWC about pain programs, my complaint to the State BWC about my individual case, and the Alto Health and medical care providers' response to paying my bills. People understood the issues, yet accepted the systems where the process was the same – deny, deny, deny – and the results were similar – reduced medical costs, meaningless health and safety statistics, and rewards for doctors, lawyers, company management, and shareholders. This tragedy was served on the backs of the unfortunate injured individual and his family. People's comment that this "was the way it is" was probably a common theme underlying a broader health care crisis in our country. Yet I was still not willing to accept for myself and others what I found with my empty safety net with its implications for many other people sick or injured and in need of medical care and other help during a very difficult transition in our lives. Yet, even while I observed this very sad situation, occasionally there were some positive exceptions, including the bill collections people at the hospital.

# # #

After I completed the pain program at Valley Hospital, I focused on healing my injury by using the pain management program designed for me. Pain management easily took half of my day every day. I also wanted to get back to work as soon as possible, so I looked hard for a part-time job. In the meantime, I called my insurance providers and Blaster to ask for workers' compensation benefits to pay my medical bills and recover some lost wages. Overall, I wanted to find a new balance in my life. I wanted to settle into a routine that fit my chronic pain and impairment. I wanted to put the entire experience behind me as quickly as possible.

I did not find part-time work for many months after being discharged from the pain program. After I finally returned to work, my safety net issues continued no matter how hard I tried to find a peaceful new balance in my life. I could not accept the denial and delay of benefits from the health care system and an emptied safety net as "that's just the way it is." Many times I felt I did not have enough energy – physical, emotional, or spiritual – to push the issues further than I already had. I also did not want to make this my life's purpose. I could not find a calm in my life knowing that injured people were treated so poorly, including me. I had to continue to do something.

Eventually, I accepted my situation as similar to many other injured employees working at many other companies. From my years of business management experience, along with what I had learned as an injured employee, I knew that Blaster, like many other businesses and organizations across the United States, probably did not fulfill their responsibility to their injured employees. The financial implications across the company were significant to shareholder wealth and management bonuses. People running the business believed that the system had to be maintained consistently for everyone at any cost because of the huge financial impact across the business. They would have to look past the additional pain and suffering to the injured. If they did not, the business profits would suffer and they would lose their bonuses and maybe even their jobs. Management knew that another person could easily be brought in to continue the legacy of shareholder and management wealth at any cost or compromise. As the competition and pressure for profits increased, more companies and their management decided that the ends justified any means. Indeed, the situations of people sick and injured were similar but that did not make it right.

While I was a patient in the pain program, I listened to many personal stories from other patients. They told me about a system for injured people where there was seldom a positive experience of recovery. This experience would start with the injury, then embrace medical care, healing, and returning to work at a natural pace. Instead, there was always a pushing for completion of medical care and return to work as soon as possible. While most pain management program patients found some recovery and healing during the program, most had not recovered enough to return to work full time. The GoWork stories were the worst I heard.

GoWork was a workers' compensation program promoted by many businesses and organizations that included an approach of aggressive physical therapy and returning to work quickly. As soon as the injured employees of these businesses finished an administratively predetermined portion of the pain program, they had to either return to work full time right away or attend GoWork. If they did not, they were fired. At GoWork, the injured were instructed to lift heavy weights to increase their strength. The weight lifting was usually more than they could handle so their pain increased dramatically. Many times the injured people were told to lift weights in a manner and amount that was not medically tailored or supervised until there was a re-injury or increased injury. At GoWork, people were also told to search for employment in jobs that did not fit their experience or capability or at places with environments that were dirty and unsafe. Some patients at the pain program were afraid and cried about the painful and humiliating GoWork experience. They had to drive long distances to the GoWork office located in a run down and unsafe part of the city. I wondered if the added pain and humiliation for the injured was part of the design of the program – humiliation on top of chronic pain and injury, on top of hopelessness and despair.

Cheryl stopped by the hospital one day while I was attending the aftercare portion of the pain program. The last time I saw Cheryl was over lunch when, with teary eyes, she held hope for a new life. She looked forward to using the tools we had learned in the pain program. After the third week of the pain program, her employer required that she attend GoWork. Now, a few weeks later, she was afraid and in pain. Her story was like many others. She told me, "They make you lift free weights at GoWork until the pain is so intense that you cry. I hurt now more than ever. The GoWork center is on the south end of the city. I fear for my safety every time I go there. I'm so scared. People are hanging out on the street all the time and make sexual comments when I walk by. The building is so far from my house. It takes me over an hour to get there and an hour to get back home. I'm so late getting home to my family. My pain is bad again ... worse." Her eyes showed her fear as she stared across the room. The red circles around her eyelids and black shadows under her eyes suggested that she had been crying off and on for some time with little rest or calm in her life. I stared at her in disbelief. I did not know what to say and began searching for words of compassion. Cheryl broke the silence with more short, distracted thoughts. "Some people stop going to the center and accept getting fired. I'm thinking about it. I can't go back to work. I'm in more pain now than ever before." She looked at me and strained to smile when she realized she was rambling as if I was not even there. This was not the same kind and caring person whom I had befriended in the pain program. I looked at her compassionately and started to say, "I'm sorry, Cheryl." She quickly replied in a strained voice, "I'm sorry, Mike, I'm sorry." She paused to compose herself, looked at me, and briefly smiled almost like she had when we were in the pain program. After another short pause, she said, "How are you doing?" I held back my overwhelming thoughts and asked her, "Is there anything I can do to help you?" She shook her head no. While abruptly glancing around, she said, "I have to go," and quickly walked away. I was stunned. It felt as if my heart sank into my stomach. I felt strongly that somebody had to do something about the system. I knew I would have to do something more than I already had. I knew we could do better for the sick and injured.

There were so many times when people were injured or in pain and reached out for help only to find people looking at them with a suspicious eye. I felt people should be given the benefit of the doubt, especially the sick, injured, and less fortunate. Yet the system and other people suspected that the injured person was looking for money and a free ride. From what I experienced, this was simply not true. Most, if not all, of the injured people I met were proud, hardworking individuals. In fact, it was that hardworking, even workaholic, personality that was most prevalent in the pain management program. Maybe sometimes the overwork caught up to hardworking people when a medical event occurred or an injury happened. Yet, no matter how hard they had worked in their past, the system pushed and pushed to get people back to work before they were ready. The system pushed until the injured people were so debilitated they had to quit their jobs. Then they no longer had any responsibility for them. Indeed, maybe it was not so much suspicion that motivated these companies and people to deny medical care to the sick and injured. Was it the cost of health care and its impact on corporate profits, management bonuses, and shareholder wealth? Was it that we were simply blinded by the greed and wealth chasing so prevalent now at the turn of the century?

Chapter 9

Insurance Web

The confusion and frustration I felt over my chronic pain with its impairment and work issues was exacerbated by the many unmet insurance promises of my safety net. At the time of the accident, there were many insurance policies and safety net promises in place for me –employee health insurance (Alto) through work that later was a COBRA policy, workers' compensation insurance, and disability insurance. All were either purchased from Blaster or provided as an employee benefit by Blaster. There was personal injury and uninsured/underinsured coverage from the car insurance Jack carried as the driver of the car. And I carried car insurance with no-fault and medical payments coverage for medical bills and wage loss regardless of who was driving the car or who was at fault for the accident. I also had an overall one million dollar umbrella policy that increased the limits for most of my car and homeowner's insurance coverage. There was also Social Security disability insurance and more. Now, two years after the accident, the medical bills from my injury exceeded $25,000, while lost wages had accumulated rapidly into the tens of thousands of dollars. Fortunately, over $15,000 of the medical bills were paid by my employee health insurance and COBRA. Yet Alto Health would eventually want to be reimbursed the benefits they paid to me once they learned that my injury was work related and from an automobile accident. This reimbursement was referred to as subrogation.

Despite my efforts to satisfy all of the requirements, Blaster's self-insured workers' compensation insurance had paid less than $1,000 of my medical bills when they should have paid almost the entire amount. Indeed, Blaster recognized the injury and acknowledged their workers' compensation responsibility after the

State BWC hearing one year after the accident. Yet Blaster paid only for limited medication and doctor visits, usually only the minimal co-pays. Blaster used various tactics and excuses to deny the remaining bills for doctors, physical therapists, massage therapists, hospital, and other charges. Meanwhile, I paid out thousands of dollars of my own for medical bills to protect my credit when the medical care providers became anxious for payment of the outstanding balances on my accounts. At the same time, there were no insurance benefits paid for lost wages. Blaster simply ignored my request for lost wages and my attorneys seemed content to let the amount owed grow, along with the fee they would charge to collect the balance.

The minimal financial help I received and the safety net issues were very frustrating and unbelievable at times. This was overwhelming, considering my safety net of insurance policies with benefits promised of well over one million dollars. And I was living on my savings and income as a part-time teacher that was less than ten percent of my previous wages as a businessman. Yet my losses were due to an accident that was no fault of my own. The entire safety net situation seemed unfair and surreal.

Fortunately, I soon found more alternatives for insurance recovery beyond Alto Health and the workers' compensation insurance provided by Blaster. Jack's automobile insurance company, Statewide Insurance, sent me a letter early in the year asking for documentation of my claim. Yet, soon after the accident, Jack and I were told that there was no personal injury insurance responsibility since my injury from the car accident was work related and, therefore, covered by workers' compensation insurance. If this was true, I wondered why Statewide Insurance contacted me about a claim. I forwarded a copy of the letter to Attorney Cliff and asked him what I should do. I always forwarded any correspondence related to my injury to the attorney I was working with to be sure he was fully informed. I also asked them to help me understand the issues and provide me with their legal advice. Indeed, whenever I felt a curiosity or discomfort in any part of my life, I had always asked questions until I had the knowledge I needed. Yet, time after time, the attorneys seldom responded. I usually contacted them again and again on the telephone when more important questions surfaced until I got the help I needed. My important question to Attorney Cliff about Statewide Insurance was not answered to my satisfaction until the day before the two-year statute of limitations for filing a personal injury claim was set to run out.

An adjuster for Statewide Insurance called me early in the week before the two-year anniversary of the car accident and offered to settle my case for $7,000. I was both surprised and intrigued by his offer. I replied, "I need at least $25,000 to cover my medical bills and some lost wages." He quickly responded, "I can go as high as $10,000 but no more. Take it or leave it." I said, "Okay," and hung up the phone. The next morning I called Attorney Cliff and explained the situation. He said, "You can take the money but workers' compensation will want an offset or will subrogate any money you take now." Even with his counsel, I was still uncomfortable. I decided to go ahead and accept the money as I continued to wonder why there was personal injury money being offered at all. That same day I called the Statewide Insurance adjuster and made an appointment to collect his offer. The next day I drove to the insurance building and waited in the lobby for him to call me into his private office. After about twenty minutes, Mr. Zeke, the adjuster, walked into the lobby area and asked, "Are you Mike?" I said, "Yes." He told me, "Come into my office. This will only take a minute." As we walked into his office, he handed me a two-page release. He quickly sat down with his desk between us, turned his chair sideways to face his computer, and said, "You need to sign this release." I read over the release and identified some broad statements releasing all parties from any claims related to the car accident. I looked at the adjuster and asked, "Would this not eliminate my workers' compensation claim?" He replied, as if agitated, "No, it doesn't say that." Then I suggested, "The words are very broad and could release Blaster from workers' compensation responsibility. For example …" I read the statements of release out loud, while Mr. Zeke became more upset and replied sharply, "No, it just releases Jack, that's all." I asked, "Can we modify the wording to exclude workers' compensation from the release?" He abruptly turned his chair to face me and angrily raised his voice. "No, no changes. Sign it and you get $10,000. Don't sign it and you get nothing. Tomorrow is the last day you have to take this settlement offer. Take it or leave it." I looked at the angry man sitting across his desk from me and became even more curious. I felt something was not right. Something did not make sense. I said, "Okay," stood up, and turned to leave, while out of the corner of my eye I noticed the adjuster as he turned his chair sideways again to face the computer. While I walked slowly out of Mr. Zeke's office, I was convinced that something was wrong as I heard the adjuster, in a collected voice, say, "The check and release will be at the front desk tomorrow if you change your mind." The next day was a Thursday and the day before the last day of the two-year statute of limitations for collecting automobile insurance benefits or filing a personal injury claim in court.

As I left the Statewide Insurance office, I was very uncomfortable with the broad release that Mr. Zeke had requested from me. I decided to fax the release to Attorney Cliff to get his advice and talk to another attorney for a second opinion. When I got home, I called Justine at work and asked her to check with the attorneys in her office to find out if anyone could help me on such short notice. After she said yes, I quickly drove to an office supply store close to our home. There I faxed the release to Attorney Cliff at his office in Columbus and to Justine at her office in Dayton. A few hours later, an attorney at Justine's work called me at home and said, "The uninsured/underinsured part of most automobile insurance policies covers phantom vehicles, as well as hit-and-run drivers. The semi-truck/trailer that drifted into your lane of traffic is considered a phantom vehicle, similar to a vehicle that causes a hit-and-run accident and leaves the scene. You might be able to recover for your personal injury under automobile insurance even though your injuries are covered by workers' compensation insurance." I replied, "Thank you for your help. I will look into this possibility."

That night, I researched the Internet to understand insurance coverage related to phantom vehicle liability. In the morning, I called Attorney Cliff to ask him to file a claim in court after explaining to him what I had learned from the other attorney and over the Internet. After he quickly checked with his partners, Attorney Cliff agreed there was the possibility of a "phantom vehicle" liability and this may have been the reason why Statewide Insurance requested the broad release. At the very last minute, this was another possible alternative for paying my medical bills and recovering some of my lost wages. That entire morning, with my help, Attorney Cliff and his staff scrambled to formally file the claim with the court. This was the last day to file a claim within the statute of limitations. A complaint and claim were filed against Jack as the driver of the vehicle we were in, his car insurance company, and the semi-truck/trailer as the phantom vehicle. To conserve precious time, I was told to find Jack's address and copies of my car insurance policies that were in effect at the time of the accident. These were needed so we could notify Jack and my automobile insurance company in case my policies could also be used for uninsured/underinsured coverage. But when I searched my file cabinet and the drawers of my desk, I could not find all of my insurance policies. I was reminded of all of the throwing and giving away of many of my possessions since the accident. We had to file the claim without copies of all of the policies that were required by the court. Hopefully, we could satisfy this requirement later with the help of my insurance company, Country Garden.

While I felt hopeful and pleased that there might be more of a safety net to help me, I was also disappointed in Attorney Cliff over the timing and how the claim was filed. We almost missed this option and had to scramble to meet the deadline with very few hours to spare. It appeared that Attorney Cliff and his law firm either did not understand the personal injury possibilities of my case or they were not interested in the work required for a lawsuit over a soft tissue injury and an invisible chronic illness like mine. Either way, I was no longer comfortable working with Attorney Cliff.

The following week, I called the attorney in Justine's office to thank him again for his last-minute help and key advice. I also asked him to handle my case or refer me to another attorney. With his advice, I hired Attorney Land to handle my personal injury claim and wrote a brief letter to Attorney Cliff to release him from working on my claim. After I met with Attorney Land, he agreed to consider handling my personal injury claim only. The workers' compensation claim would have to be handled by someone else since no one in his office had that legal expertise. Two weeks later, after reviewing a complete copy of my claim, he agreed to handle my personal injury lawsuit and suggested I hire Attorney Law as a separate attorney for the workers' compensation issues. The next day over the telephone I did just that. Then I mailed a complete copy of my claim to Attorney Law for his use.

With two separate attorneys, I was careful to prohibit the lawyers from taking fees where the insurance overlapped and would probably be subrogated by the insurance companies. In the end, I did not want to settle my claim and then have each attorney collecting one-third, leaving me with only one-third. Attorneys Land and Law agreed to the single legal fee arrangement. I quickly sent copies of my records to each of them so they could get started. In very little time, I saw that Attorneys Land and Law were much more assertive and detail oriented than Attorneys Young, Severs, or Cliff. I was comfortable with this approach and pleased that I now had legal representation that would work hard to settle my claims. In time, I realized that my feelings of discomfort with the other three lawyers had convinced me to keep looking to find legal professionals willing to work hard to fully support my situation. During this time, I was also very surprised over the difficulty I had finding lawyers interested in hard work and justice rather than small settlements taken with little effort at the expense of the injured. Sometimes I wondered if I expected too much until I later learned that lawyers called these small settlements with little effort "quick hits." These lawyers knew that the small settlements added up quickly for the high volume lawyer, unfortunately at the expense of the injured. Putting my disappointment in these quick-hit lawyers aside, I hoped the lawsuit and my new counsel would breathe some life into my safety net. Several weeks later, I wrote a letter to Nurse Jones to inform her of the change in lawyers and ask for her help. Again, and not surprisingly, she did not contact me to provide any support at all.

Shortly after filing a personal injury claim in court, I reported fraud to the BWC relative to Blaster's handling of my workers' compensation claim (Appendix 13). There were ten attachments to this letter documenting my evidence and reiterating the details of my previous complaint and appeal to the BWC. Blaster's actions relative to the pain program were the most significant and verifiable items of fraud. The prescription from Nurse Jones to attend the pain program, my letter to her stating I was filing a workers' compensation claim for the pain program, and a short time later her instructions to my doctor to not fill out the paperwork because I was not filing a workers' compensation claim for the pain program were verifiable fraud. Blaster then denied benefits for the pain program in my workers' compensation claim saying the forms were not provided as required. Blaster also lied about other forms and documentation they received, particularly those items I personally handed to Nurse Jones. Unfortunately, many of these items were not verifiable except for the contemporaneous notes I took that showed the effort I made and the response from the company and their third-party administrator. While the notes did not influence the BWC auditor who reviewed my BWC complaint and appeal, these notes would later help my attorneys pursue Blaster's responsibility through BWC hearings and the courts. Later, I also learned that Blaster lied during the audit of my complaint to the BWC by saying that I had received my full salary when I did not and that I voluntarily left Blaster. In fact, I was formally involuntarily terminated. These facts were verifiable with check stubs, letters, and a copy of the company's employee benefit plan that was used for people involuntarily terminated, including me.

Fraudulent activity of any kind was always a serious matter in my mind. Even though I felt strongly that I had to report fraud about my employer, when I actually reported fraud for the first time, it was extremely difficult for me. Regardless of my many lost employee benefits, along with the betrayal and having been fired, I felt bad. Even though they betrayed my trust in many ways with the injured employee process, I still did not want to violate their trust. Indeed, I did not even want to believe they lied like they did. Yet they did. Their actions were unacceptable. They were wrong. I had to consider the risk of more harm and negative consequences of retaliation from Blaster for reporting fraud. Would Blaster push harder to not pay workers' compensation medical bills and lost wages? Would there be other consequences that a large company with many resources could bring to bear? Regardless of any consequences, I knew I had to take the risk and do the right thing as I felt my spirit was directing me. Days after I reported fraud, I knew I had done the right thing. I felt calm – calm and even satisfied that I had worked hard and with integrity in doing what seemed right for my own life and for other people in similar circumstances.

Later I found even more examples and evidence of deceit from Blaster during the legal discovery process for my personal injury lawsuit. I reviewed copies of paperwork that were stamped "received" in July 1998 by Blaster and the third-party administrator that documented my description of my physician of record (POR) for workers' compensation. One year later, in the summer of 1999, my workers' compensation attorney told me that Blaster claimed they had never received a POR description from anyone. Yet here it was, formally recorded by Blaster as received. Their copy of my POR description was found in the third-party administrator's file. Nurse Jones made a note that I had provided the POR description to her in lieu of a BWC C-13 form. This was the first I heard of the need for a C-13 form. Nurse Jones had asked me to provide a description of my physicians of record in memo form after I repeatedly asked her if everything was properly documented. This request for a memo in lieu of a C-13 form must have been a tactic to set up another denial due to an inappropriate format for a physician of record approval. In the discovery process paperwork, there was another form copied from my file at the company's third-party administrator with a note to Kelly stating "don't pay massage" with no reason or signature. This must have been why they never paid for massage therapy despite my numerous attempts at documentation, pre-approval, and request for reasons why I was not reimbursed. Someone had directed Kelly to simply not pay.

I understood a business's need to manage workers' compensation benefits and other costs of doing business. Sometimes, too, people tried to take advantage of the system and receive benefits that were not really needed. As a former senior manager, I understood that the cost of workers' compensation insurance was important to companies simply because reduced costs improved profits, while the lowered costs suggested there were improvements in the health and safety of the company and its employees. Unfortunately, the contrary was true when businesses went beyond managing workers' compensation benefits and cut costs in any way possible, including fraud. Indeed, the tactics to deny and delay benefits were used perhaps because of the cost compounded by the implication for the company's health and safety statistics. This was done even after the costs were already reduced by business leaders who had worked with the government to set laws to limit workers' compensation benefits to employees. The BWC limits were restrictive and applied to everyone, regardless of their medical condition and personal situation. Medical care had to be pre-approved with most areas also limited in terms of cost and number of treatments. Lost wage benefits were limited to sixty percent of wages, subject to a $25,000 ceiling each year, and payable for no more than four years. The limit to lost wages was also inclusive of all other insurance and employee benefits. The BWC limits and ceilings already reduced benefits to an affordable amount. Yet many companies, including Blaster, were not satisfied and wanted even less responsibility.

The lost wage maximum of $25,000 per year must have been considered enough money for anyone to live on even though this amount was less than average wages and not much greater than poverty wages for families. For me, this was less than twenty-five percent of my annual earnings prior to the accident. Fortunately, my sons were grown and no longer needed much of my financial support. Maybe the time limit for lost wages of four years was considered enough time for an injured individual to find work and adjust his or her lifestyle to fit their lower earnings capability. Or maybe four years was chosen as the midpoint for injured people to accept the changes related to a work injury. Most psychologists report that we need two to seven years to accept dramatic changes in our lives. However determined, I understood the need to limit a business's liability for work injuries and require that the impaired individual share responsibility for his or her recovery and life changes. I did not take exception or issue with the limits or guidelines other than to say they seemed restrictive and "one size fits all." My concern all along was the deceitful tactics that businesses used to further limit or eliminate their responsibility.

According to the BWC guidelines and rules, Attorney Cliff calculated that my workers' compensation benefits for medical bills, lost wages, and disability payments should total about $159,000. Almost two years after the accident, I wanted to be done with the constant denial and deceit of workers' compensation insurance. I had asked Attorney Cliff to prepare a letter requesting a negotiated settlement with Blaster to conclude my workers' compensation claim and problems. Blaster responded confidently to my request for a negotiated settlement by offering $10,000, with the comment "take it or leave it." Blaster's offer of $10,000 was less than seven percent of the amount set by the already limited workers' compensation guidelines and rates. Then the lawyer would get one-third, leaving me (the injured) with less than five cents on the dollar of this already limited medical bill reimbursement and lost wage benefit. This analysis reminded me of Mr. Seabert's promise that I would be treated the same as everyone else as he described how Blaster would question everything I claimed and my attorney would take one-third. He was right. Yet I felt strongly that something was wrong with this picture. I did not accept the offer out of principle and my need to continue to prosecute my workers' compensation claim. Instead, I decided I would work to further understand the system and attempt changes so that injured people, including me, would be reasonably and responsibly paid workers' compensation and other insurance benefits. Meanwhile, I turned to one of my other insurance providers for help with my deteriorating financial situation.

# # #

Country Garden Insurance was my insurance company for many years with policies I purchased to cover my cars, houses, motorcycles, and other loss exposure, including a one million dollar umbrella policy. I had called my Country Garden agent in Troy and asked if I had any insurance coverage for my injuries. Ten months after the accident, when I first went on medical leave, the agent reviewed my policies and called me back to tell me that I had no coverage for my injury or loss. Now, shortly after the two-year anniversary of the accident and after I had learned of the phantom vehicle personal injury claim, I found out that there were uninsured/underinsured benefits possibly due from Country Garden

116

for the phantom vehicle claim. I was also covered for medical payments insurance. "Med Pay" was a benefit in my automobile policy that paid medical bills regardless of who was at fault in the accident. These benefits should have been offered to me when I asked the year before. Instead, they lied to me when I asked for help. I trusted and believed them when they told me there were no benefits in my policy. I also learned that a no-fault provision in my Minnesota Country Garden car insurance policy was possibly still in effect on the date of the accident since I had transferred my car insurance policy to Ohio a few weeks after the car accident. After many discussions and delays with Country Garden while they sorted out my insurance policies, I learned I was covered by the Minnesota policy. I felt relieved as I hoped my home state was immune to deny and delay tactics. Unfortunately, when I called Country Garden in Minnesota for help, I found that the insurance fraternity and their tactics reached the Midwest. Even though Country Garden in Minnesota sounded more sincere than the other insurance carriers, they responded with similar deny tactics and small benefit payments. They told me that legally workers' compensation was primary insurance in Minnesota so they would not even consider payment of no-fault benefits until workers' compensation insurance either paid the bills or at least formally denied payment with a reason acceptable to the Country Garden insurance company. This was a problem since most of the reasons Blaster used to deny benefits would have been unacceptable to anyone.

In a letter I wrote to Country Garden (Appendix 14), I submitted documentation of the difficulty I had experienced with Blaster's workers' compensation insurance. I also explained that the size of my wage loss compared to the workers' compensation limits precluded overlap or double dipping of benefit payments with my no-fault car insurance policy. Therefore, Country Garden should pay benefits regardless of the workers' compensation insurance position about my lost wages. But they were not impressed, at least for now. Instead, the Country Garden claims adjuster forwarded my no-fault claim to their lawyers for a long legal review process. They were obviously in search of more delay and deny tactics to apply to my situation. While I was disappointed, I was not completely surprised that Country Garden decided to, in effect, indirectly use the workers' compensation denial and fraud accomplished by my employer to deny or at least delay benefits under my no-fault coverage.

Over the next several months, Country Garden in Minnesota also used other tactics for delays and denial of benefits. They referenced the wrong policy number, omitted copies of related policies, overlooked umbrella coverage, and blamed my use of a lawyer for other delays and confusion. They wanted me to accept their payment of a few hundred dollars of benefits for medication co-pays that were already paid by Blaster. This further complicated the excuse and tactic that the insurance benefits overlapped and should not be paid at all. My safety net was tattered in my home state as well.

Because I was disappointed with Country Garden in Minnesota, I filed a complaint via email with the Insurance Commissioner of Minnesota. In the email, I explained the lie I was told by my Country Garden agent in Ohio to first deny then delay my claim in Minnesota for more than one year. To me, telling a lie was fraud. Here, with two states involved, there appeared to be the possibility of interstate fraud. Yet the Minnesota Insurance Commissioner's office responded, "There is not much we can do." Somewhat idealistically, I hoped there was plenty an Insurance Commissioner could do to help people injured by looking through and beyond the excuses given by insurance companies to not pay benefits. At a minimum, the Insurance Commissioner could encourage the insurance companies to make quick and appropriate benefit payments to the injured. More assertively, the Insurance Commissioner could mandate benefit payments within thirty days to the injured or into a state fund until the issues were sorted out if the company had benefit concerns with their insured. Unfortunately, there was little, if any, consequence to insurance companies for employing deny tactics, while the obvious rewards for nonpayment included improved cash flow and higher profits for insurance companies and bigger bonuses for their management. Not surprisingly, the companies continued to delay and deny benefit payments.

In time, I realized I should have done a better job of understanding and keeping track of my insurance policies in preparation for demanding the benefits when I needed them. Over the years, I had become lax, either because I trusted my insurance agents or I felt somewhat invincible and unreasonably believed I would not need the safety net I had paid for. Indeed, now I understood that by submitting well-documented requests for benefits, I could have avoided the long delay over what my insurance coverage was and proceeded to the next level of request for benefits or delay and deny tactics. I trusted that my insurance providers were telling me the truth and doing the right thing for me. They usually were not. During this difficult time, when I was overwhelmed by pain, medication, and other losses in my life, I should have used some type of an executor to help me with the many insurance requirements and tactics early after the accident. An executor would have been someone I could have trusted – a family member or good friend – who would have understood my medical needs, along with insurance policies. They could have kept more constant pressure on the insurance companies than what I did at the time. With the help of an executor, I probably could have saved some time and received medical care and benefits earlier. The lawyers I hired sure could have taken a more active and trustworthy role. After many months of my demands and the insurance company's tactics, the appropriate policies were finally identified and the insurance company paid or, more often, turned to another tactic to delay benefits.

Eventually I realized I should not have trusted my safety net no matter how strong I believed it was, how long I had worked for my employer and/or paid insurance premiums, or how sincere the agents, claims processors, business associates, lawyers, medical professionals, or government officials appeared. All along my journey of recovery, I had to clearly show them the safety net that was promised for my life when needed. I also had to demand fulfillment of their responsibility. Eventually I even had to force some of their responsibility through the courts. Along the way, I found I would first have to find competent lawyers to represent my interests, as well as their own self-interest for the customary one-third legal fee at the very least effort possible. Unfortunately, it was necessary to hire legal counsel for large claims related to an invisible chronic illness like mine. The many avenues of recovery seemed to increase the deny tactics and fraud by the holders of my safety net – an unfortunate reality that was confirmed for me by doctors, business people, and others. This reality was confirmed by personal experience and stories told when I asked them directly about their safety net promise for my situation. Most of the benefits guaranteed by my safety net would have to be fought for with litigation, while the discovery process, depositions, court time, and fees were wasted resources that could have been used for my medical recovery and return to work. Indeed, it also seemed that the bigger the loss, the more difficult were the tactics employed by the keepers of my safety net in order to deny the benefits that were promised to me. This disappointing and wasteful reality became clearer to me once I filed the lawsuit and the options for recovery of my medical bills and some lost wages increased. Nonetheless, the increased possibility for financial help made sense to me since over the years I had carefully tried to build and purchase a strong and broad safety net for my life. What did not make sense to me was how hard and long I had to fight to force my safety net providers to accept some of their responsibility and the guarantees they had made to me as an employee or insured.

PART II: A New Life

Chapter 10

The Prognosis

Part of the problem with my safety net was the inconclusive medical records recorded by my doctors. It was a problem for me too. I did not know what to expect or what to do, if anything, about my chronic pain. Everyone was initially optimistic for my soft tissue injury to heal in a few months. But it did not. After more than two years of serious pain, the ongoing medical care and lack of recovery suggested that my injury was serious. I decided to make an appointment with Dr. Hunt to find out what to expect for my future. At the appointed time, Dr. Hunt talked to me candidly about my impairment and confirmed that my medical condition would be with me for the rest of my life. He no longer held out promises of recovery with additional medical alternatives or lifestyle changes as he had in the past. Now his unspoken suggestion was one of understanding and acceptance. I must have looked surprised over his shift in perspective for, almost apologetically, he then told me that he believed half of the people he saw in his practice were faking. He had once even seen a video taken of one of his workers' compensation patients who was repairing the roof of his brother's house. His claim of patients faking seemed to be an excuse for doubting me for as long as he had. But instead of accepting his reasons for doubting me for two years, I was even more surprised and disappointed. I was not interested in understanding the reason for his suspicious medical care. After all, it caused more suffering for me and probably most of his other patients as we waited for a realistic prognosis and the corresponding medical care. We also had to wait for our safety net benefits to be tied into a realistic long-term prognosis.

I was shocked by Dr. Hunt's comment as he confirmed my suspicion that he "initially treated everyone as faking," including me.

He did not assume people were telling the truth and needed his help. His paradigm that we were cheaters until we proved otherwise delayed and limited much-needed medical care, while our pain and suffering not only continued but escalated. From my experience at the pain management program, I knew there were many people unable to obtain medical care because of these shared suspicions and a corresponding system of denying and delaying benefits. Yet I also felt that his comment, along with the hard-earned trust he now had in me, was my opportunity to explain a different reality.

As we sat in chairs directly across from each other in the small examining room, I looked into Dr. Hunt's eyes and said, "People at the pain program were further harmed with intense pain when they had to fight the system, including their own doctors, to get help. People had to experience intense pain and suffering for three to five years or more because they could not afford the medical treatment they needed even though they had insurance. People had no choice when their workers' compensation benefits or other insurance benefits were not available as promised. Many of these patients could have been helped by a more realistic assessment by their doctors. But they had to wait or find other difficult alternatives for their lives. Some of those alternatives were drastic. I was fortunate to have the financial resources to attend the pain program much earlier than the system would have allowed. For me, even the sixteen months I suffered was long enough to over-medicate and risk more physical harm or even death."

I looked more directly at Dr. Hunt and slowly and firmly said, "I could have died." My voice started to shake and intensify as I felt the collective suffering and anger of my experience. "I cannot imagine how other people waited so long." Then I paused to compose myself as Dr. Hunt sat quietly without any emotional expression. Speaking softer and in a somewhat rambling manner, I continued, "Many who survived the wait, people I met and heard about at the hospital, could not trust the hospital staff or the pain program approach and eventually dropped out of the program. They had suffered too much during their long wait to trust again. They dropped out of the system with their loss of livelihood, broken families, chemical abuse, and broken spirits. Some probably didn't survive the wait and simply dropped out of society somehow or died."

I paused and then explained, with my heart held openly in my hand, "Today I still feel chills and shake while reliving this tragedy of chronic pain sufferers. Understanding and trust were not offered to these people. I saw too much pain. I saw and experienced depths of suffering too great for any human being to endure." My emotions were now spent. I decided to stop talking and was quiet with my thoughts – thoughts I hoped Dr. Hunt considered and struggled with in his work each day – thoughts including the Hippocratic oath all medical doctors take to "do no harm."

The unnecessary continuation of torturous suffering for injured people was clearly wrong to me. I believed that good doctors, highly-trained medical professionals, should be able to judge a patient's credibility in order to manage the risk of "fakers" or "cheaters." Sick and injured people should get the medical care they need even if the system risks a fifty percent error rate for the half of the people who tried to cheat, as Dr. Hunt suggested. But I knew that the error rate would not be fifty percent when trained medical professionals made good judgment calls. My chronic myofascial pain condition is considered to be very similar to or a type of fibromyalgia syndrome (FMS). I had recently read about a FMS study where "trained examiners ... hand-picked the FMS patients out of the 'chronically ill' melting pot with an accuracy of 88%. FMS is not a wastebasket diagnosis!"[2] The study included people with other chronic illnesses and concluded that trained medical professionals were able to identify the impaired and also specify which illness they had. This study confirmed my belief that an accomplished doctor could tell who was injured and who was faking with reasonable accuracy.

After a long pause, and with this thought in mind, I looked at Dr. Hunt and said, "Doctors should make the diagnosis and move quickly to get the injured person the medical care and financial help they need." I stopped talking again and let my thoughts go ahead with the strong emotions I was feeling. We should not pull ourselves down as civilized human beings by scratching and feeding at the safety net of people with injuries and illnesses. We could do better for our injured and suffering brothers and sisters. As a civilized society, we had to do better. But I realistically knew that the problem was more than just a doctor's diagnosis and prescription for medical care.

While attending the pain program, I learned that other patients had lived with their pain for a period of between two and eight years before attending the program. Their employers and insurance companies denied them their benefits, while their employers tried as hard as they could to fire them. Eventually many people did get fired and pushed off the rolls of employee benefits, workers' compensation, and other insurance. These companies and the system had turned on the sick and injured people who had worked hard for their employers and hurt themselves in the line of duty. Once my condition improved, I challenged this paradigm with the other patients, along with the staff of the pain program. I encouraged them to push back on the system. They told me I was right to do so. They also told me I was a source of inspiration to them. I felt I had to say something to support other patients who had lived with the additional suffering, along with a sense of having been treated unfairly and even ruthlessly. I felt strongly that this subject was important to discuss with the injured people, as well as those who ran the pain program since they were part of the system. The discussion was important regardless of who was or was not responsible.

A few of the other patients, along with some of the staff, and I talked about informing and pleading with the people who were in positions to make a difference. This included the leaders of the businesses, professions, and other organizations responsible for our safety nets. I felt a need to inform everyone about the sense of greed that was going on at the expense of injured people during a time when compassion and understanding were needed. Maybe pushing back on the system through letters and lawsuits would also make a difference and wake up politicians who would see the need to act. Maybe people would make other smaller changes when they went to work for the system each day. The people in a position to make a difference included those who provide medical care for injured people – personal physicians who document their condition and prescribe their treatment.

My thoughts were spinning as I looked at Dr. Hunt sitting quietly across from me. Hoping for a response, I suggested, "The medical professionals, insurance companies, and businesses could work together to help the injured." Dr. Hunt smiled at my suggestion and said, "A team approach will never happen. But maybe you could be an advocate for chronic pain sufferers." His voice and facial expression finally showed some emotion. Unfortunately, it appeared to me to be the patronizing of an idealistically hopeful patient – me! Dr. Hunt, for some reason, did not want to attempt changes in the system. Maybe he was concerned about the risk of system changes that could impact his or his brotherhood's panoramic view of life. Or maybe he knew the system and fraternity were strong and would render consequences to people attempting change, including him. While I was not too surprised with Dr. Hunt's response, I was disappointed in him. I had known Dr. Hunt as a very capable doctor in a position to help people with physical injuries. Yet he seemed satisfied with the status quo that limited medical care for the injured. I wondered if doctors unionizing would help people like Dr. Hunt feel more comfortable pushing back on the insurance and business organizations that were forcing reduced and substandard medical care. "The American Medical Association endorsed unionization ... for the first time, lashing out at insurers it says sometimes treat doctors 'as little more than ditch diggers.'"[3]

Dr. Hunt and I changed the subject to talk about other issues of my personal situation. He confirmed that I had experienced all the tools and recovery Western medicine had to offer. He also laughed at the conclusion of the third IME doctor hired by Blaster to say that the pain program was not related to my injury. Yet he offered no assistance to help me get the pain program hospital bills appropriately paid by Blaster's workers' compensation insurance. But then I was surprised and somewhat pleased when, with a brief look of compassion, Dr. Hunt asked me, "How are you doing financially?" I replied, "I could use your help in a letter so I can keep trying to get my medical bills paid and request help with my lost wages. Could you document what we have talked about today? It would help me if you would cover my medical condition and prognosis both in terms of my physical impairment and work capability. We have also discussed my moving to a warmer climate for more recovery. All of this needs to be tied to the car accident in April 1997." He agreed and a few days later sent me the following letter:

> This is a letter to describe your condition.
>
> As you know, you have had more than two years of pain in the neck, shoulders, and back after an auto accident April 30, 1997. You have a chronic pain problem as the result of this accident that has significantly limited your physical activities. You have taken appropriate steps to manage this, including completing the hospital pain management program. You are currently working about sixteen hours a week.
>
> It is my opinion that these physical limitations in work hours will continue for the indefinite future. It is further my opinion that many of the physical activities that you have done in the past, including sports, are no longer appropriate for you to do. It is further my opinion that cold weather aggravates your chronic myofascial pain and I am fully supportive of you moving to a warmer climate to help manage this most effectively. You need to continue to do the relaxation exercises, along with the stretching and strengthening exercises, as tolerated. You have also needed to change to a job that is less stressful and have gone from a controller of a company to a part-time business teacher, as a consequence of the aftereffects of the injury.
>
> I hope this is useful to you.

I was disappointed Dr. Hunt would not write a prognosis of my impaired medical condition until after my life changes had proven what I had been telling him all along. If he had provided a projection earlier, perhaps I would have found truth and acceptance for my new life much sooner rather than grasping on to hope for a cure that always turned into torturous pain. Nonetheless, with his prognosis now in hand, my thoughts and feelings could turn to what my future might look like with an open mind and heart to understand the experience and find a place for my physical impairment. Indeed, his letter would also help me prosecute my workers' compensation insurance and phantom vehicle or other personal injury insurance claims. There was a renewed hope to recover part of my lifestyle and financial setback. I also felt hope and promise for a spiritual reconciliation with myself and with life over the entire situation as I continued to search for healing even though most of the medical alternatives had all been exhausted.

The work to recover benefits promised by my safety net paralleled my effort to understand my illness and injury, heal, and stop the pain. While the safety net problems took a lot of effort, I always tried to make my health the priority. At times, this exacerbated the safety net problems, as more benefits were needed for added medical bills, while multiple medical opinions provided more data for the IMEs to craft their reports and conclusions to deny benefits. My aggressive responsive to the safety net providers eventually worked. The process I used, along with the eventual success I found, is included in this book, *Surviving the Chronic Pain Experience: Successfully Recover Insurance Benefits and Other Promises*.

Recovering benefits to obtain medical care, lost wages and other help is very important to the recovery and survival process for people with chronic pain. There is much more to consider. In addition to this book, those with chronic pain will also want to read about the large number of medical care alternatives and other ways to manage pain and the corresponding life changes each and every day. *Surviving the Chronic Pain Experience: Understand and Manage Medical Care and Life Changes* is focused on the medical care and life changes from chronic pain. Refer to the last page of this book for more about Heywer books and resources.

# # #

Moving to a warmer climate held a promise of more pain relief. We decided to move to Florida since I had lived there once before, knew

129

the area, and still had a few friends there. To find a place to live, Justine and I flew to Florida two weeks after I confirmed my condition and alternatives with Dr. Hunt. We were looking forward to pain relief for me. And we were ready to leave the unfortunate memories of Ohio and look for a more promising future. With two months between the time our house in Ohio was rented and the apartment in Florida was available, Justine and I stayed with our families in Minnesota and worked on this book. We contemplated what had happened after the accident and wondered how much things could improve with a little more compassion, safety net responsibility, and social change.

Chapter 11

Social Change

One of my favorite movies of tragedy is *The Rainmaker*.[4] This story of an insurance company that denied medical care benefits to a terminally ill patient is one of the most blatantly immoral scenarios I have ever seen. A sick individual dies from a treatable cancer due to a denial of medical care that was promised in his insurance policy. An investigation of the insurance company identified a system of policies, procedures, handoffs, and delays that were designed to support a company strategy to deny claims until the insured became frustrated and stopped asking for benefits or died. In *The Rainmaker*, the insurance company was so confidently ruthless that they wrote to the insured's mother stating that she must be "stupid, stupid, stupid" for continuing to submit claims that had been denied in writing seven prior times. The letter was written as the "eighth and final time to deny the benefit claim." Although this story is fictional, I found similar circumstances with my injury and with other sick or injured people I met along the way.

At the pain program, I confirmed that delay and deny tactics were used at Blaster and many other companies and organizations to avoid or eliminate responsibility for the safety nets of injured employees. The companies used health care organizations and third-party administrators to deny or delay the medical treatment. Then, if the medical care was approved, the system provided excuses for why bills should not be paid. The companies also hired doctors to provide self-serving IMEs to dispute injuries and force the injured back to work where performance issues were documented so they could fire the injured employees. And they refused to give injured employees the help or equipment they needed to do their jobs, thereby indirectly forcing the injured to continue to either increase their pain or quit their jobs. Injured people were pushed on at work until eventually they were pushed out of the company when they got tired and walked away or died, physically, emotionally, and spiritually unable to continue the intense suffering. Some of the injured hired lawyers who took their one-third, many times with little effort when they settled for a "quick hit" with less money. It was a system carried on the backs of people who were injured that added despair to their lives, while reducing the natural hope and promise of any kind of a new life for the injured and their families.

The pain program itself fell short, in part, because the business and insurance communities with an excuse of affordable health care and a "health care crisis" controlled it. This was confirmed for me at my discharge when I asked the hospital staff for a better understanding of the limits of time and medical options that were offered by the pain program and why they did not adopt a more holistic approach to pain management. The hospital staff explained to me that they needed to minimize medical costs because, in the end, the businesses limit the bills they pay and demand that people return to work as quickly as possible. In effect, the medical system took patients to a certain point and then launched them back into the work force – a sink-or-swim approach. Many of the injured carried an anchor of chronic pain with them wherever they went and continuously sunk. The high probability risk was that the individual needed more medical care and was not quite ready for work, in which case he or she returned to work, failed, and was fired. Maybe the individual would never be ready for the same work he or she used to do and needed reduced time and/or responsibilities. But this did not fit the needs or desires of the business community. Instead, the return to work, failure, and termination would permanently remove the impaired individual from the company's responsibility. One question haunted my soul. Shouldn't a responsible company provide other work alternatives and/or disability benefits?

The return to work priority and goal resulted in many injured people failing at work, including me. Yet, with more time and medical care or work alternatives, the failures could have been minimized while the individual would have had a greater chance of success at work and in life. My observation was that there was always more healing possible for people in the United States than their safety nets would provide. Instead of care and compassion, our society gave in to fear of the possible adverse impact of medical care costs on economic prosperity. They did not recognize the potential benefits of greater work productivity and general social welfare with more healthy people. Indeed, many people agreed with me that the health care crisis in our country was the result of shortsightedness.

Dr. Jeffrey Sachs, the Director of the Institute of International Development for Harvard University, spoke to the Global Health Council on the need for health care for developing countries. While unintended, his studies were also good arguments for better health care in our country rather than reduced health care for short-term cost and profitability reasons. He demonstrated that productivity followed human health when he analyzed productivity and health care in the United States during the industrial revolution. From his work and conclusions, you could infer that if we improve health care today, we will reap the benefits of improved productivity over time. Alternatively, if we cut health care today, in time we will see reduced productivity in our country, along with increased welfare costs and other social harm. Add these probable economics to the morality of caring for the sick or injured and you have a strong argument for better health care despite the increased costs in the short term. Further, when you consider that at the turn of the millennium we were living in the time of greatest prosperity in our country, it made sense to me to carve off a little prosperity and face into the health care crisis as both an investment in the future and an act of compassion for the sick and injured of today and tomorrow. Yet I understood that maybe the unprecedented prosperity of today was found in part by reducing medical costs and denying medical care for those less fortunate and in need. Prior to the push in the last decade for shareholder wealth, we used to call this a short-term gain at the expense of long-term prosperity. Nonetheless, here we were at the end of the most prosperous decade in our nation's history with no health care insurance for 45 million of the 275 million people in the United States, along with significant concerns over the quality and availability of health care by people with insurance, including me and my injured friends.

For people who suffered with chronic pain for years, the abuse by the keepers of their safety net was further evidence that our business, medical, and insurance systems could not be trusted. Life became hopeless and unbearable, so they pulled back into their own world and turned to things that would always be there for them. They took drugs, drank alcohol, and smoked pot, or sometimes they stayed in bed for days or weeks at a time. They escaped from the situation in any way they could, while many times they consciously or unconsciously took a "die if I die" perspective. And I did too. This perspective allowed us to take enough prescription medication and alcohol to kill the pain. Even if the amount and/or combination was lethal, at least the unbearable pain would either be masked or stopped forever. I often made this choice because of the unbearable pain. Unfortunately, many people looked at the outward appearance and rebellious nature of chronic pain sufferers and quickly blamed their medical problems on their personality while they pushed them aside. They wanted to push them away when they should have tried to understand, maybe put an arm around them to see if they could help the injured even a little bit. People in the pain program, including the nurses and therapists, did a good job putting their arms around us. Yet we knew it was not the same as getting help from an employer, insurance company, doctor, or even friends and neighbors. Most of the time it appeared it was just too hard for others to reach out to the disabled or disadvantaged people. Instead, most people guarded and protected their own lives and their immediate family.

In time, my thoughts of abuse focused on the leadership and high-paid professionals of my safety net, not the administrative people who worked in the system each day. The business leaders promised medical benefits that were taken away by a hired doctor willing to render any opinion for a price. In my case, my own doctors limited my medical care and indirectly forced me to stay at work even when I could not. The insurance companies and workers' compensation system used a deny-and-delay approach to supplement the hired doctors' opinions. Lawyers delayed and waited for the total amount owed to grow so their one-third grew until they could accept a trivial lump sum "quick hit" to minimize their work. Government officials took political contributions from large companies to pass laws and regulations to limit benefits and allow the system abuses. These people violated the trust others and I placed in them when we put our careers, medical needs, and even some of our personal needs in their hands. After we were injured, we told them it hurt and asked for them to honor their promises. Yet they continued to abuse. They abused at a time when we were in pain and suffering, while our lives were falling apart. Our hopelessness increased, along with stress, when we could not work to pay the increasing bills left unpaid by the insurance we thought we had. This dismal cycle of mounting stress increased the muscle tension and pain that snowballed until our pitiful lives were no longer worth living. I told these high-paid professionals what was happening and watched their careless reaction. The keepers and leaders responsible for the system did not have the inspiration, courage, or strength to break the chain of abuse for fear of the impact to their lives and livelihood. I was sure this abusive behavior was encouraged by the greed of the new millennium – greed for shareholder wealth and management bonuses; greed to be part of the twenty percent of the wealthy in this country; and simply greed for big homes, sports utility vehicles, and large investment portfolios.

The leaders and professionals responded so aggressively to my suggestions and pushback that I sometimes wondered if there was more than wealth and greed motivating their actions. While many of these people agreed that a lot of my ideas were credible even when we viewed other areas of the systems differently, no changes were allowed or alternatives proposed of any substance. Indeed, I am sure they were afraid to lose some of their panoramic view of life. Upon reflection, I also wondered if there was fear controlling the behavior of these leaders and professionals. They may have been afraid to take an unpopular position for fear of losing their place in the brotherhood of wealth. Their position in the brotherhood and the brotherhood itself had to be protected at any cost. "You scratch my back and I'll scratch yours" can have great meaning in a small town or city where your family lives and your children go to school. With the world shrinking through technology and communication, the implications for people can reach across the country and throughout the world. On the other hand, sacrificing one more injured person with obviously no future was a small price to pay. And, at the end of the day, this sacrifice was required to avoid precedence and maintain the system with its many rewards provided to these leaders and professionals.

There were serious consequences to making improvements and providing benefits, whereas maintaining the status quo also maintained the brotherhood. An insurance and financial specialist told me that the businesses had to be careful to not set a new precedence of providing benefits for invisible chronic illness since the cost and lost profits throughout the United States would be great. The brotherhood was strong with many benefiting constituents. I imagined that the system itself had evolved over the years to reward its professionals until it was virtually impenetrable, with the strength of titanium I suppose. Indeed, the ruthlessness of the system in order to make an extra buck on the backs of injured employees was a very disappointing, humbling, and humiliating experience. I could not believe that so many advantaged Americans would deliver such harm upon our fellow men and women, our brothers and sisters of a universal family. Yet I also had no idea how this chain of abuse could be effectively broken. I had no idea how to impact this abuse, how to change it to make a noticeable mark to its strong metal skin. I could only imagine that it would probably take many morally inclined people to even begin to weaken the chain. We needed to challenge the leaders and professionals and help them find improvements through insight and inspiration. We needed to push back and hold up mirrors to explain the suffering caused by this abuse while also providing encouragement for positive change. We needed to embrace a constant struggle for improvements to reduce suffering while asking for unconditional acceptance of our impaired brothers or sisters. We needed to pray for inspiration.

When I look back at my experience, I realize my biggest disappointment was with the talented professionals who were unwilling to look beyond their own livelihood and economic wealth in order to keep their promises to injured people in their time of need. These high-paid professionals were unwilling to give up even a little bit of their panoramic view to help the injured and impaired that they had some responsibility for. Many gifted and talented doctors, business leaders, lawyers, politicians, and other government officials were not willing to use their gifts of life to accept some responsibility and provide a little leadership – leadership to effect even small changes to move the system in a positive direction. Indeed, the system was so ironclad that most people told me that even though my suggestions were good, I was wasting my time and energy. Yet I knew my life was greater and more meaningful for having asked the questions and fought the fight, regardless of the outcome. Struggling with a system that causes increased suffering for people already in pain was never a waste.

Indeed, the experience of the injury and response of the system that promised to treat me like everybody else was a very humbling experience. I saw the reality of this promise during my recovery when I saw that I was not the only one who went through an experience like this. There were many more people who worked in jobs more prone to injury than mine – labor jobs, blue-collar jobs in factories like I worked in during my youth, jobs of construction, driving, lifting, carrying, and more. These were people who worked jobs and made far less money than the successful business people and the medical, legal, insurance, and government professionals who supported and benefited from the health care system as it was today. These working-class people were injured and then treated as if they were faking and trying to make money off the system. I remembered growing up in a blue-collar neighborhood and realized I had somehow lost touch with my family and my heritage. Justine smiled and told me one day while I was wrestling with my feelings, "Welcome to my world." She could have just as well said, "Welcome home."

Sure, some people may have been faking and trying to game the system. Yet everyone I encountered was really hurt and simply looking for some help and compassion. Indeed, the system itself was so onerous and abusive that many injured people walked away and chose illegal drugs and a failed lifestyle over the systems that added so much harm and humiliation to an already impossible situation. The system was so bad I suspected people without a valid injury probably returned to work or some other activity soon after they realized that the abuse from the system was far more difficult than any job or other alternative.

While I struggled with this new abuse in my life, I felt good that I had done everything I reasonably could to give visibility to the issues and suggest improvements to the system. I tried to balance my actions with maintaining my own mental and emotional health and the need to recover and move on. I did everything I could to hold up a mirror to Blaster with the internal management discussions and reporting. I filed a complaint with the State Medical Review Board and a complaint, appeal, and fraud report with the BWC. I sent a letter of recommendation for pain programs to the BWC that was also copied to the staff at the pain program to further provide them with some well-deserved recognition and appreciation. I wrote a letter asking for help from the State Insurance Commissioner. There were also many, many discussions with people along the way through this process about what happened to people in need of their safety net and how we might possibly make things even a little bit better. I wanted to inform the abusers of their behavior, ask whether or not we were realizing our full potential in terms of humanity and caring for one another, and appeal to their kindness while asking for improvements. This was my idea and hope. But why was I hanging on to this abuse in my life? I wanted to embrace a larger responsibility to others – one that had more than self-interest or potential personal gain. I wanted to use my talents and strengths to make life better while embracing the mystery of life in a deeper sense than I had up to this point in my life. I knew that improvements and social changes were possible if we worked together with compassion for the chronic pain experience. I decided to use my experience and research with safety net providers to understand and encourage improvements and change to help others survive the chronic pain experience.

Chapter 12

On the Move

It took five days on the road for Justine and I to drive to our new home in Florida. Prior to the accident and my physical impairment, I had covered this same distance a few other times in thirty straight hours. On the way to Florida, we planned to spend a day in Troy where we would rest, attend a legal deposition in my attorney's office, and visit our friends. As we drove to Ohio, Justine and I took turns at the wheel of my car every two hours to help reduce my discomfort along the way. There were many times during the trip when my thoughts focused on how the keepers of my safety net were pushing hard on me to avoid their responsibility. My employee health insurance plan had paid a lot of the medical bills, while workers' compensation and my no-fault car insurance had paid very small amounts of my medical bills and no lost wages whatsoever. Yet there appeared to be the possibility of additional financial recovery through my personal injury lawsuit and no-fault insurance and workers' compensation insurance claims. Since some people had listened sincerely to my plea for keeping safety net promises, I believed there was still hope for improvements to the system that usually handled injured people with very little responsibility or compassion. But what had my life become? Over the years, I had enjoyed dreaming, hard work, negotiation, and helping other people with their goals in life. I had also tried to not be a complainer and avoided hard conflicts and legal battles. Yet I now found myself in the middle of a legal battle over my personal injury claim that included a deposition in preparation for a trial.

The day after Justine and I arrived in Troy, my attorney, Jack's insurance company's attorney, a court reporter, and I gathered on a beautiful summer morning at my attorney's office. His office was located on Plum Street in downtown Troy, two blocks away from the Miami County Courthouse where my case would eventually be heard. The building was a beautifully renovated turn-of-the-century home with light and brightly patterned wallpaper that was comfortably framed by heavy dark historic woodwork. While I waited for the deposition to begin, I stood in my attorney's large conference room looking out the window. I noticed shrubs and bright flowers that decorated the landscape around the building. With an unusual calm, given the circumstances, I imagined this could be a very pleasant and relaxing setting if not for all the legal wrestling that was promised for this day. My calm was soon broken when everyone else entered the room and sat down.

Lois, the attorney for Jack's insurance company, and I sat across from each other at one end of the large table in the conference room. My attorney sat next to me, while the court reporter sat at the end of the table to record the meeting. With a friendly manner and relatively easy questions, Lois started the deposition. It was scheduled to be two hours long. As the morning continued, her questions became more pointed and even offensive at times, while drifting into irrelevant and personal topics. Finally, my attorney objected, but I answered the questions anyway. I wanted to be truthful and supportive without hiding behind legal tactics regardless of the insurance company's approach. I was proud of the life I had lived and felt I had nothing to hide. More than two hours passed and the tight discomfort in my back became increasingly painful. I stretched and walked around the conference room for a while to try to ease my suffering. Eventually the extreme pain signaled that it was past the time for my midday meditation. I asked for a break and retreated into one of the attorney's offices to meditate. Everyone else waited in the conference room and quietly talked about topics other than my lawsuit.

After my forty-minute meditation, the pain was less and I returned to the conference room to finish the deposition. The questions from the insurance company's attorney continued with even more unusual, irrelevant, and detailed questions well beyond the normal fact finding of a typical two-hour deposition. Since I was unable to completely practice my pain management program that day,

I eventually gave in to my suffering and felt incompetent from its distraction. My answers to Lois's questions became rambling guesses that were sure to be an opportunity for errors with my memory and integrity issues at trial. During the long hours of the deposition, my physical impairment showed its full symptoms when my clarity and concentration were lost to the pain. I desperately needed medication in the mid afternoon. Lois's strategy that day was to wear me down and move in for the kill. The deposition lasted six hours and brought me a great amount of pain and suffering. This pleasant, young female attorney for Jack's insurance company had effectively kicked my pain management "wheelchair" out from under me to expose my vulnerability and uncontrollable submission. I was disappointed at more of the same with the ruthlessness of the long deposition that was played out by the insurance company's lawyer. I was not surprised. The treatment of me during the deposition followed the same pattern of company greed that had been prevalent in my entire case.

The next day Justine picked up her car from our friends' house where it was stored over the summer. We continued our travel south on I-75 to Florida. We were alone in our cars with our thoughts as we drove until our scheduled breaks every two hours to stretch and take in nourishment. While I explored the details of the deposition in my mind off and on over the next few days, I once again questioned why I continued to accept the abuse of these systems. I realized there were actually benefits to the many questions and answers given that day. A deeper and clearer understanding of my situation helped me find my way further into acceptance of my new life. I now saw that the cause of the accident was not just the semi-truck driver's for drifting into our lane. It was also related to Jack's decision to enter the high-risk construction area with the tightly drifting traffic of cars and trucks. At the deposition, after describing the accident and realizing Jack's responsibility, Lois asked me, "Are you angry and seeking revenge through this lawsuit?" My attorney objected, but I replied anyway, "No, I am not." Instead, I had probably unconsciously protected my friend from blame since the accident. To me, blame and guilt were wasted emotions that many times resulted in negative behaviors and destructive actions. This was especially true in a politically charged senior management position like Jack's and mine. During the deposition, Jack's lawyer had asked questions that required that I carefully consider the events of the accident earlier than I had in the past. From this, I saw Jack's decision to enter the high-risk construction zone. He probably did this to avoid losing the tail of our friends in the car ahead. For the first time, I saw Jack's responsibility more clearly. Yet I was still not angry with him for causing the accident. After all, it was an accident. The only negative feeling I continued to hold for Jack was disappointment – a disappointment similar to that which I held for many of the people who I worked with when they chose to ignore my impairment rather than looking with me to find recovery and a fair and reasonable conclusion to my prior life and its many responsibilities. Indeed, I was disappointed with Jack over his reaction to my injury and impairment. Yet I was also disappointed over the loss of our friendship, regardless of our changed circumstances.

Questions at the deposition also reminded me of people who asked me if I missed my work and my old life. Before I could answer, they told me how much better off I was not working the long hours, traveling so much, playing the game of business politics, running to handle the stress, and more. They told me how much better off I was living a quieter and slower life. But they were wrong, and I politely told them they were wrong. When Lois asked the same question, I replied, "I would live my life with the same level of intensity in a heartbeat if I could. The intensity and excitement of my prior life are missed very much. While there are now more moments of quiet in my life, the pain and pain management are a significant daily challenge and frustration."

Lois also asked, "Is your condition improving?" As I thought about her question and the deposition experience itself, I realized my physical condition was relatively unchanged. Pain management helped my condition, as did medication, but the tradeoff was always less work and play activity, more therapy, and less clarity, time and intensity. When activity increased, so did the pain and the need for a more significant pain management response. I made this activity and pain tradeoff each day. But I was feeling a little better emotionally.

My attempts at acceptance with the help of prayer and meditation had started to calm my emotions.

Toward the end of the deposition, Lois talked about bad days, pain management, and seeing small improvements in my condition over a long period of time. While shaking my head in agreement, I smiled at her and she smiled slightly in return. It was a moment of shared understanding and wisdom about chronic pain. She understood my chronic pain condition. I knew she was not a young, incompetent lawyer, as my counselor had suggested. All along, she had planned to press my impairment and kick my pain management "wheelchair" out from under me for the benefit of her company's profits and her career as an insurance company lawyer.

# # #

While I worked very hard to find a job in Florida, it appeared that my background and talent did not fit well in the part-time job market. Teaching or part-time business management or consulting work in the area of our new home was not available. Yet I still felt a need to work and be productive. Writing about my ordeal was the only work available to me at the time. I eventually realized the importance of this work to personally understand and find more healing in all areas of my self.

At the same time I searched for work, I also looked to Blaster's workers' compensation insurance for help with lost wages. To qualify for benefits, Ohio workers' compensation guidelines required that the claimant spend as much time looking for work as he or she was capable of working, according to their doctor. But, of course, this doctor opinion would be refuted by IMEs hired by the company. This requirement was certainly a benefit won by business to push the injured person away from the workers' compensation system. The stress of the process contributed to my pain, just as it probably did for other injured people who looked hard for work and found none. Up to forty hours of employment rejection each week probably exacerbated the injured person's despair and pain condition. Each week I looked for a job as hard as I could. Many times I spent more time than my work limitation of sixteen hours per week that was set by Dr. Hunt. The job search process and frequent rejections were very frustrating. Many resumes were sent, phone calls placed, and search firms contacted without even a single job interview scheduled other than the meetings with search firms and unemployment offices.

Later, to my astonishment, I learned that people with disabilities live with a seventy percent unemployment rate.[5] Why would the disability rate be so high? Certainly living in a society that viewed work as all or nothing, more than full time, and many times being available twenty-four hours a day and seven days a week, also known as a 24/7 proposition, accounted for part of the problem. I remembered Blaster's response when I asked for an alternative work assignment that fit my impairment. They said no and explained that Blaster management across the country did not know what to expect from me as an injured and impaired individual. Other companies probably held the same perspective to protect their company by managing the risk of hiring the impaired. This paradigm made my job search difficult, if not impossible.

But there is much more to consider. Many disabled people cannot afford to return to work. I eventually found part-time work and was denied Social Security Disability Income (SSDI), in part because the Social Security Administration (SSA) decided I could earn more than the $700 per month considered by them as "substantial gainful employment." Once you earned more than that for nine months, you are ineligible for SSDI and the Medicare coverage that goes with it after one year. My new job paid about $7,000 per year while my recurring health insurance and medical bills totaled $500 per month. The math to pay my other bills for living just did not work. But this was small considering what other disabled people pay especially those who do not have savings and retirement monies to fall back on. They also need Supplemental Security Income (SSI), along with Medicaid, for other health insurance needs, homemaking assistance, and more. Unfortunately "[m]any disabled persons want to work and are fully capable of doing so. But it's gotten to the point where we just can't afford it. We can't go without our insurance benefits, and we can't afford to pay for them ourselves

… we have to stay poor and unemployed if we want the security of the health insurance and other assistance we need."[6]

"There are other reasons why persons with disabilities have not entered the work force in high numbers. One is the way the ADA is written, using the intentionally ambiguous term 'reasonable accommodations.' This can mean many things to many employers. And enforcement of the law has been spotty, at best."[7] The result is that the disabled are not accommodated in order to be able to function in the workplace. I remembered how Mr. Seabert offered me an old broken down chair to satisfy my request for a high flat-back chair to help me with my impairment. When I mentioned the ADA to Mr. Seabert as support for my request, he was unimpressed and replied that the company could not afford to give everyone what they asked for. When the ADA was passed in 1990, many employers, like Blaster, "feared that their businesses would be saddled with burdensome expenses and many lawsuits. Since then, however, fear has been replaced by creative [low cost] problem solving … with lots of low tech ingenuity, a touch of high tech, and support from coworkers, millions of disabled people can help their employers win the battle of global competition."[8] Enacting the ADA was a definite step in the right direction for the "43 million disabled Americans [to] finally have a real chance to take their rightful place in the workforce."[9] This paradigm of support for the disabled would be my hope and encouragement as my job search continued. Like many other disabled people, I desperately wanted to work, pay my bills, and contribute to society as much as possible.

Meanwhile, the workers' compensation requirement and forms to record my job search each week in order to ask for wage loss benefits were daunting. The forms also required that "I hereby certify that the information reported on this job search form is correct to the best of my knowledge." When I researched BWC guidelines on how to report fraud about Blaster, I learned that, with this certification and other claims for benefits, the injured worker would face felony prosecution for fraud. What if I simply made a mistake on the form? Yet the company and others were free to commit fraud and employ ruthless tactics to deny workers' compensation benefits. The BWC guidelines and website did not even cover employer fraud.

Only after several phone calls within the BWC did I find an individual who would accept and consider my fraud report concerning Blaster. I eventually realized that the workers' compensation process was so complex that even an accomplished businessman like me needed an attorney. Indeed, the system did not make sense to me as a way for helping the sick or injured return to a productive life.

While I was in Florida, Blaster, along with the Ohio workers' compensation system, used more deny tactics than I ever would have imagined possible. I was required to attend two more IMEs in Florida, an IME for the Ohio BWC and an IME for Blaster to once again decide my impairment. The number of IMEs now totaled five, while each one carried indignity and disrespect from the IME doctors hired to render an opinion that the company wanted. The Ohio BWC IME was done with a fifteen-minute evaluation that was supposed to cover my entire medical history, including the dramatic change in my life over the last two and a half years, and a complete physical examination. The brevity of the evaluation, along with the disrespectful cutting off of my answers to his questions as he ignored my description of physical concerns, again suggested the report was written before the exam even started.

This BWC IME doctor provided a new level of harm during the physical examination when he held my head with his hands and forced painful movement well beyond the stretching of muscles I could accomplish on my own. Even while I immediately told him it hurt and was very painful, he pushed and jerked my head further into pain, while my eyes watered and my body shook. Shock and despair immediately crushed my spirit. It happened so fast that anger did not have a chance to surface. The exam and its painful forced stretching started a weeklong pain cycle that required more medication and stopping all activities in my life. Bad headaches also accompanied the intense back, neck, and shoulder pain as a result of this doctor's abusive examination. Eventually my anger surfaced as I wondered where was this doctor's oath to "do no harm?" How could a doctor, any person, purposefully cause that much pain to another human being? This doctor was a rheumatologist who practiced medicine for FMS, rheumatoid arthritis, and other related diseases, including my condition of chronic myofascial pain. He knew the harm he caused that day. Why would he do such a thing?

The integrity of the fifth IME doctor hired by Blaster was at first a pleasant surprise to me. He seemed interested in documenting the truth, yet was also distracted by the previous IME reports with their many errors and misstatements. While I was pleased he was willing to verify facts with me, I also did not feel violated like I did with the other IME doctors when he examined my body and asked me questions. Unfortunately, when his ten-page report was completed, I found a number of problems in his report that suggested his conclusions had been prescribed or at least inferred by Blaster like in the other IMEs. He quoted errors in his report from prior IME reports, including the IME that said I had a prior C7 cervical problem even though I had specifically discussed this error with him. Regardless of my explanation, he chose to include the error used by other IME doctors to call my cranial nerve (on the brain) problem in 1978 a cervical (neck) problem to cast doubt over the cause of my current neck and back problems by suggesting a history of related problems. There were many other mistakes included in his IME. Of greater significance, however, was an omission of the fact I had returned to work on the advice of the erroneous IME reports he quoted and was soon fired because of my medical condition. Once again the forced return to work, increased pain, and job termination were not even mentioned.

The final disappointment with this IME doctor came at the end of the exam when I asked him his opinion of my condition and he told me, "There is nothing wrong with you." Then I asked him, "Why do you say that?" He replied, "The pain is all in your head. There is nothing physically wrong with you that I can see. As soon as you conclude your workers' compensation claim and its related stress, the pain will be gone." I was astonished by his comment and assertively told him, "I would be very happy if that were true. But I would be surprised after all the medical treatment and other alternatives I have tried." I paused for reflection and looked into his eyes to challenge his conclusions. Then I continued, "We should not limit our perspective to only what we can see or measure. After all, how do we know there will be a tomorrow?" Even though he did not respond to my question, at least he was honest about his medical view of my condition. Yet why waste the time and money? He could have quoted erroneous medical opinions and colored some facts while ignoring others without pretending to examine me to render a separate IME.

The fifth IME helped me realize that my anger over IMEs was because of the carefully crafted deceit by highly trained medical professionals for a price. They pretended to render valid IME opinions that were used by businesses to get out of their responsibility for an injured employee. At the same time, their practice included treating people with similar symptoms whom they recognized had the condition and needed medical care. This seemed duplicitous and wrong. Why would they treat people with similar injuries or illnesses yet not believe in the condition? Unless, of course, some patients recovered while the other patients who were told "it's all in your head" went elsewhere for treatment and were never again seen by that doctor. He then concluded they were cured or their claim was settled or maybe they had been caught trying to obtain benefits inappropriately and went back to work. Who knows how the IME doctors rationalized their behavior?

# # #

My financial concerns were growing as no insurance benefits or work was found. To get some financial help, I decided to file for unemployment compensation for the first time in my life. Once again I found myself wide awake in the middle of the night feeling that I was desperately trying to catch some pieces of my life before they all fell to the ground. All my life I had tried to be financially responsible for my family and myself. I found responsibility, dignity, and self-respect in this and had never turned to social systems for help. This was true whether it was filing for unemployment or asking someone else to cover my bills through welfare or other social or community organizations. Now, in the middle of the night, I was sleeplessly imagining that these systems would have many questions, surprising looks, and other indignities similar to what I had already experienced with my workers' compensation and other insurance claims. There would probably be long and complex forms to fill out, difficult and ambiguous policies and procedures to follow, and evasive answers to my questions. These would be coupled with long lines to get answers to questions and forms filed. Would unemployment compensation be different?

I was involuntarily terminated and unable to find a new job even though I had tried very hard. I should qualify for unemployment compensation insurance. As I suspected, once I filed for unemployment compensation at the local office, there were long lines and difficult forms, on top of carelessness in the unemployment offices that appeared to once again be geared to deny and delay benefits. Eventually I was denied unemployment compensation because I voluntarily quit my Ohio part-time teaching job. This was decided even though my resignation was medically related to my move to a warmer climate for pain relief as suggested by my doctor. It did not matter that, as a part-time teacher, I earned less than five percent of the wage I had earned while working at Blaster. It did not matter that my total part-time earnings were less than the total possible amount of unemployment compensation I would have been paid had I not worked part time at all. Regardless of being involuntarily terminated by Blaster and qualified to collect, quitting the part-time job was the deciding factor in denying compensation. As with many others, I would have been financially better off had I not worked the part-time teaching job and instead had collected unemployment. The unemployment system denied my claim and rewarded the wrong behavior. Yet I probably would have worked part time as a teacher even if I knew at the time that it would impact me financially in a negative way. More important than the money was the fact that I needed to know how much recovery I had achieved and how my new physical capability interacted with the work world. As for so many others, I also wanted the social contact and intellectual stimulation that came from returning to work.

Soon there was another financial disappointment. When I tried to purchase health insurance in Florida, I was told, "You are not insurable because of your physical impairment. The financial risk for the insurance company is too high." I replied, "What should I do for insurance?" The agent for the insurance company answered, "We cannot help you." I called other insurance agents and got the same answer. It now appeared that even though the invisible nature of my illness was used to deny benefits from the insurance policies I carried at the time of the accident, the implications of the injury could be seen enough to deny future health insurance protection. Fear sank heavily into my stomach with this news as I wondered what I would do when my COBRA health insurance coverage from my severance agreement ran out in a few months. I could not return to work full time and enjoy the employee health plan that an employer usually provided. I would not try to qualify for individual health insurance by saying I had no pre-existing condition when I did. Instead, I could only hope life would show me the answer in time and save me from becoming one of the 43 million Americans with no health insurance. Something special would have to happen for me as I was sure our leadership in Washington would not find a solution anytime soon for this growing problem in the United States.

Even though Justine and I enjoyed our morning walks on the beach, working on this book together, and our new friends, we soon realized there were simply not enough good reasons to continue to live in Florida. Neither Justine nor I found jobs. There was very little health improvement and no health insurance for me to purchase. These problems, along with hassles with our apartment and traffic congestion, were more than we could accept. We decided to return to Minnesota to live closer to our families. We were going home.

Chapter 13

More Benefits

In early January 2000, Justine and I moved our belongings out of storage, and settled into our new place in St. Cloud, Minnesota. We unpacked our clothing and carefully arranged our furniture to fit into an apartment that was about half the size of our house in Ohio. We opted for a six-month lease in order to have the flexibility to either stay in the small apartment, find another place to rent, or buy a house. Soon after we moved in, we started looking for jobs. I began writing again and working the many issues of my workers' compensation claim and personal injury lawsuit. Working at home almost every day in a much smaller apartment sometimes reminded me of the many changes in my life. A caged-in feeling of a diminished life reminded me of the despair I had once known so well.

While preparing my income taxes, I also realized I had earned only $4,500 in the last eighteen months. This was less than what I had earned in two weeks at Blaster prior to the accident. I felt overwhelmed all over again by the harsh reality of my new financial situation, highlighted by comparing my income tax returns from one year to the next. A few days later, I was surprised when an earnings statement from the SSA arrived in the mail. I quickly read the section on disability benefits to learn that in order to receive SSA disability benefits, an individual must be disabled for at least one year and be unable to earn more than $700 per month. I quickly considered my earnings over the last eighteen months and realized I definitely qualified. I called the local SSA office to apply for benefits. A few weeks later, I was interviewed over the phone and asked to fill out many pages of forms and provide numerous documents to the SSA, including access to all of my medical records. The paperwork was, once again, very detailed and difficult to complete but seemed a worthwhile pursuant of benefits that I sure could use to help pay my monthly bills. The potential SSA benefits were significantly more than the income I was now earning and would be enough to pay most of my regular monthly bills, except for medical expenses.

The SSA application asked for a detailed description of how I spent my days and what help I needed and received from other people. Surprising realizations and mixed emotions came to me from this careful, thoughtful, and detailed analysis that was required by the SSA application process. First, I realized how important and generous Justine's help was to me with my everyday tasks. I was very grateful to have her as my helper, as well as my companion and lover. I knew I was very fortunate and felt undeserving of her and her help. Then, my heart turned sad with the realization that I needed to be taken care of, much more than I ever remembered at any time in my life. I now knew I was disabled and virtually unemployable.

In the previous six months, I had worked very hard to find a job by searching eight to ten Internet job sites and newspaper ads at least once a week, registering with local and national job services and headhunters, sending out many resumes, and calling on and cajoling prospective employers. I pursued all possible job leads, including asking people I met at stores, restaurants, and even saloons about potential job opportunities. Yet the literally hundreds of attempts at finding employment did not yield even one job interview, except for the meetings I scheduled to sell myself to prospective employers or employment search firm specialists, often called "headhunters." My frustration built along the way as I realized the most likely reason for my lack of success with finding a job was because I was virtually unemployable from a practical perspective. One rejection letter captured the essence of my problem. "Your experience and accomplishments are excellent, but our company needs an individual who is more aggressive to meet the high standards of our business." Companies were not looking for accomplished people to work flexible, part-time schedules that fit their impairments. They wanted assertive employees and business partners to work long and hard, available twenty-four hours a day, seven days a week (24/7) if necessary.

One day, several weeks after we moved into our apartment, the phone rang. It was the adjuster for Country Garden Insurance calling to ask me where to send two large checks to pay lost wage benefits under my no-fault automobile insurance policy that was in effect at the time of the accident. I was surprised and impressed that an insurance company had taken responsibility to pay benefits. I thanked her repeatedly as I gave her my address. I thanked her not only for the benefits but also for her diligence in tracking me down, as well as the company's responsible action to pay benefits. She apologized and explained that there was a long legal review and other delays in the benefit payment process. Even though her comments confirmed my concerns over the insurance benefit process, this breath of life into my safety net was very much needed and appreciated. In fact, this was the first benefit payment for lost wages from any of my insurance alternatives. The two checks I received totaled $40,000, which was the maximum amount payable as no-fault benefits. While the money represented less than five months of my lost wages, I knew that, with conservative spending, these monies could pay my living expenses for twenty months or more. Better yet, I decided to use these lump sum monies, along with my savings and retirement monies, to pay for my part of a house that Justine and I hoped to purchase together in Minnesota. Indeed, maybe this help from my safety net was another part of my welcome home to Minnesota.

The time period for my COBRA health insurance coverage with Blaster had all but run out. Good news and bad news came again when I checked into purchasing health insurance in Minnesota. To find out about health insurance, Justine and I went to see an insurance agent who was recommended by our Country Garden Insurance agent. The agent insured Justine quickly, but he could not help me no matter where he looked for coverage. Even the largest health insurance company in Minnesota rejected my application because of my injury and chronic pain. Once again I thought it was ironic that insurance benefits were delayed or denied because of my "invisible" illness, yet that same illness was used to deny me access to health insurance for the future. Fortunately for me, Minnesota was one of the few states that had an insurance pool for the uninsurable. Even the sick and impaired could get health insurance by paying premiums that were set by law at twenty-five percent over the normal premium. All that was needed was to demonstrate that I had been rejected for health insurance coverage. This was an easy thing for me to do. I was relieved that I could now purchase health insurance and receive some level of medical care if needed for a serious illness or injury in the future. That was the good news.

There was also very bad news. I asked my new health insurance agent, "Why was I rejected for regular health insurance when I now need relatively few doctor visits and prescriptions for my injury and chronic pain?" My insurance agent paused to look at me carefully. Then he candidly explained, "Chronic pain illnesses eventually lead to heart conditions and other terminal diseases. The probability of serious medical problems is greater for you." He paused again to let the words take on their full meaning. Then he continued, "Your life expectancy has declined significantly as a result of the car accident you were in a few years ago." This was horrifying to me. I now belonged in a special pool of insureds that included cancer, heart disease, AIDs, and other patients who had a less than average life expectancy.

# # #

A few weeks later, I received a phone call from Attorney Law to inform me about an upcoming workers' compensation hearing to decide my disability percentage. He explained the importance of the hearing for future wage loss benefits and encouraged me to attend an IME on my own behalf. Even though I did not want to embrace insurance benefit tactics like Blaster with their four IMEs and the one company supportive BWC IME, I decided I should at least try one IME with a doctor who had my interests in mind. Before I agreed to hire an IME doctor to support my claim, I called Dr. Hunt for a disability rating since he had been my treating physician. I thought he should report the disability percentage. He replied that the disability percentage was zero per the American Medical Association (AMA) guidelines. Yet a doctor who was one of the authors of the AMA guidelines supported Attorney Law's opinion about a disability percentage of twenty percent or more for me.

When I asked Dr. Hunt to reconcile his sixteen-hour-a-week work prognosis and restriction with his zero percent disability opinion, he replied that the AMA guidelines were specific and restrictive, especially when it came to an invisible chronic illness. I called Attorney Law to talk about Dr. Hunt's decision. Attorney Law told me that Dr. Hunt's interpretation of the AMA guidelines was that of a company or "employer" doctor. In other words, Dr. Hunt's support was for Blaster as a key contributor to his medical practice through the Blaster employee health care plan. Although I was not surprised to learn of Dr. Hunt's allegiance to Blaster, I was disappointed in his response and realized he had probably concluded his support of my life-changing injury and impairment. A subsequent phone call to Dr. Smith for a prescription refill that was denied reinforced to me that my Ohio doctors were done supporting me in any way. Then I wondered if Dr. Hunt's support of my move to a warmer climate was a way for him to conclude a doctor/patient relationship with an assertive patient. I knew it was now time to find medical care and support in Minnesota for my impairment.

I flew to Columbus, Ohio, to attend the IME that Attorney Law recommended. But first I met with my attorney to go over my file. I was surprised when Attorney Law showed me, among other things, that Dr. Hunt had reported a work restriction of twenty to thirty hours per week to the BWC at the same time he wrote the letter to me with a sixteen-hour-a-week limitation. My voice shook as I expressed my concern about this inconsistency to my attorney. He simply smiled with an accepting perspective of the many errors and tactics I had experienced and said, "He's nothing if not inconsistent." I had trusted Dr. Hunt with my recovery, while he played both sides to his advantage. The betrayal I felt from Dr. Hunt cut deeper inside of me. How could he knowingly support my new life restrictions, yet hurt my chances of receiving the financial help I needed and was promised?

After my meeting with Attorney Law, I drove a few miles and met with the IME physician, Dr. Water. He briefly reviewed my medical history and performed an examination of my injury and condition. Dr. Water referenced the AMA guidelines for disability ratings and concluded I had a twenty percent permanent disability from the sprain/strain recognized in my BWC claim. The number would have been even higher but for the chronic pain condition that was excluded from his opinion, since it was not yet formally recognized by the BWC.

The next week, the formal BWC hearing was conducted with a decision that they would recognize a six percent permanent disability to my whole person for my claim. A few days later, Blaster appealed the six percent disability decision. Before the appeal was heard, Blaster canceled their appeal and paid the $2,000 for the six percent disability that was required by the BWC guidelines. I felt good about the payment. Even though the money was small, the principle was large in that Blaster was held responsible for some portion of the long-term earnings impact from my work-related injury. And there may be more wage loss benefits in the future. At the same time, the long delay of almost three years was a tribute to Blaster's deny and delay tactics, along with recognition and reinforcement for their lawyers, third-party administrators, and the company nurse and company doctor. Nonetheless, I felt their responsibility was coming as another self-truth returned to my life. Business and life itself was sometimes an odd yet interesting and encouraging game, especially when a sense of morality accompanied a personal victory.

A few weeks later I received a phone call from Attorney Land who was working on my personal injury lawsuit. He requested I attend a deposition of Jack, the driver of the car I was riding in at the time of the accident. Jack's deposition would be held the next month in his office. I felt nervous about seeing Jack, particularly in the context of a lawsuit, since I hadn't seen or heard from him in quite some time. So I asked Attorney Land if I had to attend. He said, "Yes, we need you to verify whether or not he tells the truth at the deposition."

The day before the scheduled meeting, I flew to Ohio and rented a hotel room. The morning of Jack's deposition, I showed up at my attorney's office as scheduled. A few minutes later, Attorney Land invited me upstairs to his office where we spent some time together going over my case. Our review included doctors' opinions of my condition and the general approach my lawyers were considering in order to pursue my claim. We also talked about some of the feedback they had received from people on a witness list I had provided to them a few months earlier. I was not surprised that a respected coworker and friend of mine was reluctant to talk about me, my work, and the injury. He told Attorney Land, "I am one of the managers of the company. I am concerned for the politics of talking about a terminated former employee ... especially a former senior manager." I was also not surprised when Attorney Land concluded that Blaster would probably use their power over employees to quiet the truth. Attorney Land asked me to listen to Jack's answers during the deposition and slide him a note if Jack said anything questionable or unusual.

At the agreed upon time of the deposition, I anxiously walked with Attorney Land downstairs and into the same conference room where my own deposition had been held six months earlier. There was Jack, alongside his attorney, standing against a chair that was positioned tightly against the wall in the corner of the room. He had a disappointed look on his face as he stared at the floor. His attorney, Lois, the same lady who had taken my deposition, was looking off into the distance. It certainly was an awkward moment when I walked into the room with my lawyer right behind me. I looked at Jack and quickly remembered that he had been my friend. He had done the best he could while driving the car during the accident. I walked directly toward Jack and reached out my hand in reconciliation. I smiled and said, "Hello, Jack." He quickly looked up at me and seemed shocked. Then he smiled slightly and reached out his hand to shake mine. After Jack and I briefly shook hands, I looked over at Lois and said, "Hello." She smiled easily and reached out to shake my hand. Then we all sat down to listen while my attorney asked Jack several questions.

Jack, the court reporter, and the attorneys sat at the end of the table closest to the door. I sat next to Attorney Land at the other end of the table, more as an observer than a participant. At first, there were very general questions about the work relationship Jack and I had shared over the years, including the kind of work we did and the frequency of working together. I was surprised when Jack replied that he "was a consultant to Mr. Werb" and also avoided any reference to our personal relationship. His recounting of the number of times we had worked together was very limited. He also completely overlooked the committee we were on together for more than one year to set financial policy for the company. While on the committee, Jack and I met at least quarterly and talked on the phone many times in the interim. I put a note about the committee work on a piece of paper and slid it over to my attorney.

As Jack's deposition continued, more of our personal relationship and the committee meetings eventually came to light. He explained that we had met and shared many dinner meetings together at many different Blaster businesses around the country. Yet Jack continued to be very reserved about the amount of time we had shared and the personal discussions we had together. He obviously wanted to minimize our relationship, both work and personal, to somehow manage his responsibility. His legal counsel had probably coached him to minimize our relationship, as well as the car accident itself. It seemed we were playing a "catch me if you can" game of insurance recovery, a game that had serious implications for my future.

The deposition continued until Jack was asked questions specifically about the car accident. According to my lawyer, Jack's answers indicated that he took full responsibility for losing control of the automobile on the highway that day almost three years prior. When Jack mentioned the semi-truck/trailer that drifted and nearly sideswiped his car and caused some of his loss of control, he did not have the clarity of memory that I had over the whole situation. Nor was he able to recollect the details that he had written on the accident report that was filed with the police. At different times during the deposition, he said he was upset and distraught at the time of the accident or he simply could not remember the details anymore. A few times during the deposition, Jack was very assertive and seemed angry. I suspected he was angry for being named in a lawsuit over the car accident. Or quite possibly his counsel had coached him to be brief and firm while answering only the specifics of the questions. Indeed, I too had an angry feeling that turned to frustration and then resignation as I thought about how the process and the system was a game and such a waste of time and energy. Unfortunately, it was a high-stakes poker game about my life and my future. It seemed I was not dealt all the cards or had any reasonable chance of winning.

Jack's deposition lasted about two hours, unlike my over six-hour deposition. At least my attorney respected the process and the people. At the end of the deposition, I prepared to leave by saying goodbye to Attorney Land. As we shook hands, my attorney and I slipped into a discussion about workers' compensation insurance not paying my medical bills. Attorney Land asked me to review the files Blaster had provided to him as part of the discovery process for my personal injury lawsuit. "See if there is anything harmful to your claim, a smoking gun, and take notes about any areas of concern to you." I said, "Sure, I've got time. I can do that." I returned to the same conference room where Jack's deposition had just been held and sat down to review a stack of papers.

Of interest to me were the notes Blaster's nurse, Nurse Jones, had made that appeared to be constructed after I was fired in July. She wrote a note dated in late July that said I had approached her in her office and agreed to work with Blaster regarding my situation. I remembered making that comment in May when I returned to work, not in July before I was terminated. In the note, she also wrote that I took one pain pill each day. I remembered that during that time I had been reviewing a journal with her and the company doctor that showed I was usually taking five or six painkillers and five or six muscle relaxers mixed with a cocktail of alcohol in the evening. I did this to address the pain and relax enough to sleep a few hours each night.

One of the other notes in her file said I was unable to understand the workers' compensation system even though she had tried to help me a number of times. She also noted that I had called to let her know I had recently hired a new attorney. She wrote that she hoped this new attorney would be able to help me understand how the system worked. I felt angry over the notes as I remembered the many attempts I had made to communicate to her and others at Blaster about my condition, as well as to understand the system. Yet I was not successful. Many of these attempts were recorded in the complaint, appeal, and fraud reports I made to the BWC after I left Blaster. The nurse's notes felt like an affront to my intelligence and capability. I thought she was probably protecting her job and would have to say something defensive, particularly after I made the reports to the BWC.

I read her rebuttal to my complaint to the BWC that explained how she had told my doctor to not file the workers' compensation forms for the pain program. In her rebuttal, Nurse Jones indicated there were two doctors involved with my medical care and so much paperwork that it must have been confusing to her at the time to understand the note I had given her about the pain program. Her rebuttal seemed bogus to me since the personal face-to-face instruction and separate note I provided to her at the time were very clear. I asked her to help Dr. Hunt's office file the appropriate workers' compensation forms for the pain program. But she called his office and told Dr. Hunt's administrator that I was not filing a workers' compensation claim for the pain program. Her rebuttal now validated my understanding of what happened with the pain program forms. She had no reasonable excuse for trying to stop Dr. Hunt's office from filing the forms. Indeed, her excuse when caught in a lie was that she was temporarily confused. This was especially disappointing to me since the BWC auditors accepted it, while at the same time they accepted Blaster's explanation that my BWC problems were a result of me not understanding the system.

As I continued to review the stack of papers, I was pleasantly surprised when I saw that Blaster, as a self-insured workers' compensation employer, had actually paid almost $1,000 of my approximate $28,000 in medical bills. This was more than just a few hundred dollars that I thought they had paid up to that point. When I told Attorney Land of this finding, he smiled and said, "After almost three years, that's pathetic!" I looked at Attorney Land, smiled, and said, "That's true. I also saw that they paid their attorneys and third-party administrator almost $8,000 to accomplish this. That's pretty sad considering it's at the expense of an injured employee."

As part of my review, I also saw, for the first time, a copy of a Blaster report that detailed the reasons why they denied most of my medical bills for payment under workers' compensation insurance. Right away I knew I should have requested a status report like this every month or at least quarterly. I could have gone out and worked

160

the issues in a timelier manner. Now the files were old and people were frustrated. I also wondered if a more assertive response to Blaster's tactics would have made much of a difference anyway.

Also included in the files obtained from Blaster was the appropriate form for reporting an injury to the BWC that was dated September 1997, signed by Dr. Hunt, and submitted to Blaster. The form included the diagnosis of cervical/thoracic (neck and back) sprain/strain, along with chronic myofascial pain. Somehow the chronic myofascial pain was not formally recognized in my BWC claim. This was the main reason Blaster did not pay for the pain program and other medical bills and lost wages. Now was the first time I had seen this completed form or even known such a form existed. But Blaster knew and continued to ignore it so they could deny medical benefits and lost wages for my injury. In my view, the word "pathetic" did not seem strong enough to describe the ruthlessness of a large company going to such great lengths to cheat an injured employee.

While I noted a couple other items for Attorney Land to review, there was nothing more of great importance to discuss. When I finished my review, I gave the files over to Attorney Land's secretary, shook hands, and said goodbye. While I was driving to the airport, it dawned on me that Blaster had excluded many files, notes, memos, and letters about my struggle to perform at work and keep my job. There was no "smoking gun" or evidence contrary to my view of the situation. But maybe there was evidence of Blaster's ruthlessness and wrongdoing at the time. This could be referred to as a "hidden gun" in the sense that evidence was withheld from the discovery process for the purpose of minimizing my injury and its implications to my work. Maybe they were going to argue that I had simply quit my job. Or, I wondered, would they argue that there was a mutual agreement with the company over my departure like Attorney Law had explained Blaster had done with my workers' compensation case?

During my flight home that night, a list of information excluded by Blaster from the discovery process started to form in my mind. I remembered conversations I had had with Messrs. Blair and Seabert about my injury, the intense pain, the many different medications and medical care that I had had, and the impact my medical situation had on my work. The next day, even though I was in a lot of pain from making the trip to Ohio, I could not wait to sit down and prepare a list of "evidence" to send to Attorney Land for the personal injury case. I would also send a copy to Attorney Law for the workers' compensation claim. I looked through my notes collected over the years and chronologically outlined a number of discussions and letters that went back and forth between me and Blaster during the fifteen months after the accident and up until they fired me. As I prepared the list, I realized a story was unfolding – a story Blaster obviously didn't want other people to hear.

Mine was a story about an individual who was hurt in an accident and tried as much as, if not more than, humanly possible to continue to do his job while keeping everyone informed of his declining health. Yet the medical care, struggle over returning to work, and finally the need for a pain program was not documented or at least was not included in the discovery process papers. I had asked and written notes, some would say begged and pleaded, for lesser responsibilities and employment alternatives, including a warmer climate. But the answer that kept coming back from Blaster was no. Before attending the pain program, I had written to Mr. Blair about my preference to continue as an employee and receive medical leave benefits that had been promised to me by Blaster when I was hired. After the pain program, I wanted to return to Blaster in the position I had or a position with less responsibility if that's what made sense. Instead, I was involuntarily terminated and Blaster announced my departure throughout the company as a mutual decision. The only thing mutual about my departure from Blaster was that everyone agreed I was hurt and could no longer meet the responsibilities of my job. Everyone also agreed that I needed to attend the pain program at Valley Hospital. The only way I was able to attend the program was to accept the involuntary termination from Blaster.

The many letters, notes, and conversations I listed as missing from the information Blaster provided for the discovery process told my story of a long and painful struggle. The list I emailed to my lawyers about the missing information is included as Appendix 15. I felt good about my trip to Ohio because I saw Jack once again and found some emotional closure over our lost friendship. I was also glad I had taken the opportunity to identify the missing documents that told a story. Mine was a story that needed to be told for my personal injury and workers' compensation insurance recovery and maybe for my own emotional and spiritual recovery.

A few weeks later, Attorney Law called and asked me to return to Ohio to see an occupational psychologist about my mental condition and work capability as a result of my injury. Attorney Law explained Blaster would argue that my chronic pain was caused by depression that either existed prior to or was caused by problems unrelated to the accident. While I reluctantly agreed to make another trip to Ohio in the next two months, I also asked Attorneys Law and Land to coordinate some of what had become frequent, expensive, and painful travel. Even with the hardship of travel and the dollar amount of any benefits being questionable, I decided to continue to work the issues as much as needed. Indeed, I felt that the principle and my resolve had grown along with the deny and delay tactics and even lying that continued into the three-year anniversary of the accident. Blaster recently lied to my new doctor and physician of record in Minnesota, Dr. Bell, about my workers' compensation benefits when he referred me to Dr. Sun, an orthopedic surgeon and back and neck specialist. Nurse Jones told my doctor's office administrator that my workers' compensation claim covered only my shoulder, not my back or neck. As soon as I heard this, I sent a copy of the BWC hearing decision to Dr. Bell to clear the way for benefits from workers' compensation. The BWC decision from two years earlier had allowed my claim for cervical/thoracic sprain/strain, i.e., my neck and back.

But I knew that regardless of this clarification, Blaster would probably not provide the pre-approval I needed for the referral from Dr. Bell. After all, they had never provided a pre-approval for any of my medical care. Country Garden, my Minnesota no-fault insurance company, said they would pay if Blaster documented a valid denial of workers' compensation benefits. But Blaster seldom provided this documentation and, if they did, it was not timely. Further, since my Minnesota health insurance pool did not cover work-related medical care and had a high deductible, it appeared I would have to pay another $1,000 to $2,000 out of my own pocket if I saw this specialist without the workers' compensation or no-fault insurance coverage. Instead of incurring more medical expense, I decided to forego Dr. Sun's medical care until I sorted through the three layers of insurance benefit paperwork.

Dr. Bell referred me to a local pain center to have my medications reviewed since he, like most doctors, was reluctant to prescribe the narcotic painkillers and muscle relaxers I needed each day. For years, I took these powerful medications in the evening when the pain became unbearable and I had a need for restorative sleep. Before prescribing narcotics, the pain center doctor, Dr. Norton, insisted I try more trigger point injections, this time using steroids that could help or possibly even cure my condition. Even though I was leery about getting back on the roller coaster of hope and disappointment, I agreed to have the injections. I felt I had no other choice or I would not get the medications I needed each day.

Once again, the shots into the muscles of my back and neck provided temporary relief but also sent me into several days of an extremely bad pain cycle. Then, the pain center prescribed methadone as a painkiller that sent me into a drug stupor for two weeks. I called the pain center and insisted that this was not an acceptable medication for me. Yet, when I explained how the drug stupor robbed me of thought, emotion, and judgment, they said, "Keep taking the medication. That cloudy feeling will go away in another week or so." I paused to look at the notes I had prepared for the phone call and replied with an unavoidable slur, "I cannot take these drugs. I am in a drug stupor, spaced out, irritable, and I can't even drive." The nurse put me on hold to talk to the nurse practitioner. After a brief delay, she replied, "Then don't drive." I stood holding the phone without speaking. I was shocked and very disappointed at her response. Yet I was not surprised that they did not understand that I did not want to stop the pain if that meant I had no life to live, including not being able to drive a car.

This experience helped me see still another side to my chronic pain condition. I knew I needed some level of thought and emotion, of love and responsibility, of reality and spirituality. This also meant I would always have some level of pain in my life. Eventually I found a new balance of medication with half of the initial methadone prescription supplemented with muscle relaxers in the evening. I also held off Dr. Norton's request for more pain injections and "diagnostic" nerve blocks in my neck. I knew in my heart that my body and spirit were telling me "no more invasive medical procedures." Indeed, I also knew that as long as one of my tools of pain management was prescription medication, I would have to dance with the doctors and my safety net from time to time.

Country Garden argued that workers' compensation insurance was primary; therefore, they would not give me no-fault insurance benefits to pay my medical bills. This just seemed like another poor excuse to deny benefits. I responded by asking Country Garden to pay my bills and go after Blaster for reimbursement similar to what they did for car accidents when another party was at fault. After all, Country Garden had more resources and clout than I did to deal with a large company like Blaster and bureaucracy like the Ohio BWC. Country Garden said "no" to my general request for help, but they did agree to reimburse my medical bills for massage therapy in excess of the maximum in the BWC guidelines. I had to plead for even this benefit from Country Garden while arguing that Blaster would never pay or should pay more than the maximum in the Ohio BWC guidelines.

The summer before, Country Garden had also agreed to pay for prescription medications (usually $5 co-pays) and mileage to my medical care provider's office (even though they would not pay the bills for the medical care I had driven to receive). As the benefits were coming a little bit at a time, I tried to get their new promises in writing to ensure that they continued. As I was preparing a letter to Country Garden about our massage therapy agreement, I saw an opportunity to assertively request payment for more of the medical bills I had paid out of my own pocket. My letter requested reimbursement of $4,025 of the medical bills I had already paid for massage therapy, physical therapy, visits with MDs and a psychologist, and acupuncture. I believed they should pay all my bills. This was why I had bought insurance. I excluded unpaid bills for the BWC massage therapy limit and the pain center. I also asked for reimbursement of future medical bills (Appendix 16). Much to my surprise, a few weeks later a check came in the mail for $4,025 from Country Garden, along with a promise to reimburse future massage therapy medical bills without Blaster's review. They also agreed to pay other medical bills in the future after Blaster reviewed and formally disapproved the treatment and had given notice to Country Garden. This formal Blaster disapproval was needed by Country Garden in order to ensure that the bills would not be paid twice. This was a considerable accomplishment for me to receive no-fault insurance benefits for past and future medical bills. I felt I had, in effect, overcome the excuse that "workers' compensation insurance is primary in Minnesota." I had to in order to recover insurance benefits that had been promised to me and that I had paid for as a Country Garden policyholder. I felt good that my hard work had paid off, or at least had that appearance.

In my letter (Appendix 16), I referred to specific Ohio and Minnesota workers' compensation guidelines. I also referenced a discussion I had with an attorney at the Minnesota BWC. It was unfortunate that I had to waste so much time and suffer more pain while researching workers' compensation rules and insurance policies in order to demand the benefits I had paid for and had been promised. Indeed, benefits from my insurance policy had to be fought for when they should have been paid as promised. I was one of the insurance company's customers and insureds rather than a claimant, as they usually referred to their policyholders that requested benefits. "Claimant" seemed like an ugly term that suggested someone was looking for a handout or some type of entitlement. But that was what I was at the time – a claimant who once again, with a lot of hard work and assertiveness, recovered insurance benefits purchased and promised as part of an insurance policy for many years. Unfortunately, this recovery of benefits once again came at a much higher personal cost than necessary or reasonably expected. At least now the payment of benefits had started along with a glimmer of hope for more recovery and a much better life than initially appeared.

Chapter 14

Work In Process

My safety net issues were heating up. A few days after Attorney Law asked me to see an occupational psychologist, Attorney Land called me about my personal injury claim. He told me Blaster's attorney called him to demand that I stop contacting Blaster employees about my insurance claims and lawsuit. A month earlier, at Attorney Land's request, I had contacted two people at Blaster to ask them to talk to Attorney Land about what it was like working with me before and after I was injured.

The first contact I made was with Mark, who had worked for me the entire time I worked at Blaster in Troy. When Mark and I talked on the telephone, it seemed like old times working together. We enjoyed talking about how we were doing, both personally and professionally, including our medical problems. Shortly after I left Blaster, Mark developed a brain tumor and was hospitalized for surgery to have the problem corrected. He fully recovered after several months of medical care. Needless to say, his wife and three young children were very happy and relieved that their special young man would be healthy and with them for life. I congratulated Mark on his recovery as I held back my feelings of jealousy over the cure I could not find.

During our conversation, I explained to Mark some of the difficulty I had recovering insurance benefits and the unfortunate need I had for a personal injury lawsuit. I asked, "Could you help me by talking to Attorney Land about our work together before and after the accident? I know there may be problems for you at work if you do this. I will understand if you say no." Mark replied, "No problem. I will talk to Attorney Land when he calls." I thanked

Mark for his help. We wished each other well and said, "Goodbye and take care."

A few days later I tried to contact another Blaster employee, Sheri, who had also worked for me. During my short time working in Troy, I had hired and promoted Sheri. I recently heard that she was promoted again, this time into management after I left the company. Since we had worked together directly almost every day I was at Blaster in Troy, I hoped she could help me with my insurance problems too.

First I called her on the telephone and sent her an email directly. Sheri did not respond to my phone call or email. I asked a friend who worked at Blaster to forward an email to Sheri that asked her to contact me. Still I received no response. I was unsure why I was unsuccessful making contact with Sheri by phone or email. Maybe I had the wrong telephone numbers and email addresses and that was why I had not heard from her. After all, we had been friendly as coworkers. I was looking forward to talking to Sheri about family and children as we had done so often when we worked together. We worked hard supporting each other to balance our work with our personal lives. She helped me a lot after the injury that limited my ability to do my job. In her first year at Blaster, I worked hard and took a lot of heat from my boss so she could return home for a month to visit her family in Japan whom she had not seen in five years.

But Sheri did not contact me. Instead, I received the Blaster demand through Attorney Land to stop contacting their employees. Had Sheri notified Blaster management of my contact with her? Now I wondered if Blaster had prohibited employee contact with me. Blaster was obviously playing legal hardball by prohibiting my direct contact with their employees and theirs with me. All I wanted to do was to put the issues on the table and face them head on without all the tactics and lawyers. But this wish of mine would not come true. Indeed, many big companies preferred to push and shove hard on individuals in order to muscle their way past responsibility. Blaster would do the same to me.

Meanwhile, I continued to review the status report list of medical bills from Blaster that explained why my medical bills were denied for payment under workers' compensation insurance. Most explanations were not valid reasons to deny benefits but were simply paperwork tactics. Blaster repeatedly claimed there was inadequate documentation such as missing office notes, wrong billing codes, or no pre-approvals. This was noted even though I personally knew Blaster had received the documents directly from my medical practitioners or me. Nonetheless, to follow-up on Blaster's excuses, I mailed letters and called my doctors to request that their office notes and other documentation be sent directly to Blaster once again. I also called the hospital and asked them to forward yet another copy of the detailed bills for the pain program that were not even included on Blaster's list. Then I prepared a summary for Attorney Law to send to Blaster that detailed the recent actions I had taken to address their denial of benefits (Appendix 17).

My summary included questions for Blaster about the denials that referenced BWC codes and forms that did not make sense to me. I hoped this work would resolve most of Blaster's concerns and they would pay more bills. But they did not, and I became angry and frustrated again. Yet once I got past the anger and frustration of working the excuses once again, I found that standing to face the tactics and pushback of a large corporation invigorated me. I realized my struggle over benefits had actually encouraged me to assertively live my life once again. This was true even though my social position, status, and the materialism I once enjoyed were all gone. I also realized these social things were not really that important in my life. Instead of my past work in the business world, I was now encouraged and excited about my safety net work, this book, and the website my son, Shawn, was helping me set up to help other chronic pain sufferers. I was excited and felt positive emotions again as my truths were renewed and my spirit within was reawakened and growing stronger. I knew there was a future for me even though I still did not know what it was. The common cycle of betrayal, forgiveness, and letting go was nearing its maturity even though there was still a lot of work to do to improve safety nets for all of the sick and injured, including me.

A few weeks later, I flew to Ohio for the evaluation by an occupational psychologist that Attorney Law had suggested. I stayed in an inexpensive hotel a few miles from downtown Columbus. The next morning I treated myself to a nice breakfast and drove to Attorney Law's office. I was surprised by the austerity of Attorney Law's offices when I went there for help. And I wondered if this meant they were more interested in the practice of law than the rewards of their profession. Attorney Law was not available so I met with one of the other workers' compensation lawyers at the firm. He explained to me that he had previously worked as a member of a team at the Ohio BWC. The team was responsible for overseeing self-insured employers like Blaster.

After we talked about my claim, the lawyer told me, "Blaster is one of the worst self-insured companies. They believe they should not have to pay any workers' compensation benefits. They treat all claimants as cheaters. Contrary to their position, we know that very few people try to cheat. Most are hurt and need some help. Maybe one in a thousand people that come to us are collecting benefits while at the same time being paid under the table for working hard chopping firewood for their brothers or doing something else. Except for a few, most people have valid claims. Unfortunately, companies like Blaster will pay thousands of dollars to lawyers in order to avoid paying the injured much less. By making the system extremely difficult, people eventually drop their claims. The company avoids paying benefits that over time add up to significant savings for the company indirectly taken from their injured employees' benefits. The many complications in the system were designed by business and government with the help of lawyers to maintain a low-cost charade of security for the working masses. These companies are like the tobacco industry where they will spend any amount on lawyers, politicians, or others so as not to pay benefits to the sick or injured."

As I listened to this lawyer speak, I felt disgusted yet validated by his comments. His words rang true to me. I smiled as I told him, "I saw some of their workers' compensation records as part of my personal injury discovery process. They have paid less than $1,000 of my $28,000 in medical bills, yet they paid over $8,000 to attorneys to fight my claim." He smiled slightly and said, "We will help you pursue your claim, but it will be a long hard process." I shook my head in agreement and said, "I have already filed a complaint, appeal, and reported fraud to the BWC." He smiled as if supporting my very difficult effort. For a short time we just looked at each other quietly with an unspoken understanding. I knew I had finally found good legal representation for my workers' compensation claim. The attorneys at this firm were interested in justice over a "quick hit" even though it was a very time-consuming process and meant long hard work. They were very busy lawyers as they faced into the onerous workers' compensation system with companies like Blaster.

Next, I went to see the occupational psychologist at his office a few miles away. He was a tall, calm man who seemed suspicious of me at first. Like so many other doctors, he asked me to describe the accident, along with my medical care, impairment, and its impact on my work. During our discussion, I explained that I was frustrated over people's reaction to invisible chronic illnesses like mine and how my safety net providers tried to take advantage of the lack of objective evidence of my impairment. He seemed to warm up to my story and started to believe what I was telling him. At the end of our meeting, he even told me, "I was suspicious at first. After all, you look fine and come across confident and intelligent. Yet I understand your frustration and disappointment … like so many others who have an invisible chronic illness experience."

A few weeks later I received a copy of the psychologist's report. The report was both thoughtful and credible, at least from my perspective. He referenced the observations and conclusions of all of the IMEs I had attended, along with the opinions of my own doctors. He concluded that my impairment was both physical and psychological, and reported that I was not "malingering." The psychologist summarized that, given that I was capable of working sixteen to twenty hours per week in jobs with less responsibility, my lost wage was about $100,000 per year as a result of the accident. Indeed, I had known this for quite some time. Having this confirmed by a professional was both sad and helpful to me for my long journey of acceptance. Fortunately, now I also had a professional opinion to use to support my workers' compensation and personal injury claims. This psychologist's evaluation would be an IME in support of my request for help from my safety net providers.

# # #

My safety net struggle continued through the summer, almost three and one-half years after the accident. Pretrial meetings were scheduled in the fall by the judge assigned to my case in order to sort out issues and attempt to settle the case before the jury trial scheduled one week later. As the date scheduled for the pretrial meetings approached, I traveled once again to Ohio. The preparations for trial included my attorney and me identifying a list of potential witnesses. We had also hired an economist to quantify my lost wages and other financial considerations, excluding, of course, the expenses of pursuing my claim. Before the trial even started, these expenses grew to almost $5,000 out of my own pocket to pay for the professional opinions of an occupational psychologist, an economist, my IME doctor, and several depositions. If my claim went to trial, I would also have to pay for the time and travel expenses of my personal physicians, Drs. Hunt, Bell, and Norton, to testify. Attorney Land told me that the expenses of going to trial would easily approach $20,000. This seemed to me to be a high price to pay for justice. Again I wondered what other people did who were injured and could not afford medical care, let alone court costs, to recover benefits. I remembered my friends from the pain program and others I met along the way who suffered and gave in or gave up on the system. I felt I had to fight back for me and for them so I continued to work through more tactics from the keepers of my safety net.

The day of the first pretrial meeting was a beautiful, warm, and sunny summer day. Attorney Land and I walked the two blocks from his office to the courthouse. Jack and his attorney were already there sitting in the waiting area outside of the judge's chambers. Jack and I sat uncomfortably in the waiting area as our lawyers first met alone with the judge. The judge quickly decided to combine the question of phantom vehicle responsibility with the issue of Jack's insurance and/or Blaster's responsibility to provide its employees added underinsured or uninsured insurance coverage. Jack's attorney also provided a last-minute defense that said people could not sue a coworker. Since both sides would need time to respond to these issues, the judge rescheduled the trial for the following spring, four years after the car accident.

After the pretrial meeting, Attorney Land and I returned to his office to discuss my case. He told me that Jack's coworker defense could prevail. If it did, we would continue to pursue responsibility from the semi-truck/trailer as a phantom vehicle liability covered under Jack's and/or my uninsured/underinsured insurance policies. Attorney Land also told me that Dr. Hunt would not be very supportive of my situation in court. Recently, Attorney Land had talked to potential witnesses. Dr. Hunt told him, "Mike needs to see a psychologist. Most patients heal soon after they receive injuries like his." When Attorney Land told me this, at first I simply felt another level of betrayal from Dr. Hunt. Early in the summer of 1999, Dr. Hunt had written a letter to me that limited my work hours to sixteen per week. At the time, he knew I could not even handle the part-time job I had at the local technical college working those hours. Yet, a few weeks later, he sent a workers' compensation form to Blaster that said I could work twenty to thirty hours. Now he was suggesting I should be completely healed and working full time. I could only rationalize that Dr. Hunt must have wanted desperately to continue to be part of Blaster's lucrative health care and workers' compensation insurance plans. With a feeling of disappointment about Dr. Hunt, I looked at Attorney Land and replied, "Yes, that is true. Most patients do heal soon after the accident. But some do not."

As I searched for a better understanding for Attorney Land, I explained, "I've been told that eighty percent do heal, but unfortunately I'm one of the twenty percent that eventually finish their medical care with a physiatrist and then try other alternatives to heal, including comprehensive pain management. Learning biofeedback, meditation, and other pain management tools from a psychologist are good alternatives for pain management. Being referred to a psychologist does not mean we are crazy or it's all in our heads. As I've told others, if it is all in our heads, help us get it out. It wasn't there before the accident." Attorney Land smiled slightly as he shook his head affirmatively. Yet the distant look in his eyes suggested he did not understand, and neither would other people,

173

including potential jurors. Later I learned that the eighty percent recovery rate was overstated. This would also be hard to explain even with scientific longitudinal medical studies for proof. The studies are reviewed in *Surviving the Chronic Pain Experience: Understand and Manage Medical Care and Life Changes.*

Attorney Land then told me, "The added time until the trial will be a chance for you to work more closely with your doctor at the pain center in Minnesota." Apparently Dr. Norton's reports were more supportive of my situation than Dr. Hunt's reports, probably because Dr. Norton's work was specialized in the area of chronic pain. Suddenly it dawned on me that while both Drs. Hunt and Bell were doctors specializing in physical medicine, it was important for me to be treated by a doctor who specialized in pain. Fortunately, the area of pain medicine had evolved into a valid medical specialty rather than continuing to treat pain as a symptom to be masked with drugs. Unfortunately, the general public usually still considered chronic pain to be "in your head" or possibly faking for financial gains. Many medical care providers also held this belief about chronic pain.

The local news channel recently hosted a report on chronic pain that was given by the pain center where Dr. Norton practiced. They reported that chronic pain affects forty million Americans and contributes to half of the suicides in our country. If appropriate, the pain center implanted devices in a patient's body to regularly deliver drugs directly to the spine in order to reduce the pain without the whole body drug stupor that patients experience with pills. Yet, even with their understanding of the seriousness of chronic pain and the much-needed medical care, I had to plead for their help with insurance forms, documentation, and approvals like the work restrictions and pain management program that Dr. Bell had approved. The struggle with medical care providers made it even harder for the injured to receive the help they needed and were promised.

In a strange way, Attorney Land's discussion of different insurance options, limits in the insurance policies, and earlier comments about the amount the local small town jury was likely to award felt like an estate auction over my impaired life. I was usually

174

a bit sad when I watched an estate auction where people bid on an old couple's personal possessions. Most people at the auction were hungry for a bargain, while the old couple looked on as their life was sold to the highest bidder. The slight price on their possessions was encouraged higher by the skill of the auctioneer and deemed fair in the end. Yet the synergy of memories and the value of the items were lost at the moment of sale. Auctions were a sad and hard reality of life.

When I thought about an auction analogy to my situation, I realized that maybe I had been taking my situation too personally. The low offers from insurance companies, as well as the help or harm from my other safety net providers, were really not personal. They were playing the "maximize shareholder wealth and management bonus game" I used to play with them. Indeed, now I knew that no amount of money paid or responsibility taken by others could possibly amount to all I had lost when compared to what my life was worth to me prior to the accident. Yet here I was taking the insurance game and health care crisis personally. Maybe this was what one of my friends meant when she said I needed to forgive them for what harm I felt and forgive myself for what harm I put myself through on my road to recovery.

# # #

Earlier in the summer, Dr. Bell signed an IRS form with the statement that I was "totally and permanently disabled ... with a chance of some recovery in the future." The form he signed would allow me to take money out of my 401k and IRAs without having to pay the ten percent penalty. This penalty was levied by the IRS for withdrawals from these "pre-tax" investments by people who were not of retirement age. I withdrew some of my retirement money when I bought a house with Justine. I knew I could do it again to pay my bills for living, but eventually this money would be depleted. I was not working yet and knew part-time work would not be enough to live on.

Off and on I was thinking about my application for SSA disability benefits. Then I received a letter from the SSA with a "denial of disability benefits." The letter stated that their evaluation of my claim had determined I was capable of returning to my job as a controller. I just stood there looking at the letter and shook my head as tears formed in my eyes. The SSA letter suggested that if I disagreed with their decision, I could file a "Reconsideration of Disability Report." I decided that, rather than attempting to file the appeal myself, I would hire another lawyer for assistance with the many forms and questionnaires that were needed to appeal the SSA decision. I quickly learned I would have a difficult time finding a lawyer to represent me considering I had a soft tissue injury and invisible chronic pain. Eventually I found one to help me who worked only on SSA claims. I smiled with disbelief when I thought about how I now had four avenues for recovery of benefits from my safety net.

While I continued to handle my Minnesota no-fault insurance claim on my own, I had also hired three different attorneys to separately cover my personal injury, workers' compensation, and Social Security disability insurance claims. This required a lot of coordination on my part since the attorneys were focused on their own goals for which they would be paid a percentage of one-fourth to one-third. In some ways it was good that I had not found a job when most of the legal work occurred. The few hours each week of productive time I had was spent coordinating with lawyers and writing. The attorneys usually did not call their counterparts about overlapping issues or benefits. I had to request, and sometimes insist, they call each other to coordinate their work and find the best approach for my situation. Each time an event transpired, like a hearing, expert evaluation, IME report, or payment of benefits, I sent information to all three attorneys and encouraged them to discuss my case with each other if necessary. Meanwhile, I tried to anticipate where there might be overlapping issues or opportunities to share information or positions. This coordination effort of mine paid off with both higher benefits and reduced costs related to shared expert testimony and the avoidance of redundant work.

For example, at Dr. Bell's request, and with Justine's help, I documented each hour of my day in the context of pain management and the work restrictions I lived with each day (Appendix 18). The pain management program was first developed for me at the hospital pain management program in Ohio. I still needed to follow the program fairly religiously. My recent experience teaching at St. Cloud State University (SCSU) became the basis for a ten-hour-per-week work restriction. I first tried a twenty then a fifteen-hour workweek. I soon realized and demonstrated that a ten-hour workweek was more than enough as the pain was almost unbearable with that amount of time. The pain management and work restrictions document helped Drs. Bell and Norton and their staff better understand my condition and the medical care I needed.

A few weeks later, at the request of my workers' compensation attorney, I had Drs. Bell and Norton formally approve the document I signed and had notarized. Then I sent a copy of the signed and notarized document, along with the doctors' approvals, to the three attorneys working on my claims. Shortly thereafter, my workers' compensation attorney and SSA attorney moved ahead more assertively and confidently with my claims in their areas. I realized the formal notarized documentation and doctors' approvals of my work restrictions and pain management program were one of the keys to pursuing claims for an invisible chronic illness like mine. Medical care providers were usually very reluctant to formally approve the implications of invisible chronic illnesses. Yet my persistence, with integrity, in obtaining formal documentation eventually paid off. With written support from my doctors, the possibility of receiving more of the benefits promised in my safety net improved quite a bit.

While meditating a few days later, I recognized that another important self-truth had reappeared in my life. Taking value-based positions with my medical care providers, former employer, and the insurance companies felt good and, at times, exhilarating. On that day, my safety net work seemed to change its complexion from frustration to more of a game where the odds were against me. Each play of my hand was a clear victory, even if the benefits were small or nothing. With this encouragement, I decided to push more on Country Garden to pay the no-fault insurance benefits according to my insurance policies. They eventually paid some benefits, but only after we argued the merits of their approach of litigation rather than my suggestion of partnering with their insureds to achieve medical care and reduced costs together.

First, I tried to hold Country Garden to an earlier promise that they would pay for my prescription medications pending Blaster's payment under workers' compensation insurance. When Country Garden reneged on their promise, I responded with a letter to document both our agreement about reimbursement of medical bills and my concern for the company's business practices. Their company had used a long list of deny and delay tactics, including lying to me about my insurance benefits. Along with detailing my concerns with Country Garden, I also suggested they adopt a partnering approach with their insureds, including me (Appendix 19). Several weeks later, they responded with a three-page letter, along with more than forty pages of attachments that concluded:

> After careful review and consideration of your claim, it is our position we are being fair and reasonable. We believe our handling of your claim is consistent with the language in the policy contract you signed as well as the laws and statutes in both Minnesota and Ohio ... If you disagree with our handling or our position on your claim, your remedies in Minnesota are mandatory arbitration or District Court.

Their response shot through the pit of my stomach as I was reminded of Blaster's response to my concern about their injured employee and workers' compensation insurance process. They seemed to be saying indirectly that lying and cheating was fair and reasonable. What about my policy and the laws and statutes in Minnesota and Ohio?

From what I could see, they had not followed the policy or law except when it supported their position to deny benefits. They mixed the two states' laws together to create a nearly responsibility-free scenario for their company. Even the letter they finally sent to Alto Health about their subrogation rights to benefits included a reference to my policy that was in error and favored Country Garden.

178

Even though it referenced my policy incorrectly, at least they finally sent a letter to Alto Health about the $15,000 of medical bills they wanted reimbursed. I knew I needed legal help, but there was no way I wanted to hire another lawyer, especially for what should be fairly routine no-fault insurance benefits. And I knew arbitration or District Court would be stacked in their favor. Or maybe Country Garden suggested this option as an indirect threat intended to encourage me to stop asking for benefits. There must be other alternatives I could explore. I decided to do more research myself and posture my claim for a hearing in the court of public opinion. I decided to use my website and ask for help from others like investigative reporters or the State Attorney General. But first I had to complete my commitment to teach two classes at SCSU, which was more than enough for now. My safety net issues would have to wait.

Chapter 15

A Better Understanding

During the few weeks of winter break at SCSU, I reviewed Country Garden's latest letter to me with the forty pages of attachments, studied my insurance contract, and researched state laws on the Internet. My response to their letter grew to six pages with two attachments (Appendix 20) to dispute their positions for denying no-fault insurance benefits. I also asked them to consider the impact their process and demands had on people suffering from chronic pain, like me. I once again asked Country Garden to partner with their insureds as I documented the benefits to their company of such a positive approach. But I knew my request for partnering was wishful thinking and possibly quite naïve. Yet, in hindsight, it seemed I found some success each time I assertively pushed back on Country Garden to pay benefits. They either slowly paid more benefits or considered the merit of my arguments by asking their lawyers for a review. I hoped they would eventually pay more even though I knew their reviews were focused on finding legal arguments to deny benefits. These legal reviews seemed like such a waste of time and resources. The no-fault part of my automobile insurance policy was supposed to pay benefits to me as their insured for medical care and lost wages regardless of whose fault the accident was. Yet they first told me I had no benefits and later found other excuses. After I assertively worked with my no-fault insurance claim, Country Garden paid $5,200 of medical bills and $40,000 for lost wages. Even with these payments, my unpaid medical bills were adding up, as were my lost wages.

At the time of the accident, I carried insurance for my car and my son, Johnny's, car with Country Garden. I had elected $20,000 of no-fault benefits on each car with a stacking option so benefits were added together if there was an accident. I was now glad I had elected stacking. I contractually had $40,000 of no-fault benefits available for medical bills and $40,000 of no-fault benefits available for lost wages. That is what my insurance contract said and what I thought would be paid. Country Garden did pay the maximum no-fault lost wage benefits of $40,000 based on a maximum of $4,000 per month for the ten months after my severance pay ran out in January 2000. They delayed payment while saying their lawyers were reviewing my claim. I called them frequently to demand a resolution. Eventually they sent me a lump sum after the fact rather than paying monthly in order to get the time value of money and interest benefits for the company. Or maybe they hoped I would eventually go away or hand this claim over to an attorney, along with my other insurance claims. This would have caused more delay and maybe even a reduction somehow. At times, it seemed the tactics to deny or delay benefits would never end.

In the summer of 2000, I was very pleased when Country Garden paid $5,200 of my medical bills while promising to look at the entire more than $25,000 of medical bills incurred since the accident, along with those into the future. Meanwhile, Alto Health wanted to be paid back for the medical bills they had paid for my work-related car accident. I had already paid a few thousand dollars out of my own pocket for overdue bills. And the medical bills and lost wages continued to add up. I had to continue requesting insurance benefits not only from my no-fault policy but other car insurance and an umbrella policy I had in effect at the time of the accident. Should not my own insurance policies pay these medical bills and more lost wages as outlined in my insurance policies?

My focus for now was on my no-fault policy, while Attorney Land was supposed to be working on the others. With our collective effort, it seemed we were slowly repairing parts of my safety net that had been torn and tattered by the insurance company's deny and delay tactics. Although the benefits I collected were oftentimes hardly worth the effort, I continued my efforts to recover them. When benefits were paid, I celebrated the positive results of my work. I hoped my work would also benefit other people injured and in need of help. Each time I received benefits, I knew I had weathered their tactics. A true, fair, and reasonable solution had prevailed over their cheating of another injured insured.

My letter to Country Garden began:

> While I apologize for the length of this letter, I hope to have captured the essence of Country Garden's unreasonable and inappropriate excuses for denying benefits that suggests Country Garden has little or no interest in paying the benefits promised in the insurance policy I had contracted with Country Garden for years. These concerns include looking at the facts ... potential fraud and other delay/deny tactics, inappropriate policy language you referenced for my claim, insurance laws of Ohio apply to my claim, a reasonable interpretation of Minnesota statute, my satisfaction of all the requirements for no-fault insurance, recovery of workers' compensation insurance benefits has been exhausted, the arbitration and court cases you sent to me do not apply, looking beyond questions of contracts and law at other issues of a more personal and heartfelt consideration, and benefits of partnering that can accrue to Country Garden as well as the insured. Please seriously consider these concerns and recommendations not only for me but, more importantly, for so many other people who are unable to ask the questions and/or request satisfaction from their insurance providers for the benefits they were promised in the policies they purchased.

Attachment I to this letter was a request for additional no-fault medical benefit payments of $19,000, including reimbursement to Alto Health of almost $15,000 for medical bills they had paid as part of my health insurance policy. I also asked for $2,300 for the interest on the benefit payments they delayed to me where Country Garden reaped the benefit of the interest on the money. This request for interest was only included to make a point. I never expected they would give up any of the profits the company realized from their tactics to delay and deny benefits.

Two months later, Country Garden responded in a brief letter stating that they still believed they were being fair and reasonable. I decided to take my concerns to the next level by publishing my letters and summarizing their response on my website. I also forwarded this information to the Minnesota Attorney General. At first, I sent an email to the office of the Attorney General. An individual in the Attorney General's office sent me a reply email to ask that I file a formal complaint and be very specific about what I wanted them to do for me. In a one-page complaint form, I summarized that I wanted the Attorney General to (1) have Country Garden pay the benefits that were denied and delayed as specified in my letter to them (Appendix 20 which I attached to the complaint); (2) conduct a third-party review to determine the validity of my one million dollar umbrella policy to the car accident; and (3) review the insurance company's business processes for improvements after determining if prosecution for fraud and other improprieties was needed.

The Attorney General's office forwarded my complaint to Country Garden for their review. Country Garden replied that workers' compensation insurance should pay benefits rather than my no-fault policy. They acknowledged my umbrella policy but said they were working with my attorney relative to its application to the accident. This response, more than four years after the accident, suggests to me that the umbrella policy was applicable despite Country Garden's certified response that the umbrella policy was <u>not</u> in effect at the time of the accident. Country Garden chose to respond with legal delays and incorrect statements rather than begin to pay. This was probably because my policy had such a large limit and my losses easily exceeded this amount. In their response, Country Garden also said they were honoring their commitment to pay some of my current medical bills even though this was a mistake on their part. Again, they did not respond to my allegations of fraud and other improprieties on their part. No surprise here.

The Attorney General's office gave me ten days to respond to Country Garden's reply to my complaint. In my response (Appendix 21), I summarized my experience with contract law and ethics over the years in many venues. I said I believed Country Garden should make substantive changes to their business practices and asked the Attorney General's office to review my records and those of Country Garden to draw their own conclusion. My response also included a more detailed and factual review of the reply Country Garden had provided to my complaint. What I most hoped for from my reply and complaint was that the Attorney General would visit Country Garden for an audit. From there, I was sure they would find many improprieties and be in a position to request changes that would benefit me and all of Country Garden's insureds. Hopefully, the audit and findings would also be made public, whereupon other insurance companies would have notice that they should also treat their insureds fairly. This was my hope.

#

Dr. Bell was my physician of record for workers' compensation insurance. He was supposed to be able to prescribe additional medical treatment with specialists, including Dr. Norton, and workers' compensation benefits would pay the bills. Yet Blaster would not pre-approve or pay my medical bills for regular visits with Dr. Norton as a pain specialist. Blaster did this even though Dr. Norton was formally referred by Dr. Bell to prescribe medications and consider other therapies for me. In an attempt to have more bills paid by Blaster, or possibly Country Garden, I asked Dr. Norton to approve my daily pain management program and work restrictions (Appendix 18). I sent him a letter (Appendix 22) asking for this approval and for help with other insurance benefits. He had a nurse call me about my request. She said, "No, he will not approve your daily pain program and work restrictions." When I asked, "Why? Please help me understand," she said, "He has not worked with you long enough to sign the form." I was not sure what this meant other than I had possibly not tried the facet injections and other physical therapy he had prescribed for me several months earlier. I was in a "catch 22." I needed the medical care but could not get the insurance benefits I needed for the treatment because I did not have a formal diagnosis and prognosis of my condition. The doctor would not approve the diagnosis and prognosis of my condition unless I already had the medical care he felt he needed to form his medical opinion.

At my next office visit with Dr. Norton, I told the nurse, "I must see Dr. Norton about the help I need for insurance." She left the room to see what she could do. After a few minutes, Dr. Norton walked into the small examining room where I was sitting and said, "No, I cannot sign this. I have not worked with you long enough. You should have facet injections, pool therapy, and other treatment as we have discussed." Here was the "catch 22" I anticipated. The patient is told to have the therapy first so the doctors can provide the diagnosis and prognosis needed for insurance benefits. But the insured risked losing benefits because the pre-approvals were not obtained. With all of my outstanding medical bills, I decided to try harder for the doctor's approval. I was more assertive and direct with Dr. Norton about my injury and problems with insurance. I looked him directly in the eye and told him, "Blaster is sending me to a fifth IME next week to refute my injury and need for additional medical care. I need my doctors to support me with the documentation I need for insurance benefits to pay for medical care." He looked frustrated over my request and the deny tactics of insurance. Yet, after I repeated my request, he looked down at the paper in disgust and said, "I will sign this ... but I must see you monthly from now on. The opiate medications you take sometimes end up on the street." I shook my head in agreement and said, "Yes, I will do whatever you need. The medications are a small but important part of my overall pain management program. My program has allowed me to return to work and participate in life as much as I do." I later learned that having a second doctor's approval of my pain program and work restrictions turned out to be helpful for my ongoing safety net struggle.

Before the workers' compensation hearing was held to determine wage loss benefits, Blaster sent me to another IME. This IME doctor, Dr. Cain, was an orthopedic surgeon like Dr. Sun. Earlier Dr. Bell referred me to Dr. Sun for an orthopedic evaluation. The medical specialty of Dr. Cain and Dr. Sun was where their similarities ended. Dr. Cain was in his late sixties with a much slower and informal approach. He told me he was disappointed over the limited medical information Blaster had provided to him. I told him, "Blaster usually only gives the IME doctors what they want them to see. Yours is the fifth IME I have had. The IME reports you were given by Blaster include many errors carried forward from the first IME that is grossly inaccurate, along with others added along the way. Those errors say I had a prior neck problem and a car accident only one year earlier than the one in April 1997. The C5 problem in the IME report refers to an inflamed cranial nerve I had in 1978, whereas the other car accident was in 1966 when I was eleven years old, not in 1996. There are many more errors and problems in the reports." Dr. Cain smiled at first, then leaned back in his chair and laughed. "That's the system." I assertively looked him directly in the eyes and said, "It's not funny. Many people are denied the medical care they need and suffer greatly because of IMEs and other tactics to deny benefits. Some people don't make it." He suddenly became more authoritative and said, "You are just angry." I replied, "No, I have seen a lot of suffering. I'm not just angry, confused, or uninformed. My prior work experience is extensive with the Department of Defense, National Contracts Management … on the Board of Directors, and Financial Executives Institute. These IMEs are not simply system issues. There is cheating and fraud." He became serious and said, "There is no objective evidence for your symptoms. Your problem is psychosomatic." I asked, "So if you can't see it and can't cut it in an operation, it's all in my head?" He said, "No, it's real to you. You just need to quit thinking so much about it. If I were your doctor, I'd be all over you to physically work hard to recover. I'd be like a gunnery sergeant. You wouldn't have time to think about or feel the pain."

For the next hour we talked about all the times I pushed myself intellectually, physically, emotionally, and spiritually without success. I explained how my recently approved pain management and work restrictions allowed me to work and enjoy some of my life without the intense pain, medicated stupor, and eventual failure that came each time I pushed too far. I assured Dr. Cain that I had pushed the limit and would keep trying. But he was not satisfied. He told me that my pain management schedule was too rigid and I was too focused on pain. He said, "You even meditate about your problem." I replied, "You don't seem to understand how meditation allows me to relax my muscles so the pain is reduced dramatically for a while. My pain management program works. On the other hand, a doctor's excuse that the pain is in my head is self-serving. Obviously the patients you tell this to will never come back to see you if you offer no medical care other than pushing them into failure." He explained, "My approach worked once for a close friend of mine who was hurt in an accident." With a serious demeanor, he explained the recovery his friend realized by using his hard-working gunnery sergeant approach. I could tell he was proud of his accomplishment so I listened respectfully. When he finished I replied, "I'll keep trying and maybe some day it will work for me. Meanwhile, there are over thirty studies spanning a forty-year time frame covering people with soft tissue injuries. The studies show that one-third improve soon after the accident, one-third improve slowly over time, and one-third stay the same or get worse." I handed Dr. Cain the studies that Dr. Sun gave to me and he looked them over quickly. He handed the papers back and said, "I've seen these from *Spine Magazine*. You need the gunnery sergeant approach to get well." I said, "What about the people who have surgery and end up worse? Everyone's different." "Yes that's true. It doesn't work for everyone" was his reply. We both were tiring of our intellectual duel and became quiet. He asked me to sit on the examining table and did a quick physical exam of me while telling me about his childhood. I respectfully listened as I looked out the examining room window. I could see the twin towers of classrooms at the University of Minnesota Business School where I graduated with honors almost twenty-five years ago. I never imagined I would be sitting here today being questioned about an injury while lecturing a doctor on IMEs, chronic pain injuries, and safety net issues, and listening to stories about his childhood.

# # #

The next, and now third, workers' compensation hearing was held almost four years after the accident. It resulted in allowing the condition of chronic myofascial pain to my claim. I was pleased to hear this as it validated what I had been struggling with all along – a chronic pain condition. But since no lost wages or medical bills were allowed, the hearing was a victory for Blaster. Blaster's lawyer used a shotgun approach to dispute my claim, my injury, and my integrity. She picked through my medical files and IME reports to convince the hearing officer that my problem was psychosomatic, especially considering that I had worked for ten months after the accident. At first, I felt I was being penalized for trying so hard to hang on to my job. But I also knew there were many other issues, tactics, and concerns wrapped up in Blaster's victory at this hearing.

After I returned home, I reviewed my business calendars and medical bills to better understand how I had actually worked full time for those ten months after the accident. From this review and careful contemplation about that period of time, I realized how much help I received from others at Blaster that allowed me to hang on to my job. I also remembered how hard I had worked for recovery while searching for a job and/or working part time after I was fired from my full-time job. I thought about the incredible scrutiny I had been under since the accident that did not identify any other reasons or behaviors to suggest anything other than the accident was the cause of my medical bills and lost wages. After completing this thought process and analysis, I wrote a Hearing Response to prepare for and read at my BWC appeal. The Hearing Response (Appendix 23) described how little I had worked even while at work, how much help I had received from the people at Blaster, and the scrutiny I had been under. It also described medical research that supported my claim that my myofascial pain syndrome and soft tissue injury were caused by the accident and was the reason for my symptoms and losses. I referenced the financial losses and medical bills I had, along with a plea for help from workers' compensation insurance. The analysis and Hearing Response gave me a much deeper understanding of what had happened since the accident. I sent the Hearing Response to Attorney Law and called him to insist that I read it at the BWC appeal. He reluctantly agreed to let me read the response.

Two months after the first hearing, I flew to Ohio for the BWC appeal. While sitting in the waiting area of the BWC offices, at the last minute Attorney Law said, "You cannot read the letter. You can sign it and submit it to the hearing officer." I objected, "But I came all this way. I must have an opportunity to present my findings." But Attorney Law would not budge. Fortunately, I had highlighted key points in the response that summarized my findings and addressed Blaster's position from the initial hearing. After my name was called, Attorney Law and I proceeded to the hearing room where Blaster's lawyer was already seated. We sat across from her at a table large enough for five people. Blaster's nurse and human resource manager did not attend this hearing as they had in the past. The hearing officer sat at a desk positioned high above our table similar to what exists in a formal court of law. Actually, the decisions at the BWC are in lieu of a court of law. Only under extreme circumstances could the decision from this appeal be considered in a court of law. This was my last chance.

As soon as the hearing started, the Blaster attorney introduced a work record into the BWC files. The exhibit was supposed to be my attendance record at Blaster from the time I started in Troy until I was terminated. My heart pounded as I flipped through the multi-page document and found many errors. First, the company nurse said I took more than a month paid time off before I even started my job. Then there was no time off recorded for doctor visits or days off for the injury until after the first BWC hearing that determined my injury was work related. Even after Blaster started recording time off for my work injury, the dates and times were significantly understated. I was scared that this final act of deception by Blaster would carry the hearing in their favor. Fortunately, I had reviewed my business calendars for that time frame so I could knowingly and truthfully say that the records were incorrect. But I felt my comment about the work record being incorrect would not be enough. I had to respond well at this appeal in order to tell my story and have the truth be heard.

Blaster's lawyer immediately started her shotgun approach once again to gain the upper hand at the appeal. I quickly took notes about eight of her assertions and tried to tie them into the response of rebuttal I had prepared. As soon as she stopped, I took a deep breath and asked everyone to refer to my Hearing Response. Once I had their attention, I began noting Blaster's position and the appropriate rebuttal in the response. Then I read the highlighted summary out loud. Attorney Law fidgeted in his chair and motioned under the table for me to wrap up my comments. I was exhausted as I finished my rebuttal as best as I could. With the stress of the hearing, my muscles had tightened and the pain was severe. I stood up and swayed back and forth to address the increasing pain. I was soon completely drained from the experience. The hearing officer wrapped up the appeal by saying we would hear from him in a few months. I was hurting but glad that I had told my story regardless of the outcome of the appeal.

Blaster's attorney seemed surprised that I was grateful for the help I received from the company. I was not only grateful, I felt I better understood why the people at Blaster did not understand my condition and maybe why they tried to cheat the workers' compensation process in order to deny benefits to me. Maybe they simply felt they had already done enough for me. While this was understandable, I still believed their lying and deceptive tactics were wrong. I was so moved by the experience that I showcased a description of it on my website to bring public attention to the irony of a workers' compensation system that brought more harm to an already injured worker. Here is the introductory part of the description which is included in its entirety on the Heywer website (www.heywer.com):

Workers' Compensation Systems that Harm the Injured Worker

The shiny copper and glass "Green" building in Columbus, Ohio, stands thirty stories high and covers more than a half a city block. Attached to both sides of the building are two much shorter wings that house the hearing rooms and medical exams area to support Ohio's Industrial Commission (IC) and Bureau of Workers' Compensation (BWC) offices. Today's Industrial Commission's mission is to "serve injured workers and Ohio employers through expeditious and impartial resolution of issues arising from workers' compensation claims and through establishment of adjudication policy ... the Industrial

Commission held hearings on 182,335 claims ... in 2000. The IC and BWC employ approximately 1,700 at the William Green Building ... William Green sought to improve the life of Ohio's working men and women ... he proposed a system to care for injured workers ... in 1913, the Green Compulsory Workmens' Compensation Act was enacted. The Legislation was so successful that it served as a model at the time for other states' workers' compensation systems. In His Own Words: 'Through social provision against the hazards which menace a man's opportunities to work and earn – unemployment, disability, illness, old age – we can establish the basis for freedom of the worker, freedom to make a living without relying on charity.' ... Construction of the William Green Building and Three Nationwide Plaza was the largest coordinated office building construction ever undertaken in the United States by government and private business. Its aesthetic qualities and downtown surroundings give the building its charm ..." (Ohio Industrial Commission and Bureau of Workers' Compensation, William Green Building, Columbus, Ohio, April, 2001.)

With a closer view of what happens inside the building, it appears that its wings do not quite allow the place to soar into accomplishing today's mission, let alone the vision of Mr. Green. Today, because of risks to the people working there, the building is protected by numerous armed guards who patrol the entrances, exits, and each floor twenty-four hours a day, seven days a week. Several years ago, a workers' compensation claimant entered the building and took hostages at gunpoint because of the impact to his injured life from the onerous workers' compensation process and his employer's injustice. I understand this injured employee's struggle and share his pain, literally. I have come to appreciate the plight of people who were injured at work and cannot get help from workers' compensation insurance even though the law says they should. They do not get the medical care they need to recover or the help they need with their lost wages in order to eat and feed their families.

Achievement of the vision held by Mr. Green to help the injured worker seems as distant as ever. The BWC has evolved over the years into an adversarial system that seems to support business and economic constituents ahead of the injured. The goals they prioritize have changed even though they are still commissioned by the government to help the injured worker. Today, the only people consistently helped are the businesses who pay less to their injured, while reporting safer work environments than really exist at their place of business. The companies' lawyers and workers' lawyers are also helped with work that pays nice salaries and benefits. Indeed, most injured employees eventually must hire a lawyer when we learn that the process is so complex and onerous that legal help and formal hearings are needed if we are to recover anything. Oh yes, and the 1700 inhabitants of the thirty-story building enjoy a nice job and comfortable place to work. All of this is essentially carried on the backs of the injured worker.

Imagine if these resources were paid to the injured worker instead. Many BWC administrators, business managers, lawyers, and doctors have smiled or even laughed at this thought. But I'll bet Mr. Green would share my image. And so would the many injured workers and their families across our great nation.

Chapter 16

Greater Recovery

My BWC appeal was decided primarily in my favor. Blaster was directed to pay working wage loss benefits and medical bills as of the date of the request for the first hearing. The appeal decision did not allow for wage loss when I was not working even though, as required by BWC guidelines, I tried hard to search for work at least ten hours a week per my doctor's approved work restriction. I filled out the forms and met the BWC requirements, but it appeared the BWC did not like to pay lost wage benefits to the unemployed. Attorney Law told me that the "Hearing Response" I prepared, submitted, and presented at the hearing was probably the main reason we prevailed over Blaster and had most of the previous hearing decision overturned. I was glad I did it and wondered why this was not standard practice for an injured worker's claim. But there was so much work involved in its preparation, which was usually required of lawyers already overwhelmed by the onerous BWC system. My recommendation for others who are injured is to prepare such a response by themselves for their lawyer's review. This will help their claim and provide a better understanding and acceptance of what happened in their life after the accident.

Even with this legal directive from the BWC, Blaster continued to delay payments by incorrectly calculating the benefit amounts and stalling over reimbursement and direct payment of medical bills. With the tactics continuing, I assertively asked Attorney Law to reach a lump sum settlement with Blaster. He explained that a negotiated settlement would take three months. Unfortunately, Ohio was not like Minnesota when a BWC decision was made. In Minnesota, the judge calculates the present value of lost wages and medical care. The company then pays the claimant that amount and the claim is over. My Ohio BWC claim would have to be wrestled through more delays and tactics, including a broad release I was asked to sign that would have adversely impacted my personal injury claim. Then, as we worked through the issues for months before Blaster paid any monies to me, Blaster informed my medical care providers that my claim was settled. Because of this, one of my medical care providers became anxious to be paid and turned to a collection agency to collect my debt. I had to scramble to respond to this bill collector to protect my credit while Blaster enjoyed the cash flow and pressure it put on me to sign a broad release and settle. But I did not sign or settle yet. Meanwhile, another medical care provider wrote off my bill since they had not gotten a pre-approval as required of medical care providers in Minnesota. I offered to pay a portion of their bill per the settlement, but they declined. I appreciated their help.

As the four-and-a-half-year mark of the car accident approached, I continued to delay facet injections and other medical care while waiting patiently for a workers' compensation settlement. Eventually, more benefits were paid beyond the small amount of medical bills paid by Blaster since the accident. A final lump sum settlement was decided, which was less than half of what the BWC guidelines said Blaster should have paid. Their tactics paid off once again, but not entirely. I recovered much more than their initial settlement offer of $10,000 when they said, "Take it or leave it." Legal fees, of course, reduced the amount I received from Blaster, as did the cost of the IME and occupational psychologist hired on my behalf and other legal expenses. As a pleasant surprise, Attorney Law reduced his fee because a lump sum settlement was less work for him than a continuing legal battle with Blaster. But, in the end, it was definitely not financially worth all the effort I had put into the claim. I would rather have gone to work and earned my pay through hard work and successful job assignments as I always had. Nonetheless, even though the money was small compared to what I earned before the accident, the principle was great. For this I was grateful.

Even though chronic myofascial pain was confirmed by the BWC at the appeal as an allowed condition, Blaster had avoided their workers' compensation responsibility for about $16,000 of medical bills for the pain program. It was obviously too late for the pre-approval I needed before I attended the program almost three years earlier. There would be no payment without a pre-approval or BWC hearing-directed responsibility for the pain program or other medical expenses. But I still felt like asking Attorney Law to continue requesting payment for the program from Blaster anyway. I reminded him that Alto Health had formally requested that I pay them back for the medical bills from the pain program I attended since it was needed as a result of a work-related injury. From my conversations with Attorney Law, I confirmed something I had learned earlier when I reviewed the Ohio statutes that cover insurance. Ohio law says that it is not the insured's responsibility to sort out multiple insurance sources. It is the insurance providers and companies themselves who must sort out overlapping responsibility for insurance benefits. In my situation, this meant Alto Health was supposed to sort this out with Blaster, who was self-insured for workers' compensation insurance. Blaster was also self-insured for their employee health insurance, as most large companies were at the time. Alto Health was a bill payer and administrator of the Blaster employee health insurance plan. After the employee's medical bills were paid according to the plan, Blaster reimbursed the actual medical expenses plus an administrative fee to Alto Health.

Blaster was self-insured for both their employee health plan and workers' compensation insurance. In the business world, we called this left pocket/right pocket health care costs attributed to the same company for the same expense. Unfortunately, most people, including lawyers, did not understand this and reimbursed the employee health plan out of their workers' compensation insurance settlements from the company. This reimbursement directly or indirectly through insurance rates went back to the company. The company was repaid for what was their responsibility under workers' compensation insurance. To address this issue, I drafted and sent a letter to Alto Health explaining that their right to recovery or subrogation should be against Blaster not me (Appendix 24). Both Attorneys Law and Land helped me draft this letter which would reduce the likelihood that Alto Health would later ask for reimbursement of medical bills from any of my insurance settlements. This was a great relief to me from the threat of Alto Health subrogating my insurance settlements sometime in the future.

The trial date for my personal injury lawsuit was scheduled almost four and one-half years after the car accident. First I had to attend another deposition since we had added the insurance company for Blaster as well as my own, Country Garden, to my claim in court. My personal uninsured/underinsured insurance, Blaster's uninsured/underinsured insurance required for their employees, and Jack's uninsured/underinsured insurance were responsible for the "phantom vehicle." The semi-truck/trailer that drifted on us and caused the accident was known as the "phantom vehicle" for legal and insurance purposes and was covered under underinsured and uninsured motorist automobile policies. Jack was no longer part of the lawsuit since his coworker defense had prevailed. The judge had ruled earlier that Jack was not liable since he was my coworker. Suddenly this made sense to me since my workers' compensation claim had finally prevailed. But what if Blaster had won at the BWC appeal? Then no one would have been held responsible for the driver's culpability. While this was interesting to me, the source of insurance coverage had now shifted to uninsured/underinsured liability.

Justine and I flew to Ohio for the deposition and an opportunity to visit our friends in Ohio one more time. I appreciated her company even though I was once again nervously focused on my deposition. To prepare, I read the almost two hundred pages of testimony recorded at my first deposition. With this comprehensive testimony, the lawyers for my second deposition agreed ahead of time to cover only the circumstances of the accident. This was needed to apportion fault between Jack and the phantom vehicle, which would be the subject of the upcoming first trial. A second trial would be conducted next year to determine the amount of my loss from the accident. The phantom vehicle percentage of fault would be applied to my total loss per the jury trial. The result would be paid to me as insurance benefits from the three insurance companies. This was the plan.

The lawyers for the insurance companies had copies of my first deposition that lasted six hours and covered the details of the accident and my entire life. At my second deposition, the lawyers talked fast and pushed hard with the hope that I would lose my credibility when they compared what I said now to the two hundred pages of deposition I had previously given. They quoted answers from the first deposition out of context in an attempt to discredit a previous answer, along with my credibility overall. But I did not waiver. I asked for pause and clarification when needed and answered truthfully and thoughtfully. They told me not to guess but later asked me to give them estimates. I assertively asked them to clarify what they wanted with each question. I imagined that this was simply a taste of what I would experience during a trial. I decided I would continue to do my best no matter what the situation or the pain consequence. Of course, the stress of the deposition intensified my pain and my answers began to ramble. The irony was that my own insurance company caused most of this added pain.

The first lawyer to ask questions represented Country Garden in Minnesota even though he lived and worked in Ohio. He immediately repeated questions about my life rather than focusing on the accident. Because of this, a scheduled one-hour deposition turned into two and a half hours, and my pain intensified beyond what I could handle. Jack's attorney asked only a few questions, while Blaster's attorney asked none. It appeared that it did not matter whether I lived in Ohio or Minnesota. Country Garden's legal tactics were complete throughout the process and halfway across the country. Indirectly from this experience, the Country Garden lawyer convinced me to continue to work on this part of my safety net. As I sat there, I planned to share my experience on the Heywer website and continue my formal report to the Minnesota Attorney General.

# # #

As the time for the trial approached, I was nervous even though I kept reminding myself that the onerous process was nothing to be afraid of or nothing personal, as many people told me along the way. But my loss and safety net felt personal to me. I was simply asking for help with an injury that had changed my life dramatically through no cause of my own. Any help I could get with my great loss would be appreciated. I could not help the feelings of loss, distrust, betrayal, and anger as I asked for help from my safety net providers. I also knew that, to the lawyers, doctors, and other keepers of my safety net, it was just a job or maybe even a game. I remembered that my personal injury claim was almost lost just prior to the two-year time of the statute of limitations running out. The attorney I was working with at the time had not seen the validity of a personal injury claim in my situation. Fortunately, I eventually found attorneys willing to work hard with me in pursuit of responsibility from several different sources of insurance. Now I was glad for this "repair" of my safety net. And I was very appreciative of Justine for her support during the years that led up to the trial. She was truly a godsend during a time of great pain and suffering. She was a great help as I worked hard to repair my safety net while hoping to find ways to repair the safety nets of other people sick or injured.

To my surprise, Attorney Land called me a week before the scheduled trial date. He said "hello" and started talking fast. "Your case is a textbook example of complex insurance issues. You are probably not aware that the lawyers at my firm are experts who speak at professional gatherings and colleges about insurance contracts and law." I was not sure where he was going with this, but he did remind me of the times when I spoke at professional gatherings and colleges about finance and contracting. I was glad to hear that he was doing the same. Attorney Land continued, "Yours and Jack's uninsured/underinsured insurance may or may not have to pay anything. There is an anti-stacking provision in Ohio law. The most you could get is $100,000 from both. There also needs to be independent corroborative evidence for a phantom vehicle claim. Jack's testimony may not meet this requirement. Just last year, the law that companies are held responsible for their employees' uninsured/underinsured coverage changed. They could make an issue about whether or not this change is retroactive to your case. If you won in court, there are so many issues that it would probably take five years before the appeals would be concluded." Attorney Land appeared to be painting a gloomy picture of my case. I thought about the additional $15,000 of expenses for the first trial alone. How much more would it cost? It seemed that whenever justice was pursued in court, the legal expenses were terribly significant. Maybe I could use some of my retirement savings. But what did other people do? The threat of appeals and court costs made me wonder whether or not we really had "justice for all" in this country.

Attorney Land finally reached his point. "Your insurance company and Jack's have offered to settle your case for the $100,000 policy limit," he said. I replied, "What about Blaster?" He answered, "They may still be responsible. I'll call them and ask them to contribute." After a long pause, Attorney Land said, "You need to look at this as a business decision. My advice to you is take the $100,000 and settle."

Then I remembered my one million dollar umbrella policy. We discussed the applicability of the policy and whether or not it had uninsured/underinsured coverage. Attorney Land said, "Even if you did have coverage, a jury will not award you more than what you have received already. You need to add together what you got from your Country Garden no-fault insurance, Blaster's workers' compensation insurance, and the $100,000 they are offering you now. That is well over $200,000. The highest award I have seen from a jury in Miami County is $200,000. If you go to court, it could be as little as nothing. If you are awarded less than what you have received so far, you will have to pay back the difference. I've seen that happen. It's a very sad situation." I reminded Attorney Land of my report to the Minnesota Attorney General and how Country Garden had lied, denied, and delayed for so long. I told him, "They still owe $33,000 on my no-fault policy. That is like a separate policy that should pay without any hassle. It should be a no-brainer. If Country Garden only kicks in $50,000, they will have settled everything for an additional $17,000 over the no-fault benefits promised. That just doesn't seem right. And there's the one million dollar umbrella policy."

My voice was beginning to shake as I became upset over the insurance company's success at cheating their insured. He replied, "I know you are upset with Country Garden. They are one of the worst insurance companies. They take your premiums, and then fight as hard as possible to not pay benefits. They could have stopped paying benefits on your no-fault insurance at any time with IMEs or other tactics. You know this is true." I agreed, "Yes, I have wondered sometimes why they didn't, other than the visibility and pushback I have given them. I understand what you are saying." Attorney Land replied, "This is a business decision now." I said, "I know. You're right." I felt increasingly upset, even nauseous during our conversation. I asked Attorney Land, "Let me think about it overnight." He agreed and we said goodbye.

I discussed my dilemma with Justine when she arrived home from work. She empathized with my situation and asked, "What good did the umbrella policy do? Why did you even buy it?" I replied, "I don't know. They probably never pay benefits for their umbrella policies ... unless you are totally disabled and using a wheelchair ... if even then."

The rest of the day and into the night I prayed and meditated about my situation, but my feelings were silent. There was no intuitive response as I tried to imagine what my future would look like in either of the two scenarios where I took the offer or not. Eventually I thought about those helping me with my struggle for safety net benefits. The lawyers were convinced it was almost over. Attorney Land said we would still go after Blaster, but the work was done as far as the other two insurance companies were concerned. I also thought about Justine and how more and more she told me she had tired of talking about safety nets and the ongoing tactics and disappointments I experienced. "But what about me and the others I wanted to help with their safety nets" was a question I asked myself. Would I learn any more if I continued? The abusive tactics up to now seemed to be a repetitive theme of the ends justifying any means. I am sure a trial would be like the workers' compensation hearings and depositions with tactics, lies, innuendos, personal attacks, and more. I wondered if I would not only lose financially, but also lose Justine and others in the process. Five more years was a dark thought. But if I wrapped things up soon, I could finish my book and get more involved with helping others. I had learned enough about safety nets.

These settlements, after the lawyers were paid and the legal expenses were subtracted, would be about $140,000. Earlier no-fault payments added another $40,000. Most of this would be used to pay for my "share" of the house Justine and I purchased and medical bills with enough left for my living expenses for the next several years. My severance pay from Blaster was already spent on living expenses over the last few years. What would I live on after all the insurance and other benefits ran out? Maybe I would eventually get SSA disability benefits. Then I could make it to retirement age and my pensions and SSA retirement benefits. But what if I didn't? Maybe I could eventually work more hours. This was what I wanted the most, to be able to work more and earn more.

I tossed and turned all night about my decision. The final amount I would receive compared favorably to Blaster's and the insurance company's initial positions that I was not covered at all. Then the two offers from Blaster and Jack's insurance company were $10,000 each with the same comment "take it or leave it." The amount I would recover with this settlement was also much more than my lawyers had estimated of $40,000 to $50,000 for a soft tissue injury like mine that went to trial in Troy, Ohio, where the county court was located and the jury trials were held. This trial amount would yield maybe $25,000 after the lawyers were paid and the legal expenses were subtracted. My assertive approach of self-help and social change resulted in roughly ten times the amount of the two early offers or usual trial amount. This was good news. The risk was also much less than going to trial where the result could be zero. The total amount would be much less than the many insurance and employee benefit sources of hundreds of thousands of dollars and my own policies exceeding one million dollars. The amount I would recover also paled against my total loss, conservatively estimated by experts at close to two million dollars. To recover what our safety net providers promised would never happen. Their lawyers and deceitful business practices had seen to that.

The next day, Attorney Land and I talked about the same things at least twice more. The answer kept coming back the same. Attorney Land had checked with other lawyers and concluded the same thing. This was the best we were going to do. He promised they would work hard to recover from Blaster, but this was the best for now. I reminded him, "I am in effect building a bridge to take me from today until I am old enough to retire. The greater my settlement amounts, the longer the bridge and the closer I will come to my retirement age when the companies I have worked for will pay a pension and I can collect Social Security retirement benefits. I told you I filed for Social Security disability." I paused. He said, "Yes." Then I continued, "But my request was denied and appealed. It will be a year before I know if I can collect disability benefits from Social Security. Meanwhile, the personal injury and workers' compensation settlements are all I have to live on." I wanted my situation to be real for Attorney Land, as I had tried to convey to others who worked with our safety nets every day. I always hoped people would take their jobs and responsibilities more seriously. Maybe if they did, it would be less of a game and more helpful to people trying to get by in life with a disability. People with disabilities wanted to be as responsible as they could. We needed our safety nets to be responsible.

I agreed with Attorney Land and told him to accept their offer. After accepting the offer, my emotions and thoughts swirled for several days. What had I expected? Over the years, I had planned that if I was disabled, my insurance would pay my medical bills and some amount of lost wages until the ceilings on my policies were reached. This was why I had purchased a one million dollar umbrella policy. I figured I would be adequately covered in any accident and never reach such a ceiling. I knew I would not receive the full amount of my wages before the accident, but I thought I would get enough to live on. Maybe the $4,000 per month ceiling in my no-fault policy would be paid during the time of my disability. Or the $2,240 per month ceiling as provided by workers' compensation insurance would be paid. Either was free from income tax at the time and would be enough to pay my bills and occasionally some of the extras from my lifestyle before the accident that I sometimes missed. I wondered about emergencies such as my health or even my car wearing out or the furnace needing repair or replacement. If my insurance providers had worked together and provided the $4,000 per month or even the $2,240 per month until the policy limits were reached, I would have been satisfied. This would have been enough for me to live on. But instead of help, they said no, pushed, cheated, and attacked my situation and good name to make the number as small as possible. They would have to be forced to take the responsibility they had promised when I paid insurance premiums and/or went to work each day. My own employer and insurance company were the worst. What an incredible betrayal!

The courts were the final battleground where the tactics, lying, and character assassination would be played out publicly. Enough doubt would be created in the minds of the jurors that the injured, especially with an "invisible" soft tissue injury, would be lucky to get five or ten percent of their insurance benefits promised, if they got anything at all. There would be opportunities for appeals where the costs to the injured would grow and the potential benefits would become riskier. An adversarial legal approach benefited employers and insurance companies. The courtroom was not used to find the truth. Instead, it was a place for the final legal battle of wits, tactics, and deception that artificially established a ceiling for the injured's loss. An invisible chronic illness was an especially fertile ground for the lawyers to plant their seeds of deception. High-paid defense lawyers would make sure the precedence for jury awards to the injured was set at an artificially low ceiling. This amount would be touted in the future to convince other injured people to settle their cases out of court for pennies or nickels on the dollar. The expensive legal process of depositions and expert testimony was another threat. The legal battles would eat up more than one-third of an already reduced amount of benefits. My own employer and insurance company for many years were the worst. This was what upset me the most. This was abuse of power. This was simply the abuse of employees and insureds that trusted them, employees and insureds that had become ill or were injured. Once again I suspected that people who did not have a valid injury probably returned to work or some other activity soon after they realized that the abuse from the system was far more difficult than any job or other alternative. This left the truly injured people to be abused.

My lawyer told me that I received more settlement benefits than anyone whether they went to trial or not in the small town of

Troy, Ohio. I had worked hard to recover these benefits from my safety net without having to go to trial. Now I wanted my direct view of human deception and betrayal to be over. A trial would only expand this view for me. My desire to move on was also reinforced because I felt the keepers of my safety net had been held responsible for some of the benefits they promised to me as an injured individual. Each time the keepers of our safety nets had to pay some of the benefits they had promised, the better the chance was that they would see their responsibility more clearly for other people injured now and in the future. I learned a lot too. By working the issues and writing about my experience, I found more clarity, good and bad, that helped me understand more about my safety net, my life and disability, and life itself. This deeper and clearer understanding furthered my acceptance and recovery, while allowing me to look more optimistically toward the future. Along the way I also helped others understand their situations and get help from their safety nets. For this I was pleased and proud.

After several days, I realized that not going to trial was really good news. I had already received the high end of settlements for soft tissue injuries like mine. I did not have to throw the dice, which was what the courtroom experience sounded like. I did not have to go through the additional humiliation of examinations and innuendoes from the insurance company lawyers that occurred during depositions or hearings. I had already paid those dues along the way as I assertively pushed back on my safety net providers. Yet I also realized that my safety net providers would not have paid so much had I not been entitled to it through my insurance policies. As Justine told me one day while on our daily walk in the neighborhood streets of Troy, "They will never really believe you unless they have to pay." Some of them already knew I was injured all along. I could tell by their questions at depositions and the defense arguments they presented. They knew a settlement was appropriate but wanted to save their companies some money. This was accomplished at the expense of the injured.

Perhaps having to pay more than usual for me and others who push assertively would eventually convince the insurance companies and employers to pay more benefits to the injured rather than paying expensive lawyers and others to fight their responsibility and cheat their employees and insureds. My encouragement to others to push back for benefits was not only for the money and precedence for others in the future. More importantly, the injured can find a better understanding of their injury and its impact on the environment of their lives. The injured can find a new place in the world. This was the greater benefit to me. I know my impairment, capability, and options for the future. I know where I stand and now I can make plans for my future.

Some people told me that the reason I received over $200,000 in settlements was because I earned so much money before the accident. My response was that even if you earned $18,000 per year before your accident and could not work any more for the next twenty years before retirement age, the present value of those lost earnings is about $200,000. This should be your settlement if you had insurance policies for at least that amount. Alternatively, if you earned $38,000 and could only earn $20,000 because of an injury, you would come to the same conclusion. The numbers added up. The problem would be convincing your safety net providers to pay. If you do and this seems like a lot of money, the lawyers usually get a third and there are other legal expenses. You will probably also have ongoing medical bills and health insurance that costs more because of your impairment. The money goes fast. We have to be careful how we spend it.

Other people suggested that my settlements were easy money. I would rather have worked at my job and earned more than that in just two years. There was no financial reward for this experience! I no longer had the ability to work enough to even pay my bills for living expenses. Maybe if I did, the settlement monies would be some kind of windfall. But I had to make the monies last for the rest of my working years – which was most likely my retirement age in twenty years.

# # #

About the same time as we were discussing my personal injury settlement, I received a letter that said my request for SSA disability benefits was denied. This news came twenty months after I applied for help from my SSA insurance. While working through the SSA process, I learned they had their own difficult set of forms, decisions, and court appeals, along with a disability perspective that was hard to understand. The SSA was reluctant to award benefits to younger workers (under 55) for fear they would stay on SSA disability for the rest of their lives. Maybe younger people stayed on SSA disability because they were, in fact, permanently disabled. Like my personal insurance and workers' compensation insurance, the difficult SSA process weeded out able-bodied people and more. The SSA did their best to deny benefits throughout the process of multiple administrative reviews and hearings. It would have been much easier to go to work than suffer through the long and difficult SSA process. The past several years would have been much easier and more meaningful if I would have been able to go to work as a businessman and enjoy a well-earned paycheck. Unfortunately, no more than part-time work was possible for my frail condition. I needed the benefits promised by my safety net providers.

Surprisingly, I was uncomfortable when I thought about receiving SSA disability benefits even though I had paid for this insurance for many years. This was probably because I did not want to be disabled even though intellectually I knew the facts said I was. The fact that I was disabled was as surreal to me as it was to anyone who had questioned my impairment over the last four and a half years. I was very upset at my SSA hearing in court three months earlier when the judge and state employment specialist discussed my situation out loud. They noted how much I earned in a year, $6,500. They discussed whether or not this and whatever else I could earn, considering their view of my impairment, exceeded the amount considered by SSA as "gainful employment." If I earned more than the $7,000 the SSA defined as gainful employment, I would be disqualified from receiving SSA disability benefits. But what sense or magic was there in the $7,000 SSA rule? My recent earnings were close to this amount, yet pathetic considering the cost of food, lodging, transportation, and medical care for anyone living in this country. Eventually the SSA judge and state employment specialist agreed that I was truly unemployable given the work restrictions and limited number of hours per week approved by my doctors. But my claim was still denied.

The SSA judge's opinion was that I was able to work full time. The judge ignored the discussion and conclusion in court about my employment status. The judge also did not give consideration to the pain management program and work restrictions that Drs. Bell and Norton had approved. She justified her position by saying that early after the accident my doctors in Ohio never referenced a permanent disability or work restriction as a result of the car accident. She also extracted positive comments and medical treatment goals from hundreds of pages of medical records, employment records, and the SSA forms I completed and submitted. From this, she wrote a seven-page opinion that made my situation sound like an enjoyable and minimally challenged voluntary retirement on my part. There were definite shades of the story Blaster's attorney told during my workers' compensation hearings.

My SSA lawyer sent me a letter the day after I received the SSA opinion. He simply said that the judge's opinion was "patently" wrong and suggested we appeal the decision. Fortunately, I had copies of Drs. Hunt's and Lee's early reports months after the accident that said I had a permanent disability and later reported work restrictions as a result of the car accident. I also thought the Hearing Response I prepared for the workers' compensation appeal would help explain my situation and address some more of the SSA judge's concerns. And I had more current job search and medical bills as records to support my situation. With these documents as attachments, I prepared a response to the SSA judge's opinion. This was attached to the SSA appeal form, signed, and mailed to Virginia where the next appeal would be heard. Unfortunately, this next appeal would take one year and the SSA rules only allow for retroactive benefits for twelve months. This patently wrong opinion would deprive me of insurance benefits that I was entitled to once again. It was certainly a good thing I had the insurance settlements to use while I waited for the SSA appeal decision.

Even with this SSA struggle, I was still glad I had SSA disability insurance that I had paid for over the years while I was working. I was hopeful this insurance would pay benefits until I was able to work more than "gainful employment" or reach retirement age. This would be the rest of the financial bridge I needed in order to pay my own way in life. Meanwhile, I would continue to try to heal, recover more physical capability as soon as possible, and work more so that one day I would not have to rely on SSA disability benefits, insurance settlements, or any other benefits from my safety net providers.

# # #

As I reviewed the release I was asked to sign for my personal injury settlement, I tried to have the settlement referred to as compensatory damages so the IRS did not consider the amount I received as taxable income. And I made sure the insurers did not have subrogation rights to another settlement that could be used later against me. This way I could retain as much as possible in order to pay more of my medical bills and living expenses in the future.

As the workers' compensation settlement agreement was written, I was careful to coordinate the release of responsibility I approved in the agreements. Blaster wrote the workers' compensation settlement agreement and used a broad release to try to get out of their uninsured/underinsured responsibility provided for by Ohio law. I objected to this and asked them to exclude the release of their uninsured/underinsured responsibility. I also asked that the workers' compensation settlement be fairly allocated between lost wages and medical bills. The SSA system seemed to be structured around a disabled person receiving workers' compensation or other insurance benefits right away. After a one- or two-year delay, SSA benefits would be available. Any overlap would be adjusted. I wanted the lost wages to be identified as starting as early as possible since any SSA benefits would be reduced for workers' compensation wage loss benefits. By detailing this allocation, any SSA disability benefits I might receive next year would be higher. This seemed appropriate to me since the long delay in the workers' compensation award was due to legal and other tactics rather than because the benefits were not earned earlier. Unfortunately, Blaster ignored my request for changes. Instead they did not define anything specifically except that they were no longer responsible. I almost accepted this release in order to finish my tired and worn workers' compensation claim that even Attorney Law seemed no longer interested in supporting. With Attorney Law's disinterest, I assumed I had gotten everything I could from the extremely onerous Blaster workers' compensation process.

At the last minute, Attorney Land suggested I ask for a mutual release from Blaster to settle both the workers' compensation and uninsured/underinsured claims. With a mutual release, I would completely release Blaster and they would do the same to me. With a release from Blaster, I would not have to worry about things like Blaster or Alto Health subrogating my insurance settlements and other payments. I liked Attorney Land's idea and asked him to make it happen. Attorney Land also explained that Blaster had a two million dollar insurance policy with a two million dollar deductible for uninsured/underinsured coverage. Because of this the insurance was worthless, and since I could not sue my former employer, Blaster was probably free of responsibility for uninsured/underinsured insurance related to the phantom vehicle. Attorney Land explained that this approach to get around the law was working for many companies like Blaster. Meanwhile, the Ohio lawmakers kept trying to change loopholes like this one. We could wait for new legislation or court rulings or accept that Blaster's lawyers had succeeded in avoiding responsibility once again. This loophole was probably why the attorney for Blaster's insurance company said nothing at the recent deposition. He knew they would not have to pay benefits.

The mutual release delayed the settlement six more months. Every few weeks, I became nervous and called Attorney Land for a status report. Attorney Land kept asking Blaster and its outside attorneys for mutual release words that reflected what we agreed to, but Blaster kept delaying the writing of their verbal agreement. This was no surprise to me, but I became anxious anyway. Meanwhile, Attorney Law wrote a letter that reflected his frustration, while virtually handing the issue over to Attorney Land. Now I would have to pay Attorney Land for his time, as well as the amount Attorney Law was entitled to receive out of the settlement. Eventually, the release was accomplished, but only after Blaster's outside attorneys had increased their billable hours. My settlement amount was then reduced to pay Attorney Land even though he left any additional fee amount to my discretion. It seemed only fair for me to pay him since he worked so hard on my case and in the end accepted a lower fee on the insurance company settlements. I did not want to spoil his willingness to work the details hard for other injured people who would need his help in the future. I sent him $500 for handling the mutual release. I was glad it was over.

As the dust settled, I felt good about the financial help I received from my safety net. I had recovered enough for a large down payment on a house and to pay my living expenses and medical bills for the next few years. Fortunately, I had reduced my living expenses to one-fourth of what they were before the accident. I was proud I had reduced my living expenses to less than $1,500 per month including over $500 each month for ongoing medical bills and increased medical insurance premiums because of the accident. Even with my impairment, I wanted to take full responsibility for all of my living expenses. Since the accident, I had met and become friends with many people with disabilities. This was the same sense of responsibility they had told me they also wanted.

I viewed *Surviving the Chronic Pain Experience: Successfully Recover Insurance Benefits and Other Promises* as primarily a self-help book with an element of consumer advocacy and request for social change. As I studied Ralph Nader's work, I realized he also tried to accomplish both with some of his work. His book, *Winning the Insurance Game*, is a very practical self-help book everyone can use with his or her insurance needs. I wished I had applied the suggestions in *Winning the Insurance Game* when I purchased insurance earlier in my life. I would have avoided some of the struggle with insurance after the car accident. After I studied Mr. Nader's book, Justine and I switched our insurance policies from Country Garden to a company with more integrity. We checked consumer reports and Insurance Commissioner complaints to make sure the new company was secure and fair when settling claims. Justine and I also made sure everything was put in writing with the new insurance company to avoid excuses or misunderstandings should a claim be filed in the future.

Ralph Nader also wrote a high-level moral review of "lawyer aided corporate abuse" in *No Contest*. High-paid lawyers help businesses avoid or limit their responsibility for unsafe products, contamination of our environment, monopoly and other antitrust violations, and more, including injured employees. The legal tactics identified in *No Contest* include many of those I refer to in my book. Prolonged and degrading depositions, "hide and seek" discovery processes, limited jury awards, "hired gun" experts, unenforced insurance promises, litigation ahead of responsibility, complex rules, and more were parallel themes in our books. *No Contest* goes further with a review of tort reform (called tort deform in the book), political ties, lobbyist activities, government agencies and professional organization's limitations, and more. The deck is definitely stacked to favor business over the consumer, including the injured. Our books also share a plea for social change and include suggestions for others to use. My findings over the last five years were again verified.

I studied both books in detail and realized how my story fit somewhere between the two Nader books. *Surviving the Chronic Pain Experience* is more personal and detailed than *No Contest* and *Winning the Insurance Game*, while very similar messages and suggestions of self-help and social change are in all three books. How far could we reach out with Heywer and help others meet the daily challenge of living with chronic pain?

Chapter 17

Into the Future

The State of Minnesota provided health care insurance for uninsurable people like me through a government mandated and privately managed health insurance risk pool. There were large monthly premiums, large deductibles, and twenty percent co-pays for this insurance coverage. But at least I had some health insurance. My health insurance provider recently sent me a letter with questions to identify the appropriate source of insurance benefits for my medical bills. Over the last several months I had steroid shots and radio frequency (RF) blocks where they cauterized the nerves in my back, shoulder, and neck on my right side. This series of shots and nerve blocks were very expensive. I thought I had worked through the paperwork very carefully. I was wrong. My health insurance provider did not want to pay benefits for an injury where the responsibility was with workers' compensation, automobile, or any other insurance provider. After all, my health insurance was intended to cover medical care for an illness or injury not covered by other insurance policies. I agreed with their position but also knew that the question of responsibility was not very simple. I also knew that several thousand dollars of medical bills for my recent shots and RF blocks were on the line for me to possibly have to pay.

Chronic myofascial (musculoskeletal) pain was recently added as an allowed condition for my claim by the BWC at a formal hearing. Soon after the last hearing, Blaster appealed the workers' compensation decision in district court. Attorney Land told me that Blaster had a good chance of prevailing in district court given the invisible nature of chronic pain, IMEs, and other tactics. Fighting Blaster in court would also be very expensive for me and difficult for my lawyer. Attorney Land suggested I settle with Blaster with no provision for future medical bills. Meanwhile, Country Garden held fast to their position that workers' compensation was primary; therefore, it was up to Blaster to pay my medical bills related to the car accident. I had hoped that my health insurance would pay my future medical bills that Blaster did not pay. If my health insurance provider decided that my medical care was not their responsibility either, I would have to pay my future medical bills or get a lawyer to fight their position. Once again I feared I would become harmed by the onerous system of medical care and insurance. There must be a legal and reasonable way to make sense out of my situation and get future medical benefits from my safety net.

Dr. Norton and his nurse practitioners at Medical Pain Specialists first diagnosed my condition as a cervical thoracic sprain/strain, which was the same as the condition first allowed by my workers' compensation claim. After two visits, Medical Pain Specialists changed my diagnosis to cervicalgia. Cervicalgia was a different and broader diagnosis than the cervical thoracic sprain/strain or even the chronic myofascial pain recently allowed in my workers' compensation claim. Probably because my diagnosis had changed to a condition not allowed by the BWC, Blaster paid for my first three office visits to Dr. Norton but no more. This different diagnosis was a serious issue for my workers' compensation claim, which did not and would never recognize a broader diagnosis of cervicalgia. I asked Dr. Norton why they changed my diagnosis, but he did not have an answer. His billing people told me that when a diagnosis changed, the workers' compensation insurance people usually recognized the similarity in diagnoses and paid the bills. I told them that this was not true for Blaster and possibly other companies. Consistent diagnosis was important. Was this Dr. Norton's way of avoiding expert testimony in court, which he told me he disliked so much? If so, it was again at the expense of the injured. My workers' compensation case was weaker from inconsistent diagnoses and lack of expert testimony from my doctors. I should have carefully reviewed all my doctors' office notes since the accident to make sure the diagnosis was always exactly the same. Along the way I had tried at times, but it was now too late.

213

I was not sure what to do about my health insurance so I called Attorneys Law and Land for advice. At first they told me that my settlements were intended to cover future medical bills. After I called them on such a frivolous response, they agreed with me that there was no money in the settlements for future medical bills considering my huge wage loss and prior medical bills. Attorney Law suggested I accept the cervicalgia diagnosis and respond to my healthcare provider that this condition was not included in my workers' compensation claim and, therefore, not a direct result of the car accident. After emotionally swirling for days about adopting diagnosis and paperwork tactics like Blaster did, I accepted this different broader diagnosis as my condition. In a letter, I informed my health insurance risk pool of this different diagnosis, as well as my reliance on my doctor to make this judgment call (Appendix 25). I sent a copy to Attorney Law as documentation of his advice and to Medical Pain Specialists as notification of my reliance on their medical diagnosis. Then I continued to recover health care benefits from my health insurance provider, at least for a while.

It was appropriate for me to deflect questions about my diagnosis from my health insurance company to my health care providers, including Dr. Norton. The responsibility of medical care providers to obtain insurance pre-approvals and the insurance company's responsibility to sort out insurance issues was part of the law in Ohio, Minnesota, and other states. The doctors made the diagnosis and the insurance companies were supposed to pay benefits based on their judgment. This made sense, unless, of course, the insurance companies ignored the law and succeeded in pointing fingers of responsibility at each other and no one paid. This happened quite often and left many injured people alone to shoulder the entire responsibility. This was not acceptable to me so I pushed back using a similar diagnostic code tactic to that used by Blaster to refute my claim for workers' compensation benefits all along. This time I used a similar argument about diagnosis in order to have my health insurance provider pay some of my bills. I hoped others received the help they needed with such a complex and onerous system.

I was reminded that my safety net providers had used any tactic, including fraud, to minimize their responsibility. The IMEs had reported errors that supported a worse condition than was my history. The IMEs ignored the great physical capability I had prior to the accident. They also did not document the relative change in my condition after the accident. They and other safety net providers lied about paperwork and created scenarios in order to deny or delay my benefits and medical care. "Anything goes" was their approach to minimize their responsibility. This approach worked with me as it had and continues to work with so many others injured and impaired. This was what I also knew and believed was wrong. I reviewed my approach to be sure I was not breaking the law or stooping as low as them for my insurance benefits. I believed I had not. My own safety net issues were now concluded. I felt a reckoning that encouraged me to continue my work as an advocate for surviving the chronic pain experience separate from my own safety net issues.

# # #

Writing and seeing more of my safety net's point of view was an important part of my recovery and acceptance. I wrote and edited for quite some time before I truly believed what I felt. Seeing a shared cause and responsibility for my impairment became more enlightening and peaceful. This understanding was needed for more recovery and acceptance in my entire life. While this shared responsibility was now apparent to me, so was the validity of my earlier attempts to encourage everyone involved to realize the benefits of partnering with the injured and insured. We need less litigation and more health care. We need less disbelief and more compassion for the impaired. Health care, recovery for the injured or sick, and company profitability are not mutually exclusive. At a minimum, they are integrated within the concepts of a civilized culture, economics, and humanity. This is still true.

Along the way, I simply wanted Blaster, Country Garden, and the other insurance companies to pay the benefits they had promised and were their responsibility. But maybe the safety net providers were not so sure about my injury or their responsibility. There was no verifiable measure or picture of my injury. Because we were unable to prove pain or maybe, more importantly, prove the extent of the pain, we had to experience the doubt and suspicion of others. I knew invisible chronic pain was real for millions of people, including me. I also understood that we were unfairly given the burden of proof left by people who got caught when they lied about having chronic pain and tried to cheat the system. How could we ask our safety net providers to take on responsibility for what possibly was not real? Unfortunately, many companies believed they had to say no to everyone who had invisible chronic pain regardless of the person's individual circumstances. Some companies said no again and again simply because of the potential cost to their companies. Some lied to say no. They said no until people (like me) somehow forced them to take some responsibility and pay benefits.

Blaster's Human Resources Director tried to discourage my workers' compensation claim by telling me that (1) I would be treated no differently than anyone else with an injury, (2) any workers' compensation benefits would be subrogated from other insurance payments to the injured, and (3) the lawyers would take one-third of any settlement. I believed him at first. I knew companies had to follow consistent human resource policies for all of their employees so they would not be accused of discrimination. Blaster had no choice but to treat me the same way they treated all employees. Or did they? Consistent business policies are one thing; however, deciding what tactics would be used to deny and delay benefits to cheat all sick or injured employees did not make it right. His comment about subrogation was also wrong. Subrogation was common for insurance so the insured collected only once. That was fair and all I ever asked for. In Ohio, it is the insurer's responsibility to sort out who has to pay without burdening the injured insured. But Blaster and others ignored this statute. In Minnesota, workers' compensation benefits are primary and paid first. Any duplicate insurance payments are returned to other insurance sources ahead of the workers' compensation insurance. Finally, most lawyers do take one-third, but not all of them. The standard fee for Attorney Law was one-fourth and Attorney Land was one-third, which they voluntarily reduced or I requested when they suggested I take a settlement rather than continue on a path of expensive and time-consuming legal battles. These were some of the things Blaster told me to influence my request for insurance benefits from the company. It was good that I did not believe everything they told me.

Part of the reason companies denied benefits was to reduce medical costs. This made sense in times of rising medical costs. But it was wrong to deny benefits that were promised to employees and planned for by employees to use when there was an illness or injury. I knew the implications of goals and strategies of the business world that were measured financially and not morally. Many times this "for-the-good-of-the-business" approach meant that the ends justified any means. Reducing medical costs on the backs of injured employees or insureds embraced this approach. The ends justified any means. Indeed, prior to the accident, my career and bank account had seen the benefits of working successfully within a "strictly business" paradigm. Maybe it was now my turn to feel more directly the personal impact of making financial results the highest priority of a business. Maybe it was part of my journey to fully understand the impact of a strictly business paradigm. This furthered my resolve to encourage morality as an important element of business management.

Many business managers viewed their primary and many times only responsibility as maximizing the company's short-term profitability in order to increase shareholder wealth, along with their management bonuses. To control medical costs, most companies first tried to reduce the amount of money doctors charged for services by using managed health care programs and the cost of prescription medications through the use of generic brands and volume discounts. Alternative medical treatment and other services were limited or not allowed. Deductibles and co-pays were increased for the employee and his or her family. When these cost-reduction opportunities became less and less, many companies turned to ways of reducing their responsibility for injured employees that at times went too far. Overly aggressive use of paperwork tactics, fraud, and IMEs by the workers' compensation system, third-party administrators, and managed health care plans was too much. Insurance companies, with the support of a cadre of corporate and hired legal counsel, pushed the denial of benefits beyond moral boundaries. More and more organizations and individuals embraced a legalistic or "force-me-to-be-responsible" approach to their business and social interactions. As long as there were no consequences, then the approach was considered okay, no matter how aggressive or potentially immoral.

Paperwork was no longer simply a tool to document an individual's medical condition, approval for treatment, medical bills, and/or lost wages. Paperwork became a tool to deny benefits and responsibility for the sick or injured and their families. Difficult forms, unnecessary pre-approvals, and onerous contract details, along with shuffled and lost paperwork, were used. Leaders of businesses and government communicated an aggressive deny and delay approach directly or indirectly to their clerical and administrative people, the working professionals who administered the system day in and day out. In order to reduce medical costs, they were told to work aggressively at denying benefits in order to support the company, the BWC, insurance companies, or others. This was expected as part of their job. While this approach sometimes went against their own values and affected morale at work, over time the administrators of the system became numb to the impact the denials had on injured people. This was what some of them told me when we discussed problems with the "system."

After three years of asking people to help me with my workers' compensation claim, I wanted to better understand why my bills had not been paid by Blaster and what I should expect to be paid. I called the Ohio BWC and asked for copies of their rules and guidelines. Several days later, UPS delivered a box to my apartment that included the Ohio BWC manuals and papers that were two inches thick with print so small that in some cases I could not read it at all. Right away I knew there was no way for me to completely understand the BWC rules and represent myself. This was certainly good for businesses that wanted any excuse possible for denying benefits. As I perused the materials, I realized I should have reviewed the BWC rules early after the accident to learn that companies, including Blaster, could require pre-approvals for most medical procedures. Without pre-approvals, the medical bills did not have to be paid by insurance. The implications for my situation were common for many other people. Pre-approvals could be used to deny benefits until hearings were scheduled years later and too late to help.

It was several months before I understood that my injury, with its chronic pain, was a permanent impairment and medical care would probably be necessary for the rest of my life. Once I understood, I realized that I needed help from more than just health insurance to cover my medical bills and lost wages. By the time I filed a workers' compensation claim form, I had already received $2,000 in physical therapy that required a pre-approval. I did not have a pre-approval. Then Blaster rejected my claim as not being work related, which further delayed benefits. Close to $10,000 of medical bills were incurred in the first year after my injury, including a second round of physical therapy, along with a number of massage therapy sessions. Because of the requirement for pre-approvals and other paperwork, a one-year delay in the approval of my claim made it uncertain whether or not any benefits for these bills would ever be paid. I had hired an attorney and trusted that he was taking care of the necessary paperwork. But he was not. Instead my "case" was building.

When I reviewed the BWC guidelines, I learned I had attended twice the number of physical and massage therapy appointments allowed. In the three and a half years after the accident, $7,000 of medical bills were incurred for physical and massage therapy alone that should have been pre-approved but were not. Looking back, even if I would have known about the BWC limits, I am sure I would have kept pushing for recovery with the added massage and physical therapy despite having to pay some of the bills out of my own pocket. I could not expect Blaster to pay for my assertive approach. I wanted them to at least pay per the guidelines, which they did not. I paid all of them myself. A similar review of the medical bills for the pain program shows more tactics even though Dr. Hunt, who was a doctor in Blaster's health care plan, recommended the program. But Blaster lied about the paperwork, hired another IME, and never paid a dime of the $16,000 of medical care. This too was wrong.

Fortunately, Alto Health paid almost 80% of the pain program bills. But, of course, they wanted reimbursement for these medical bills related to a work injury that should have been paid for by workers' compensation insurance. Eventually my lawyers helped me draft a letter to Alto Health directing them to Blaster for any reimbursement for these charges. I had read the Ohio statutes on insurance and learned that I could take such a position. Ohio statutes require that redundant insurers, not the injured, sort out who pays. Why didn't my lawyers handle this for me? In terms of costs paid out, it did not matter to Blaster anyway whether my employer health care plan or workers' compensation insurance paid my bills. The company was self-insured for both employee health care and workers' compensation insurance. The end result to Blaster was simply a matter of where the costs were reported. Alto Health paid the bills according to the health plan and billed Blaster for the medical costs, plus their administrative effort. I paid the Alto Health plan deductibles and co-pays. For workers' compensation insurance, Blaster either paid the employee directly or reimbursed their third-party administrator for any costs they paid to Blaster employees. By not paying the bills as workers' compensation insurance, Blaster saved what I paid as deductibles and co-pays while protecting their government-required health and safety statistics.

During the discovery process for my personal injury claim, I received a status of the medical bills considered for payment under Blaster's workers' compensation insurance. I realized I should have formally asked Blaster for a monthly or quarterly status of the medical bills I had submitted for reimbursement. Blaster had denied payment of many of my medical bills simply due to missing doctors' office notes, diagnoses, or other easily obtainable information. Had I known what was needed, I could have tried to provide this information to Blaster on a timelier basis. And I would have learned earlier that I needed a lawyer like Attorney Law to help me with their tactics. Because of the difficult deny tactics and lies from Blaster and their third-party administrator, I did not work the workers' compensation details as often or as much as I could have. Instead, I pursued medical benefits from Alto Health that came easier, while planning to work the Blaster issues later. At the time, most of the Blaster issues seemed impossible to address, so I reported complaints and fraud to the BWC. I am glad I did this, but I should have also demanded a status report to work through at the same time. Early on,

I should have found a better lawyer who was willing to work the details and demand hearings as often as needed. It was obvious that Blaster was not going to pay benefits unless they were forced to at a BWC hearing. The same was true of my approach to car insurance benefits where I took their word when they told me I had no benefits. I should have been less trusting even while I was suffering and reaching out for help. I should have talked to other impaired people, learned from their struggle, and found out who the good and caring doctors and lawyers were who could help me survive instead of causing me further injury.

The "force me" or "legalistic" business practices are not unusual in the United States. Business practices that "bully the customer, insured, or employee" were and are on the rise. At the time, I was still behaving as a trustworthy, respectful individual who was accustomed to being treated fairly by my employer, insurer, or other businesses from whom I purchased goods and services. I saw and felt these changed business practices first with my safety net. As I became aware, I saw them more and more when I purchased products and services that frequently had to be returned or disputed. There was the Ridden rental truck that had not been serviced as promised and blew up on our way from Florida to Minnesota, unsafe and dirty apartments, and issues when I bought or sold houses. When I raised concerns, hard-nosed landlords and realtors smiled when they said no and suggested an expensive legal process if I was not satisfied. I should not have expected any better treatment from Blaster or Country Garden.

Upon reflection, I know I should have been more guarded in whom I trusted. I should have gone to the hospital to be checked out immediately after such a significant car accident. Then I should have filed claims with all the insurance companies I could think of, demanded formal proof of any assertions about benefits they made, and quickly hired and fired lawyers until I found assertive and competent counsel as I finally did. Would my struggle with safety net providers have been less? Could I have then focused more on my recovery? Why was I put through such an onerous and deceitful process with my safety net providers? The accident was not my fault and I had several sources of insurance. They simply did not want to pay regardless of our contract, the law, or morality. I read and heard stories about people who gave in to their chronic pain and/or gave up on their safety nets. They seemed to carry regret, along with pain, into their future. Even though it took a lot of work and time, I was fortunate to find the satisfaction that came from receiving some measure of responsibility from my safety net providers.

I could have speculated reasons and paradigms forever. What I did know for sure, now more than ever, was that human beings have an incredible ability to rationalize any of their behaviors or means to their desired end. Invisible chronic pain and illness is a fuzzy playing field for both the injured and safety net providers – a fuzzy playing field subject to all kinds of beliefs and interpretations. These usually make for legal and hopefully moral struggles for honesty and integrity. From moral struggles like these is birthed the possibility of a better future for everyone.

For years prior to the accident, I pushed back or stood up for my beliefs and for fairness in many situations. When I did, I almost always found fair and reasonable solutions from adversaries who at least respected me through the process. But this was not always true with my safety net struggle. I had to demand responsibility and reasonableness, but received very little of either. There was something very wrong with the system. I felt strongly enough about this to file complaints and report fraud to the Ohio BWC about my employer, to the Ohio Medical Review Board about IMEs, to the Minnesota Insurance Commissioner and Attorney General about my automobile insurance, and more. I filed the complaints and wrote the letters even as I suffered with pain and was trying desperately to recover. Whenever I had enough pain relief to do the work, I dictated the words, while Justine supported me with typing and editing. This safety net work was extraordinary for me. I had never been a serious advocate. Now that I was, most of the business managers, doctors, or lawyers did not disagree with my observations or complaints. They usually only disagreed with the possibility of having a positive impact on the system. Many told me that writing letters was "a waste of time, don't do it" rather than saying "hey, I can help you draft a letter" or "I can suggest whom you might talk to about your concerns." These professionals discouraged my filing of complaints.

Then my safety net providers ignored my suggestions for improvement. They wanted to maintain the adversarial nature of the process to continue to profit by its onerous and conveniently complex nature.

In the end, I was disappointed with my safety net and its many professionals who promised a safe and secure life for people who worked hard, paid their bills, carried insurance, and lived respectably. Fortunately, I did not give up on God or life while I struggled for recovery and I never blamed either for my physical misfortunate. Instead, I no longer trusted the social systems that I had trusted and served all my life. Business, medicine, government, insurance, and law appeared to be increasingly geared toward a self-serving goal of generating wealth regardless of the consequences to human beings and regardless of the consequences to the suffering people that their professions promised to serve. The economic measure of our world and the material seduction was too great for many professionals. Their nobility in our society seemed to have all but disappeared. We must do something. But what?

The help I received from the Minnesota Attorney General included an unsuccessful attempt to mediate my concerns with Country Garden. The Attorney General also explained his limited jurisdiction unless there was a "pattern and practice" suggested by a large number of consumer complaints. A recent city newspaper reported a small victory for chronic pain survivors and others who need insurance benefits for medical care and lost wages. The insurance company, pseudo named Country Garden in this book, was the subject of the article. The heading of the article read: "[Country Garden] Insurance has agreed to pay $775,000 in civil penalties and investigative costs for allegedly violating Minnesota insurance laws, the state Department of Commerce said Wednesday."[10] More important than the money they had to pay was that the company agreed to change their business practices in the future in several areas. "As a result of the agreement, auto-accident victims could get faster payment on medical claims … [Country Garden] agreed to: Stop forcing policyholders to go to court to get benefits they are entitled to by law … Set up rules to prevent the company from influencing or changing the results of independent medical exams …

Provide medical records to those conducting medical exams before the exam ..."[11] and more. The results of this investigation and settlement with Country Garden should help those in pain today and into the future recover the insurance benefits they need. Imagine if even more people took up the cause with us!

The article also reported, "[The Minnesota Insurance Commissioner] said [Country Garden] officials never told him or investigators why they engaged in behavior the state considered illegal. 'I think greed and bad judgment got in the way,' he said ... [Country Garden] was accused of pressuring the independent medical personnel who checked out no-fault medical claims to change their opinions in order to reduce costs. (The no-fault law was intended to reduce lawsuits and provide prompt treatment for accident victims regardless of who caused the accident.) [The Minnesota Insurance Commissioner] said he's aware of complaints that other insurers in the state have violated the no-fault provisions as well, and the state will take action against them 'if these companies do not change their practices.'"[12] Many people must have reported their concerns regarding Country Garden to build the case for a pattern and practice supporting the investigation. Heywer pushed hard with letters to government officials to review Country Garden's business practices and my personal situation as an example. These letters must have helped show the pattern and practice too. Many of these letters are included in the appendixes at the back of this book. The letters can be used as templates to report your concerns. We can help the Insurance Commissioners and other government officials in all states understand the problems with insurance and what needs to be done.

As consumers, our individual efforts many times do not make a big difference, whereas our collective efforts definitely do at some point. Please add your letter, complaint, and/or specific request to the letters from other consumers who share our plight. Push back wherever you can with requests and demands for the benefits that were promised, for the medical care you need. ABC News recently reported on a new Harvard study on health care. The study concluded that almost half (48%) of patients under age 65 had problems with their health insurance. The biggest problem the insureds encountered was the seemingly inappropriate denial and delay of benefits. You may have already joined with others in the increasing number of class action lawsuits over medical care and insurance benefits. Imagine if each of us acted and our voice was amplified with millions of people sick, injured, and/or disabled demanding the promises made by our safety nets. The systems would have to change. I wish you and your individual cause great success. I anticipate success for our shared cause.

Consider those safety net providers who renege on their promises as business terrorists preying on our country's sick and injured for their own benefit. My memory of the recent terrorist attack on our country is very upsetting. I prayed for those killed or injured and their friends and families. I thought about the many new lives of chronic pain that were born that day. And I cried. I also saw how the American people responded with great compassion and caring for the victims and their families. My faith in Americans was restored at the sights and sounds of such an incredible outpouring of love from others. One man took a disabled woman out of her wheelchair, strapped her to his body, and carried her down more than fifty stories to safety. Another person stayed by the side of his disabled friend who was unable to find his way to safety. They died together. Many firefighters and rescue workers gave their lives to try to save or help others. I prayed for them and knew my advocacy for the chronically ill was not naïve or a waste of time. Americans simply need to see the suffering and injustice around them. Then, out of compassion, we can figure out what needs to be done.

I could not help but make a connection to the faceless safety net providers who, through their companies and employees, exact great suffering on the less fortunate in our great country. As a nation, we collectively stand together to stop the foreign terrorists who dare challenge our freedom and compassionate way of life. It is my hope that we can do the same to regain the safety and compassion of our entire society of people with its great diversity of thoughts, emotions, and different physical capabilities.

If you are fortunate enough that a chronic illness or other tragedy has not yet been your experience, take up this cause with me on behalf of other injured people and yourself, our children, and their children in the future who may need the safety nets they were promised. Review my work in prior chapters and use the letters I wrote as templates for ideas or guidance in your letters to push back on the system. Write to elected officials, business leaders, medical professionals, and other organizations to cast your vote for a strong and moral safety net for the future. Support the politicians working for health care reform and other safety net improvements. Be heard even when they will not listen. Consider that we may not always appeal to their morality, especially if they have an amoral perspective. But if nothing else, we can appeal to them through their pocketbooks. If the cost of responding to our collective pushback is high, then the keepers of our safety nets will consider providing medical care and paying benefits as a more cost-effective approach to managing what they like to call a "health care crisis."

Beyond medical care, you can also let your purchase of goods and services cast a vote in the marketplace for moral companies and business practices. We can practice justice in all aspects of our lives to help our social systems work better for everyone into the future. This will also help our country regain its moral promise to our children and us, and as a positive example to the world. There is much we can do even while we face the daily battle of either our own chronic illness or the many other challenges in our lives that seem to be spinning faster and further out of control.

Please consider as many suggestions and other actions as possible to help this cause. Know that our collective efforts can make a difference. My passion is great for this extremely worthwhile effort and far-reaching issue. This passion further awakened my spirit, flooded my mind with ideas, and strengthened my entire being. Your passion for this work may do the same for you. While some of these ideas may seem obvious or trite, please accept them in the spirit of helping the injured of today and tomorrow.

We can use a partnering approach with negotiation instead of litigation to provide help to people in need. Partnering to accomplish a greater good for the sick and injured can bring wealth to each of our souls rather than material wealth for a privileged minority. We become true survivors by helping each other survive whatever hardship or impairment it is we face. We all long for balance in our lives and we can find it. We can experience soul wealth in our hearts and spirits much greater than the material wealth we so readily use as the measure of our life's value and happiness. We can make a difference.

#

You may want to learn more about the medical care alternatives, pain management process, and other life changes referred to throughout this book. A complete recovery was always my goal. I tried Western, Eastern, and alternative medicines for the most physical and emotional recovery possible. Psychological, physiological, neurological, and pain management evaluations directed my care. Various physical and massage therapies, medications, trigger point injections, use of special exercise equipment, meditation, heating pads, cold packs, chiropractic adjustments, acupuncture, aromatherapy, essential oils, magnets, herbs, diet, and other medical and non-medical alternatives were all tried. Various medical and self-help books and literature were studied to understand my condition and challenge me and my medical care providers to find the most healing and the most recovery. There were no limits to my quest for recovery. This approach and process is included in *Surviving the Chronic Pain Experience: Understand and Manage Medical Care and Life Changes.* There was also a spiritual journey to the survival process which is included in *Surviving the Chronic Pain Experience: The Complete Journey.* Refer to the last page of this book for more about Heywer books and resources. We look forward to providing other information and resources in the future to help each other survive.

ENDNOTES

[1] Kazuaki Tanahashi and Tensho David Schneider, *Essential Zen*, Castle Books, New Jersey, p. ix.

[2] "Fibromyalgia Syndrome (FMS): A Patient's Guide," reprinted from *ARTHRITIS AND RHEUMATISM Journal*, copyright 1990.

[3] Julie Appleby, "Organizing movement gains steam," *USA Today*, 24 June 1999.

[4] *The Rainmaker*, 16 mm, 135 min., Paramount Pictures, Hollywood, 1997.

[5] "Getting to Work/For the disabled, opportunity remains out of reach," Kenny Fries, *The Progressive*, August 2000.

[6] Id., p 32.

[7] Id.

[8] Robert Kreitner, *Management*, Seventh Edition, Houghton Mifflin Company, Boston, New York, pp. 327, 328.

[9] Id., p. 327.

[10] Donna Halvorsen, "State Farm fined $775,000 for alleged violations," Minneapolis *Star Tribune*, 5 December 2002.

[11] Id.

[12] Id.

BIBLIOGRAPHY

BOOKS

Kreitner, Robert, *Management*, Seventh Edition, Houghton Mifflin Company, Massachusetts, 1998.

Nader, Ralph and Wesley Smith, *No Contest*, Random House, New York, 1996.

Nader, Ralph and Wesley Smith, *Winning the Insurance Game*, Doubleday, New York, 1990.

Tanahashi, Kazuaki and Tensho David Schneider, *Essential Zen*, Castle Books, New Jersey, 1994.

MOVIES

The Rainmaker. 16 mm, 135 min. Paramount Pictures, Hollywood, 1997.

NEWSPAPERS

Appleby, Julie, "Organizing movement gains steam," *USA Today*, 24 June 1999.

Halvorsen, Donna, "State Farm fined $775,000 for alleged violations," Minneapolis *Star Tribune*, 5 December 2002.

PERIODICALS

"Fibromyalgia Syndrome (FMS): A Patient's Guide," reprinted from *ARTHRITIS AND RHEUMATISM Journal*, copyright 1990.

Fries, Kenny, "Getting to Work/For the disabled, opportunity remains out of reach," *The Progressive*, August 2000.

Gore, Donald R., MD, Susan B. Sepic, MS, Gena M. Gardner, BS, and M. Patricia Murray, PhD, "Neck Pain: A Long-term Follow-up of 205 Patients," *Spine*, Volume 12, Number 1, 1987.

Hohl, Mason, "Soft Tissue Neck Injuries, Abbott Northwestern Hospital, Minneapolis, Minnesota.

WEBSITES

Heywer Books and Periodicals: http://www.survivingpain.com

Heywer: *Surviving the Chronic Pain Experience*,
http://www.heywer.com

Introduction to Corporate Social Responsibility, http://www.bsr.org

Appendix 1

LIFE ANALYSIS
MICHAEL J. WERB

As of 09/22/1997
Impact of 04/30/1997 Car Accident

LIFE WAS:	LIFE IS:
Intense, active, exciting, intuitive, engaged	Uncomfortable, pain, struggle, reactive, distracted, balance pain with engagement

Personal

Running - 4 miles per day, races (past ran marathons)	Occasionally 3 slow miles struggling
Lift weights, physical yard work, moving, etc.	Stretching, cut back activity
Motorcycle	Motorcycle - less time, hurts later
Exciting relationship and sex	Needy (massage) relationship and frustrating sex
Travel - plane, road trips	Travel - uncomfortable/pain
Emotion based, intuitive	Frustrated, back focused
Drug free	Daily medication to maintain
Restful sleep	Broken sleep, tossing and turning, excessive snoring

Work

Intense, 60 to 70 hours per week, engaged	Less than 40 hours per week, performing much less
Thinking, assertive/aggressive	Relaxing, missing things, pain aware
Intuitive, proactive	Reactive
Work through lunch typical	1- to 2-hour lunch to relax

Other

Purchased items I liked

Purchased support couch, wheeled luggage, other supports

Goal: Return to "Life Was"

Appendix 2

10/1997

Mr. Tom Young
Attorney at Law
Address
City, State, Zip

Dear Attorney:

I went to see my primary physician, Dr. Smith, on Thursday, (date), to follow-up on my back and get prescriptions refilled. I explained to him that I was keeping a journal relative to my back and concluded that the pain is related to the activities and level of stress in my life. I explained that there are three levels of pain. The first is general discomfort on good days when I have no stress and limited activities. The second is muscle pain in my shoulders and back which I manage each day. The worst is intense and sometimes sharp pain in my shoulders and through my back which comes from the higher levels of activity and stress during the day that I used to embrace quite often. I shared with Dr. Smith the enclosed comparison of how my life was before the accident and after.

Dr. Smith's comments were rather interesting. He explained that my life will never be the way it was. If I try to get there, I will have pain, illness, and stress. I will need to cut my activities and can't stop medication. He said, "You're doomed."

I was surprised considering he noted in his report to you that my chance of full recovery was excellent. He explained to me that because I was now in my 40s I should expect that my life will change. I told him it didn't make sense that it would change that dramatically so quickly. He seemed uncomfortable and cut our session off. He gave me three new prescriptions. He told me to come back in three weeks. I don't see my primary physician as a solution for this problem. Is it advisable for me to change primary care physicians at this point?

I saw Dr. Hunt on Friday, (date), for trigger point injections for pain relief and to see if I could further reduce my medication over the weekend while I relaxed. I shared with him the enclosed comparison and he seemed to better understand. When I asked his thoughts, he explained there is a legal/medical opinion and a medical opinion shared with his patients. With the legal/medical opinion, he wants to protect his patients; whereas in discussions with his patients, he wants to provide a more optimistic and encouraging perspective. [I later learned the emphasis was always optimistic for both opinions.] He talked briefly about chronic pain and suggested I read a book. He explained that my situation needs to be viewed in the long term, and I should plan and create goals with small steps of improvement rather than expecting to find the solution quickly. He also seemed to suggest that my life will never be the way it was. His discussion was in the context of a book I reviewed today on chronic pain.

Mr. Young, it's obvious to me that I need your help. If, in fact, this is a lifelong situation, I want to be sure that my interests are appreciated. I need to find a way to significantly cut back my work and my career, along with the rest of my life, so that all of it can be meaningful and with tolerable levels of pain. I'm still not sure how to do that. I look forward to your comments.

Sincerely,

Michael J. Werb
Address
City, State, Zip
Telephone
Enclosure

Appendix 3

04/1998

Dr. Hunt
Address
City, State, Zip

Dear Dr. Hunt:

I have treated with you for my back injury related to a car accident on April 30, 1997. Per Dr. Lee's advice, I went on medical leave from my job on February 18, 1998. At this time, I ask that you provide me with the following information:

1. What is my current diagnosis? Was this diagnosis caused by the April 30, 1997 auto accident?

2. What medical treatment has been prescribed and what is suggested for the future? (Medication, physical therapy, massage therapy, home stretching, exercise, meditation, chiropractic adjustments, etc.)

3. Have I reached maximum medical improvement? If not, why?

4. I have been requested to return to my Controller position at Blaster (see job description attached) and fulfill all responsibilities (no "ramping up") based upon the report from Dr. Blunder (also attached).

    In your opinion, am I able to perform this job as described without limitations?

5.   If you feel I am not able to return to the full duties of my job that I have described, please explain the medical reasons for your opinion.

Thank you for your help.

Sincerely,

Michael J. Werb
Address
City, State, Zip
Telephone
Enclosures

Appendix 4

Life Analysis
MICHAEL J. WERB
Impact of 04/30/1997 Car Accident

LIFE WAS:	LIFE IS:	04/1998
(prior to 04/30/1997)	(09/1997)	(on medical leave)
Intense, active, exciting, intuitive, engaged	Uncomfortable, pain, struggle, reactive, distracted, balance pain with engagement	Half day clarity, little pain & discomfort in AM, most drugs in PM & night for sleep

Personal

Running - 4 miles per per day, races (past ran marathons	Occasionally 3 slow miles, struggling	Walking 2½ to 5 miles/day
Lift weights, physical yard work, moving, etc.	Stretching, cut back activity	Exercise, m.t., p.t., etc. avg 4½ hrs/day (Att 1)
Motorcycle	Motorcycle - less time, hurts later	Motorcycle - less time & hurt
Exciting relationship and sex	Needy (massage) relationship and frustrating sex	Good in AM, less aggressive massage
Travel - plane, road trips	Travel - uncomfortable/ pain	Travel cut - still pain
Emotion based, Intuitive	Frustrated, back focused	Mix, good in AM
Drug free	Daily meds to maintain	Meds in PM
Restful sleep	Broken sleep, tossing & turning, excessive snoring	Sleeping better, more snoring from me
Social alcohol	Excessive alcohol during pain sessions	
Meds - occasional aspirin, albuterol	1 Daypro, 4-9 Skelaxin 8-12 OTC, trigger point injections, albuterol	2-4 Soma, 2-4 Tylenol No. 3, occasional Skelaxin & albuterol

239

Work

Intense, 60-70 hrs/ week, engaged (Att 2 -job description)	40 h rs/week, perform less (see 09/1998 perf. review, Att 3)	Not working since 02/18/1998
Thinking, assertive/aggressive	Relaxing, missing things pain aware	
Intuitive, proactive	Reactive	
Work through lunch typical	1-2 hr lunch to relax	

Other

Purchased items I liked	Purchased support couch, wheeled luggage, other supports	No sports car, new car, windshield on motorcycle

Goal: Return to "Life Was"

Medical reports:	Attachment
Dr. Lee	4
Dr. Hunt	5
Physical therapist	6
Massage therapy	7

Appendix 5

April 1998 Back Routine

	Number of minutes	
	Each Day	Daily Average
Daily		
Stretch in morning and at noon	15	30
Ice and relax at noon and 5 PM	30	60
Meditation in afternoon	45	45
Walking 2.5 miles in AM and afternoon	45	90
Medication (generic equiv); 2-4 Soma, 2-4 Tylenol #3 (in PM)		
Weekly		
Gym workout T and Th (90 min including travel)		25
Massage therapy 90 min (140 min including travel)		20
Relax through pain session (avg 1 per week)		?
Journal entry and review		?
Reading		?
Monthly		
Doctor follow-up		?
Total average time each day (270/60 min=4 1/2 hours a day)		270

Appendix 6

04/1998:

The physical injury specialist I was sent to, Dr. Hunt, describes a permanent impairment. My general practitioner, Dr. Smith, told me I am "doomed" when I asked him to help me return to the active life I enjoyed prior to the accident. Both doctors are included in Blaster's managed health care plan. Dr. Lee provides "adjustments" and a more aggressive physical therapy approach to a serious ongoing injury and he put me on an eight-month medical leave. This medical leave was decided after ten months of medication, physical and massage therapy, trigger point injections, meditation, and other alternative approaches to manage and overcome the daily pain that was getting worse as the medication became less effective.

After two months of the medical leave with no work, limited personal physical activities (daily walking of 2.5 to 5 miles and no running), aggressive physical therapy, and continued massage therapy, along with meditation and other alternatives, there is some improvement as I have some relief from the pain in the mornings and a clarity of my mind and heart that I have not enjoyed in almost an entire year. A few pain-free hours in the morning have brought me such excitement that I want to live fully again but know I must continue with this approach to find as much improvement as possible and, of course, return to work. This approach takes six to eight hours per day, time that will need to be cut back to balance my life and get back to work. I still dream of returning to a position as challenging and rewarding as I have enjoyed lately but know I may need to consider alternatives. Dr. Hunt has suggested that a less intense, 40-hour-a-week job may be realistic. Dr. Lee says it may or may not be possible to return to my present position after the aggressive therapy (to be completed as of 10/18/1998).

Blaster has been informed of my condition and struggle over the last year. I have shared all of this information with my supervisor and the director of human resources. I tried for the first few months to handle my job while taking medications. My doctor indicated that the majority of people with this type of injury would recover in a few months. My plan was to do the best I could, cover the medical expenses, and return to my life ASAP. The medication is causing me to be irritable, and I feel nauseous. I have lost my intuition and drive needed for this work. My emotions are masked along with the pain. Yet the recovery does not come. It seemed I was one of the 10 to 20 percent that Dr. Smith indicated would have continuing problems. On vacation for a week in late June last year, I cut the medication in half and turned to the doctors to help me find a natural and physical solution to my problem. This approach was repeated with my vacation in October. The results were more pain but very little improvement in the muscle trigger points in my back and shoulders.

I looked to an attorney in August and the car insurance company as I could see that this problem was going to be bigger and more costly than I hoped. I looked to an attorney in September to handle the bills and paperwork as I was struggling to get by at work and in my personal life. The car insurance company said it was a workers' compensation issue. I was advised to protect my interests and I filed for workers' compensation in September. My supervisor asked me what I was trying to pull. I explained the injury in greater detail and asked him for help. While I believe he tried to be supportive by listening, the responsibilities remained and, in my performance review, this period of time was referred to as lacking in performance. In the latter part of 1997 I requested a move to a position in a warmer climate as I had determined that the cold weather tightened the muscles and made the problem and pain much worse. I was more convinced in December over the holidays when there were fewer demands at work and time off work to conclude that the current approach was not effective, even with the benefit of medication. I am determined to eliminate this medication as much as possible. Two business trips were scheduled in January which I knew I would not be able to handle as travel also made the problem worse. And I was not effective on medication or in pain. I respectively told my supervisor, and he responded that this was not acceptable and he was disappointed. We met with the director of human resources to face the situation. I asked them to find me a position at The Blaster Company which I could handle with lesser demands in a warmer climate. They asked around with the reply that another business would not be interested as they did not know what to expect. No alternative positions have been offered that would fit my new and lesser capabilities.

My situation continued to deteriorate as the medication became less effective and the physical therapy was not working. I was not willing to take more drugs and not be able to perform my work even to minimum standards. I was not sleeping and was awake at times in the early hours of the morning crying over my situation and the pain. After discussions with the physical therapist and an honest evaluation of the situation, I approached Dr. Lee for alternatives. He gave me an eight-month medical leave that I now see as a necessary time frame to, in effect, relearn the process of physical and emotional stress and relaxation for my back and shoulders. When I met with my supervisor and the director of human resources the next day, I broke down crying which I had never done in any difficult and challenging work situation. I believe this was an emotional release of ten months of daily pain and work performance shortcomings, and a realization and start of acceptance of the magnitude of the injury I was struggling with every day.

My supervisor asked me what the probability and timing were of my return to work. I met him in March for lunch and advised him of Dr. Hunt's and Dr. Lee's opinions after asking them that same question. Mr. Blair's response was to consider the medical suggestions as not necessary and that diet can be a factor. I explained I had done a considerable amount of independent research of Western and Eastern medicine and was trying everything, including diet, exercise, medication, herbs, oils, meditation, magnetic mattress, spiritual prayer, physical and massage therapy, etc. There are no limits to what a person will try when they face this level of pain every day. He responded with the analogy of a wolf pack where they will check on the injured and leave them behind if they slow the pack.

The following week (04/02/1998) I was required to attend a workers' compensation hearing to respond to Blaster's denial of my claim. The hearing officer determined that this injury is work related and that Blaster should pay the medical bills. No loss of compensation had been incurred to that point so that issue was deferred. I do appreciate the medical pay I have received to date as part of my employment benefits.

Blaster notified me on 03/26/1998 that the 12-week Family Medical Leave clock had started. Then, on 04/10/1998, they notified me that I am okay and should return to work. They apparently feel it is time to conclude this situation. Their conclusion is based on an independent medical evaluation which they sent me to in February 1998. This doctor concluded that I was injured in the accident but that I was completely healed. His medical exam lasted approximately 15 minutes and covered my complete medical history, a neurological and physical exam, and review of my present symptoms and medical approach. He frequently interrupted my response to his questions and ignored my questions. His physical exam of my back was accomplished with a light brushing of the skin with his hand. He did not attempt to feel into the muscle to understand the trigger points (knots or spasms) that have been a part of my life this entire time. These spasms have given me a lot of pain every day since the accident. The IME report has a number of errors, omissions, and misstatements (more than 30). These errors are all in support of a conclusion that there is no continuing injury or medical improvement possible and I should return to work.

I shared this information with the Director of Human Resources when he explained that I should return to work based on this report. I told him that while I have experienced some improvement during this medical leave, if I returned to work now I would probably fall flat on my face. I explained that I did not believe this made sense for me or the business. He told me this was not personal. When I tried to make sense out of this situation with a friend with workers' compensation experience, I was told that it is at this point that most people either return to work injured and are fired when they find they are unable to perform their job or they find a less demanding job at another company. This results in eliminating the company's responsibility at the expense of the employee. While I was not comfortable with this for me, I feel bad for the people who live paycheck to paycheck to support their families and have to accept such an inequity. There may be a few folks who are looking for a paycheck without work, but it appears the system has shifted to hurt the majority of people that believe in an honest day's work for an honest day's pay, but may need some help from time to time from the company they have worked so hard for.

Appendix 7

09/1998

Administrator
Bureau of Workers' Compensation
Address
City, State, Zip

Dear Sir/Madam:

The purpose of this letter is to recommend pain programs as soon as possible for people injured in work-related accidents that result in chronic pain conditions. I have just completed a four-week pain program at Valley Hospital. The impact of what I learned from this program is very positive in my life compared to when I started the program. While my chronic pain will probably continue for the rest of my life, I am able to function more and better in my personal life and look forward to returning to work, albeit part time at first and always in a less demanding position than I worked prior to my injury. I believe pain programs like the one at Valley Hospital can provide other people with chronic pain conditions similar improvements in their lives, including an earlier return to a productive work and personal life. Unfortunately, what I found with other patients at the pain program is that people have to wait between two and seven years before they are allowed by the workers' compensation system to attend the program. The longer people have to wait, the more medical problems increase, and it seems harder for people to trust the pain program and realize its full potential. The following will describe the pain program as I understand it and suggest its greater and quicker use for other people with chronic pain conditions.

The pain program at Valley Hospital takes a multifaceted approach to managing chronic pain which includes physical and psychological healing, along with behavioral modification. On the one hand, the physical approach is similar to sports medicine where the individual is taught how to maximize their physical condition, as well as conserve their physical capability through proper body mechanics and relaxation techniques. At the same time, the psychological and emotional implications of the limitations to an individual's life as a result of chronic pain are addressed. There is also training provided for proper nutrition, medication, and communication, all of which are important components which require change in the life of a person living with chronic pain. The entire program is structured in 40-hour weeks similar to what one could expect while working. This provides the opportunity to introduce pacing and balancing of activities for the individual's behavioral modification. Finally, the success of the program is enhanced by the staff of the Valley Hospital pain program. The staff works as a team to balance the program's vision and goals for all the patients while tailoring specific treatment for each individual. They are the most professional and talented groups of medical professionals I have ever encountered.

While the pain program holds varying degrees of success for the patients participating, there was a common thread for people with work-related injuries. These people also had to deal with the difficulty related to the administration of workers' compensation pre-approving and subsequently paying their bills and providing appropriate wage benefits. People primarily experienced frustration and disappointment with the workers' compensation system and the lack of support from case managers, third-party administrators, and others working in that system. I was very saddened to know that these people could have been helped years ahead of when they were if workers' compensation was administered in a quicker and more compassionate manner for injured employees with chronic pain conditions. These people not only would have experienced less pain for a number of years, but could also have returned to work earlier and enjoyed a fuller and more productive life in general.

I ask for your help to improve the workers' compensation system to provide the pain program option as quickly as possible to people with chronic pain conditions resulting from work-related injuries. I would be glad to discuss any of the above in more detail at your convenience. Thank you in advance for your consideration and help.

Sincerely,

Michael J. Werb
Address
City, State, Zip
Telephone

c: State Senator
c: Company Nurse/Blaster
c: Valley Hospital Pain Program Staff
c: My Attorney
c: Company Third-party Administrator

Appendix 8

09/1998

Administrator
Bureau of Workers' Compensation
Address
City, State, Zip

Dear Administrator:

I am writing this letter to request your assistance to accomplish reimbursement of valid medical bills related to my workers' compensation (WC) claim. I will need your help with the process and system used by self-insured employers and their third-party administrators. It appears I will not be successful in recovering my medical bills unless I get help with the process. My efforts over the last year have been frustrating and unsuccessful. Many of my bills date back to May of 1997. Less than $200 has been reimbursed of over $8,000 of valid bills with medical care continuing and the bills increasing.

First, by way of background, I would like to briefly summarize my situation with respect to my WC claim. I was injured in a work-related accident on 04/20/1997. In the accident, I was a passenger in an automobile traveling to a work function from work with fellow employees. I filed a workers' compensation claim a few months later as I had hoped that the injury would resolve itself upon the advice of my family doctor. And I was concerned with the possible consequences at work associated with filing a claim. When I filed the workers' compensation claim, I was counseled by my employer that filing a WC report and claim might not be the best thing for me to do. When I reported the injury and filed for WC, the management of the company explained to me that the injury may not be work-related, is not worth the effort or visibility for the individual (me) at work, hired lawyers that just take a third of the reimbursement, the reimbursed bills will be subrogated, etc. My response has always been "I'd just like to get my bills paid." The WC claim was denied by my employer and brought to a workers' compensation hearing on 04/02/1998 (the record of proceedings is attached). The company lawyers did not dispute the work relationship at the hearing and the injury was concluded as work-related. At the hearing, a grossly erroneous independent medical evaluation was used by one company as a basis to refute the extent of the injury. I subsequently filed a complaint with the State Medical Board of Ohio with respect to that independent medical evaluation.

I had anticipated the need for a lot of work and a correct approach to filing a claim and hired an attorney, Mr. Young, after calling the Dayton Bar Association for a recommendation. Ms. Jones, the company nurse, explained to me that all workers' compensation bills have to go through her. She acts as the initial screen for the third-party administrator. During 1997, Ms. Jones and Mr. Young had difficulty working together. When this was explained to me, I asked Ms. Jones on several occasions to provide a listing to Mr. Young and directly to me with respect to the information and support that she needed. This listing was never provided. She explained that she did not believe Mr. Young understood workers' compensation law. Mr. Young explained to me that he had 150 to 200 workers' compensation cases and had been working in that specialty for about 15 years. He cautioned me about the company tactics, which I should be sensitive to, and he eventually dropped me as a client as too difficult to support. I tried to handle this claim on my own but got very little help from the company and eventually had to hire another attorney, Mr. Severs. Mr. Severs supported me at the 04/02/1998 hearing. With the approval for the WC claim from the hearing, I attempted to assertively accomplish reimbursement of my medical bills. I met with Ms. Jones on frequent occasions at this time since I had also returned to work after being on medical leave for this injury.

I had returned to work and was seeing Ms. Jones on a daily basis for medical treatment.

On 06/10/1998, I provided a summary and all documentation required for medical bills up to that point. The total was $4,581.58. I also indicated that a number of medical bills from Dr. Lee, one of the doctors I had been seeing, were not included in this summary. I believe those bills exceeded $3,000 at that point. On 07/02/1998, I was reimbursed a total of $153.21 of $233.21 from that summary with adjustments made for service for "unrelated condition" and "repriced by bill reviewer." The remaining $4,348.37 was not addressed nor have the Dr. Lee bills exceeding $3,000. When I asked Ms. Jones to help me and to tell me what I needed to provide, she gave me BWC C-161 forms to be filled out by my doctors that provided for approval of the medical bills for treatment, including massage therapy, physical therapy, psychologist evaluation, alternative pain management, various drugs, and related doctor visits and other medical bills. On 07/16/1998, I provided the completed C 161 form from Dr. Hunt, who was one of my physicians of record, and on 08/04/1998, I provided the completed C-161 form from Dr. Lee, the other physician of record that I had for this injury. At the request of Ms. Jones, on 07/17/1998, I also provided an explanation of the timing of the two physicians of record and the time frame that they covered in support of my injury. Copies of the C-161 form and the letter to Ms. Jones are also attached for your review. On 08/15/1998, I provided a second summary of medical bills. These bills are in addition to the previous summary of bills and total $777.71. Again, this was provided directly to Ms. Jones as she had requested. On 08/21/1998, I contacted Ms. Jones and asked the status of the bills being paid. She indicated to me they were part of a file review, that the Bureau of Workers' Compensation was busy on audits, and that they were probably too busy to participate in the file review. I did not think the Bureau participated in file reviews for self-insured employers. At that time, I also asked for the status of a pain clinic pre-approval requested in July. She indicated there was no word from the third-party administrator and that they were reviewing the necessity of the pain clinic. I followed up with Dr.

Hunt, my physician of record who had recommended that I attend the pain clinic, and I learned that his office had sent the required forms to Ms. Jones on 07/20/1998. I still have not heard from the third-party administrator with respect to approval of this pain clinic.

On 09/01/1998, the third-party administrator issued another check for $44.48 in payment against the second summary that I had provided. They responded to $669.74 of the $777.71 submitted and indicated they adjusted $595 for "no prior authorization" and $30.26 as "repriced by bill reviewer." On 09/10/1998, I called Ms. Jones who gave me the name of an individual, Ms. Bumer, to contact at the third-party administrator. Ms. Bumer's voice mail indicated she was not available until the following Monday so I called and asked for Adjuster 59 as indicated on the explanation of review from the third-party administrator. The receptionist forwarded my call to Laurie. Laurie forwarded me to Kim, who was not available, so I left a message with her voice mail. She did return my phone call and I called her back on 09/11/1998. She indicated to me that the records were not appropriate for approving these bills. She indicated to me that she only had one of the doctor's C-161 form, the one where the doctor had omitted the diagnosis. I should note that once this omission was identified to the doctor, his office support faxed the revised C-161 form, which included the diagnosis, directly to Ms. Jones at her request. That same day, 09/11/1998, I followed up with a phone call to Ms. Jones and told her that the third-party administrator did not have two completed C-161 forms from my two physicians of record that I had been treating with. She indicated she had given these to the third-party administrator directly and that I should call the first person that she suggested. At this point I indicated to Ms. Jones that I felt I was going in circles with trying to get these bills paid. I had submitted all the documentation and requested help directly from her as she had instructed me early on in the process that all information had to go through her. When I was talking to Ms. Jones, she indicated that I should not talk to Kim, but should talk to Ms. Bumer. Ms. Bumer is the field rep and the person that Ms. Jones handed details to directly that supported my claim.

When I step back and look at the many, many phone calls and many personal visits and all the information I have tried to provide, it appears to me that the comment by the first attorney I had worked with was on point, i.e., I should be sensitive to this company's tactics. The system and process that is used for reimbursing workers' compensation bills by this company and by the third-party administrator appears to be geared towards, first of all, repeatedly denying reimbursement and/or responsibility for the medical bills and, secondly, creating so much difficulty to the individual for getting the bills reimbursed that they will either hire an attorney or people just get tired and stop trying to work the process. The warning that the individual is given early on that the claim is not worthwhile or lawyers will just take a third becomes a self-fulfilling prophecy.

I ask that the Bureau of Workers' Compensation help me in getting reimbursement for the medical bills that I have submitted. In order to do that, I am also requesting that they review the process that is used by the company and their third-party administrator and request appropriate changes to ensure reimbursement of appropriate medical bills in a reasonable time frame with minimal difficulty.

Sincerely,

Michael J. Werb
Address
City, State, Zip
Telephone
Enclosures

c: State Senator
c: Ms. Jones, Blaster
c: Ms. Bumer, Third-party administrator
c: Kim, Third-party administrator
c: (My) Attorney Cliff

Appendix 9

08/1998

State Medical Board
Address
City, State, Zip

RE: Complaint to Medical Review Board

Dear Medical Review Board:

I am writing you regarding medical opinions provided by two medical doctors in our state which were in error. The opinions suggest medical incompetence, gross inaccuracy, and possibly falsifying information to force an injured employee to return to work prematurely ahead of completing a medical approach that was beginning to show promise and success. As a result of these opinions, I incurred a great deal of additional pain and indignity, and I eventually lost my job. I believe this approach to medical treatment is inappropriate, and I would like your help.

The following is a brief background of my situation. I was in a work-related car accident in 04/1997 which resulted in, among other things, chronic myofascial pain. After ten months of unsuccessful medical treatment, my personal physician put me on an eight-month medical leave in 02/1998 and into an aggressive therapy program. This program provided me with the most relief from my chronic back pain after many months of trying several medical and non-medical alternatives to address the pain. My employer sent me to an IME (by Dr. Blunder) within a week of my doctor putting me on a medical leave. Dr. Blunder's exam was inadequate and the subsequent report is grossly inaccurate.   I have noted more than 30 errors, misstatements, and omissions in the report (Attachment I) all to support a conclusion of no impairment. After I explained the inaccuracies in the Dr. Blunder's report, my employer sent me to a second IME. While this second IME was fairly credible, I believe it was influenced by the letter (Attachment II) from my employer to Dr. Waits (who performed the second IME). My employer included a copy of Dr. Blunder's IME with the letter, as well as a statement by the company physician that "[he had] determined that [I was] fit to return to work immediately." At that point in time I had never even met the company doctor. I believe it is inappropriate for a doctor to provide such a medical opinion without even seeing the patient.

I believe that because of the Dr. Blunder's IME and the company doctor's opinion, my career and credibility at work were seriously damaged, I suffered great indignity, and I eventually lost my job. In 05/1998, I was forced to return to work before I had completed my doctor's intensive therapy and for two months the pain and inability to function at work or home increased and returned to the level it was at prior to the medical leave. In 07/1998, at the request of the company doctor, I went to a physiatrist who had treated me prior to my medical leave. The physiatrist recommended I return to medical leave and go through a four-week pain clinic. After the pain clinic, I was to ramp up from 20 hours a week to 40 hours a week over a period of six weeks. The job I had at Blaster requires 50- to 70-hour workweeks. I was unsure if I would be able to meet these job requirements given the various medical treatments and results over the last fifteen months, along with the medical prognosis. Blaster involuntarily terminated me at the end of 07/1998. I start the pain program the next month.

From the above, you can see that the Dr. Blunder's IME and the company doctor's evaluations have caused me great harm during a time when I was actually healing. I believe that this approach to medical treatment is inappropriate and would like to help in any way to ensure or at least mitigate the possibility of other people having to go through a similar experience. Please consider my complaint and contact me at your convenience for help in your investigation of this matter.

Sincerely,

Michael J. Werb
Address
City, State, Zip
Telephone
Enclosures

Appendix 10

10/1998

Summary of Workers' Compensation (WC) process with self-insured employer:

Many of my bills date back to 05/1997. Of over $9,000 of valid and documented bills with medical care continuing and the bills increasing, less than $200 has been reimbursed.

Soon after my injury, I had anticipated the need for a lot of work and a correct approach to filing a claim so I hired an attorney, Attorney Young, after calling the Dayton Bar Association for a recommendation. Ms. Jones, the company nurse, explained to me that all workers' compensation bills have to go through her as she acts as the screen for the third-party administrator. During 1997, Nurse Jones and Mr. Young had difficulty working together. When this was explained to me, I asked Nurse Jones on several occasions to provide a listing to Mr. Young and directly to me with respect to the information that she needed and the support that she needed. This listing was never provided. She explained she did not believe Mr. Young understood workers' compensation law. Mr. Young explained to me that he had 150 to 200 workers' compensation cases and had been working in that specialty for about 15 years. He cautioned me about the company tactics, which I should be sensitive to, and he eventually dropped me as a client as too difficult to support. I tried to handle this claim on my own but received no help from the company and eventually had to hire another attorney, Attorney Severs. Mr. Severs supported me at the 04/02/1998 WC hearing where my claim was disputed by the company and decided to be allowed by the Industrial Commission. With the approval for the WC claim from the hearing, I attempted to assertively accomplish reimbursement of my medical bills. I met with Nurse Jones on frequent occasions as I had returned to work after being on medical leave for this injury. I was seeing Nurse Jones on a daily basis for medical treatment in the company medical office.

On 06/10/1998, I provided a summary and all documentation required for medical bills up to that point. The total was $4,581.58. I also indicated that a number of medical bills from Dr. Lee, one of the doctors I had been seeing, were not included in this summary. I believe those bills exceeded $3,000 at that point. On 07/02/1998, I was reimbursed a total of $153.21 of $233.21 from that summary with adjustments made for service for "unrelated condition" and "repriced by bill reviewer." Of the remaining $4,348.37 that was not addressed, $2431.27 was denied primarily because of no prior authorization (massage therapy). Dr. Lee's bills, which exceed $3,000, were also not addressed. When I asked Nurse Jones to help me and to tell me what I needed to provide, she gave me BWC C-161 forms to be filled out by my doctors that provided for approval of the medical bills for treatment, including massage therapy, physical therapy, psychologist evaluation, alternative pain management, various drugs, related doctor visits and other medical bills. On 07/16/1998, I provided the completed C-161 form from Dr. Hunt, who was one of my physicians of record. On 08/04/1998, I provided the completed C-161 form from Dr. Lee, the other physician of record that I had for this injury. On 07/17/1998, at the request of Nurse Jones, I also provided an explanation of the timing of the two physicians of record and the time frame that they covered in support of my injury (split roughly 50/50 since 04/30/1997). The completed C-161s and the letter were given directly to Nurse Jones who told me they would be forwarded to the third party administrator. To date, the third-party administrator has indicated they do not have the Dr. Hunt C-161 that covers a lot of the above bills. The third-party administrator only has one of the two doctor's C-161 forms, the one from Dr. Lee where the doctor had omitted the diagnosis. I should note that once this omission was identified to the doctor, his office staff faxed the revised C-161 form in early August, which included the diagnosis, directly to Nurse Jones at her request. They also mailed me a copy of the completed C-161.

On 08/15/1998, I provided a second summary of medical bills. These bills are in addition to the previous summary of bills and total

$777.71. Again, this was provided directly to Nurse Jones as she had requested. On 08/21/1998, I contacted Nurse Jones and asked the status of the bills being paid. She indicated to me they were part of an individuals file review for medical bill reimbursement, that the BWC was busy on audits, and that they were probably too busy to participate in the file review at this time. Does the Bureau participate in individual file reviews for medical bill reimbursement for self-insured employers? At that time, I also asked for the status of a pain clinic pre-approval requested in July. She indicated there was no word from the third-party administrator and that they were reviewing the necessity of the pain clinic. Nurse Jones also indicated I should attend the pain clinic, and I took this as a verbal approval and began the pain program on 08/24/1998. I followed up with Dr. Hunt, my physician of record who had prescribed the pain clinic for my medical condition, and his office had sent the required WC forms to Nurse Jones on 07/20/1998. The third-party administrator has verbally disapproved this pain program to me but has not formally rendered an opinion.

On 09/01/1998, the third-party administrator issued another check for $44.48 in payment against the second summary that I had provided. They responded to $669.74 of the $777.71 submitted and indicated they adjusted $595 for "no prior authorization" and $30.26 as "repriced by bill reviewer." On 09/10/1998, I called Nurse Jones who gave me the name of an individual, Ms. Bumer, to contact at the third-party administrator. Ms. Bumer's voice mail indicated she was not available until the following Monday so I called and asked for Adjuster 59 as indicated on the explanation of review from the third-party administrator. The receptionist forwarded my call to Laurie. Laurie forwarded me to Kim, who was not available, and I left a message with her voice mail. She returned my phone call and I called her back on 09/11/1998. She indicated to me that the records were not appropriate for approving these bills. She indicated to me that she only had one of the doctor's C-161 forms, the one from Dr. Lee where the doctor had omitted the diagnosis (they claimed to not have the revised C-161, which included the diagnosis, that his office staff had faxed to Nurse Jones at her request, as soon as they were

260

notified). Kim said they also did not have the completed C-161 form from Dr. Hunt. I called Dr. Lee's office and they faxed another copy of the completed C-161 form to Kim. That same day, 09/11/1998, I also followed up with a phone call to Nurse Jones and told her that the third-party administrator did not have two completed C-161 forms from my two physicians of record that I had been treating with (Dr. Hunt or revised Dr. Lee C-161 forms). Nurse Jones indicated she had given these directly to the third-party administrator Ms. Bumer and that I should call the first person that she suggested, i.e., Ms. Bumer. Nurse Jones also indicated that the revised Dr. Lee form had initially been faxed directly to the third-party administrator. I checked with Dr. Lee's office. On 08/12/1998 they had faxed the revision to Nurse Jones. At this point I indicated to Nurse Jones that I felt I was going in circles trying to get these bills paid. I had submitted all the documentation and requested help directly from her as she had instructed me early on in the process that all information had to go through her. I indicated to Nurse Jones that I might request some help from the BWC. She said I should go ahead and call the self-insured department at the BWC if I have concerns. When I was talking to Nurse Jones, she indicated that I should not talk to Kim, but should talk to Ms. Bumer as Ms. Bumer is the field rep and the person that Nurse Jones handed details to directly that supported my claim.

To be sure everyone had the needed documentation, on 09/15/1998 I left a voice mail with Ms. Bumer that told of the C-161 forms that were provided to Kim and I left my phone number. On 09/15/1998 I asked Dr. Lee's office to again fax the C-161 form that included the diagnosis to the attention of Kim. On 09/16/1998 I talked to both Dr. Lee's and Dr. Hunt's offices to fax the completed C-161 forms again to Nurse Jones and to the third-party administrator. On 09/16/1998 I talked to Kim. She said she did not receive the C-161 forms that were faxed from both doctors' offices. I confirmed the fax number that Kim provided me on 09/15/1998.

On 09/16/1998 I talked to Ms. Bumer. She indicated that Bureau guidelines do not provide for massage therapy. I asked her what guidelines and Ms. Bumer indicated Kim has a thick book. I asked her if we could review it together. Ms. Bumer indicated she would send me the appropriate sections. I told Ms. Bumer that Nurse Jones had said she had all the C-161 and required forms for reimbursement of my medical bills. Ms. Bumer indicated she would talk to Nurse Jones. I indicated I would follow-up with Kim on propriety with the rules as the hearing on April 2 said these bills should be paid. Ms. Bumer indicated Kim may have the needed pre-approvals. I indicated to Ms. Bumer that I incurred many of these expenses before the hearing and that the C-161 forms covered these expenses.

On 09/17/1998 I left a voice mail with Kim to follow-up again on the C-161 forms and also to see if she had received the summary of the physicians of record that Nurse Jones had asked me to prepare. I also asked Kim to mail me the workers' compensation guidelines relative to reimbursement of massage therapy expenses. On 09/18/1998 Ms. Bumer returned my phone call indicating she still needed the diagnosis code from Dr. Lee. Ellie said she did check with Nurse Jones and Nurse Jones did not have the completed form. Ms. Bumer indicated she would check with Kim on the C-161 forms and would pull the file and review it with Kim. She also asked me to explain the nature of my injury and a little bit about the accident, which I did. Ms. Bumer also asked if I would consider a lump sum. I told Ms. Bumer that I might consider a lump sum sometime in the future, but that for now I wanted to get the outstanding bills sorted out and paid.

On 09/21/1998 Ms. Bumer indicated they only had the Dr. Lee C-161 form with no diagnosis in their file. She also indicated that Dr. Lee had written the diagnosis on the existing C-161 form that had been denied by the third-party administrator. That tells me they have received a complete C-161 form with a diagnosis but they appear to be nit-picking about revising existing forms versus filling out a brand new form each time there is an issue. Ms. Bumer also indicated the guidelines provide for 20 massage therapy treatments, 10 without authorization and 10 referred by a physician, at $51.52 per day. She indicated she had a quarterly review with Nurse Jones the next day and I asked her to call me if they needed anything else. I also told Ms. Bumer I was concerned and frustrated with the confusion relative to my claim. I indicated I had prepared two letters to the Administrator of WC, one covering a recommendation to encourage and facilitate pain programs for injured employees as appropriate, and that I would copy Ms. Bumer on that letter. I was also preparing a letter that included details of the WC process that I had been going through with very little success.

On 09/23/1998 I left a voice mail with Ms. Bumer to call me and follow-up relative to her review of my file with Nurse Jones.

On 09/25/1998 I called again and left a voice mail. This time I asked specifically what forms were required to pre-approve massage therapy as now additional massage therapy had been prescribed through the pain program. I also asked if they had found Dr. Hunt's C-161 form and asked her to follow-up relative to her review with Nurse Jones and I asked her again for a copy of the relevant rules.

Ms. Bumer is no longer returning my phone calls. The company, nurse, Ms. Jones, insists I work through Ms. Bumer. On 10/12/1998 I called Nurse Jones to ask what forms and documentation were still needed and that I had additional medical bills to forward for payment. Nurse Jones suggested I get a new attorney to start the process over from the beginning with all the forms and documentation as the rules and requirements are too difficult (for me). I have hit a dead end with respect to the medical bills and I have not made any progress relative to lost wages for the three months I was on medical leave earlier this year or since I have been out of work since 07/31/1998.

When I step back and look at the many, many phone calls and many personal visits and all the information I have tried to provide, it appears to me that the comment by the first attorney I had worked with was on point, i.e., I should be sensitive to this company's tactics. The system and process that is used for reimbursing workers' compensation bills by this company and by the third-party administrator appears to be geared towards, first of all, repeatedly denying reimbursement and/or responsibility for the medical bills and, secondly, creating so much difficulty to the individual for getting the bills reimbursed that they will either hire an attorney or people just get tired and stop trying to work the process.

I ask that the BWC help me in getting reimbursement for the medical bills that I have submitted and recover lost wages as appropriate. In order to do that, I am also requesting that they review the process that is used by the company and their third-party administrator and request appropriate changes to ensure reimbursement of appropriate medical bills and lost wages within a reasonable time frame with minimal difficulty.

Appendix 11

03/1999

Valley Hospital
Patient Financial Services
Address
City, State, Zip

RE: Pain Program Billings for Michael J. Werb

Dear Sir/Madam:

Thank you for your help on 03/17/1999 by telephone relative to my outstanding bills with Valley Hospital. Please consider the following status and list of actions we discussed.

Overall, I was quoted an estimate of $12,000 for the pain program. The total billings have exceeded $16,000. While I understand why there may be some difference due to added physical therapy, the remaining difference should be addressed by Valley Hospital. I am not willing to cover this significant amount in excess of the estimate.

Relative to the psychology portion of my bill, I have contacted Psychology Insurance repeatedly only to learn that their request for documentation was sitting in the records area at Valley Hospital. On 02/23/1999 I contacted the hospital's billing department as part of a regular statusing of the situation and was told there was no problem with the outstanding balance. Less than two weeks later I received a letter that my overdue balance was turned over to a debt collector! As I told you, I will pay any balance in full once I have substantiated the charges and the insurance company has had an opportunity to pay on my behalf. I received my copy of the records today. Psychology

Insurance has yet to confirm receipt of their copy. Further, a referral was not received for the psychology portion of my bill, $2,149. Ms. Simon at the pain center attempted to get the required referrals but did not succeed in this area. As a result, I may only be covered for between zero and 50 percent rather than 90 percent from Psychology Insurance. Further, the discounts related to network negotiated charges are not reflected in my billing balance.

The larger balance of $5,750 for therapy and miscellaneous charges has also been a problem. Alto Health Insurance first had trouble with the referral, which I straightened out directly. Alto Health has also not addressed billings from 09/08/1998 through 09/18/1998 claiming they have not received the billings even though, through my efforts and the hospital's efforts, multiple electronic submissions and paper copies have been submitted, along with requests for payment. Please verify multiple copies have been provided from Valley Hospital to Alto Health. I expect Valley Hospital to continue to submit copies and follow-up with Alto Health with respect to billing receipt and payment for this period of time. A check for $4,737 was indicated by Alto Health to me and the hospital to be processed 2/25/99 but has still not been received by the hospital ($1,403 was received 03/03/1999). Yesterday, I mailed a formal request for review to Alto Health and Blaster to investigate and address this matter. This formal review takes 30 to 60 days.

Your lecture to me about patient responsibility and accountability, along with Valley Hospital's "strategy of aggressive patient collections," was disappointing and not appreciated. Responsibility and accountability applies to Valley Hospital as well as to patients. I will continue my weekly and/or biweekly follow-up with the insurance companies and the hospital, but I will not be bullied into paying outstanding balances I do not understand and where the hospital has not addressed outstanding issues. Valley Hospital could also benefit by quicker response to telephone calls. The amount of time and the local long distance charges are further frustrations to the collection process.

I am disappointed Valley Hospital takes such an aggressive approach to collections. My experience as a financial controller relative to collections found greater success with an assertive and understanding partnering approach with customers. Further, the circumstances surrounding most people's lives that go through a pain program make this understanding even more important – not only relative to compassion for people faced with dramatic changes to their lives and financial situations, but relative to the emotional and financial priority we are able and willing to allocate to an "aggressive patient collections" approach.

Please forward this letter within Valley Hospital as you feel appropriate. I look forward to a comprehensive response within ten (10) days relative to the above issues and recommendations.

Sincerely,

Michael J. Werb
Address
City, State, Zip
Telephone

c: Consumer Relations
c: Psychology Insurance

Appendix 12

04/1999

Bureau of Workers' Compensation
Auditor
Self-Insured Department
Address
City, State, Zip

RE: Complaint #_____
     Filed for Claim: _____
     SSN: _____

Dear Auditor:

This letter is in response to your letter dated 03/22/1999 that I received 04/01/1999 relative to your investigation of my complaint about my workers' compensation claim. I was generally disappointed that the Bureau chose not to talk to me with regard to specific details of the complaint I filed and chose only to review the files of Blaster and the third-party administrator. I am sure their files are in order, but I suspect that many of the issues that I have identified are not detailed in their files.

In response to specifics relative to your investigation, the following is offered:

I did not receive my salary during my period of disability. This issue also relates to the required use of vacation/sick leave. I did receive full pay as part of my medical benefits with Blaster from late 02/1998 through 04/06/1998. For the period of 04/07/1998 through 05/19/1998, I only received half pay. That period of 31 days times 4 hours equals 124 hours. My hourly rate was $45.01 during that period of time, so my total lost wages were $5,581.07. Please let me know if you need to review my pay stubs for substantiation. Some portion of the lost wage was covered by use of vacation pay as required by Blaster against my wishes. I have letters and notes documenting this issue with Blaster for your review. The calculation of $5,581.07 is the lost pay in 1998. There is considerable lost pay beginning in 1999 that has not been documented.

You also indicated that I voluntarily severed my employment with Blaster on 07/30/1998. This is not correct. Under the company's Employee Termination Policy, I was involuntarily terminated. Blaster has a copy of the Employee Termination Policy and the release forms that were signed at the time. The Employee Termination Policy is fairly large and my personal release under that involuntary termination program is a multi-page document. I request that you either review that policy and document directly with Blaster or call me and we can make arrangements to get together to review these documents.

You indicated that a review of requests for treatment indicates there were several on file from Dr. Hunt and Dr. Lee requesting similar duplicate services and that these requests were denied by the employer. I was not informed of these denials. Without the denials and to attempt to resolve outstanding issues, I made numerous phone calls that I detailed as an attachment to the complaint I filed with the Bureau. Should I not be the recipient of these denials and be provided assistance by the self-insured employer to resolve the issues?

You indicated there was a C-9 Physician's Report/Treatment Plan and a C-161 from Dr. Hunt filed 07/22/1998 that did not have a written response from Blaster. Further, the physician's office indicated they received a verbal denial on 08/28/1998. You indicated this was an untimely response for Blaster that is in non-compliance with the laws and rules that govern the administration of the self-insured claim. Therefore, I do not understand your comments later in your report that says Blaster has complied with the rules for processing claims and that they have complied with the laws and rules that govern the administration of self-insurance claims. Please explain this inconsistency to me. Further, in a review of my files, I found a note from Nurse Jones given to me early in 07/1998 that prescribed a TENS unit, certain medication, and the pain program at Valley Hospital. The pain program was also the prescription of the C-9 and C-161 from Dr. Hunt filed 07/22/1998. At that time, Nurse Jones had also given me verbal approval to go ahead with that pain program.

I also found in my notes that on 08/12/1998 I talked to an individual in Dr. Hunt's office who told me that Nurse Jones told her I was processing the pain program request through my Blaster insurance company managed care health plan and that I would not be filing a pain program request through workers' compensation. The attached note from myself to Nurse Jones dated 07/29/1998, clearly states that I was going to process the request for the pain program through workers' compensation and the insurance company, and I would be sure that only one payment came from Blaster in the end. (Note: Blaster is also self-insured with the insurance company.) I believe this represents fraud on the part of Nurse Jones and Blaster in that she knowingly misrepresented my position with respect to filing a workers' compensation claim. The comment from Nurse Jones to Dr. Hunt's office obviously delayed the filing from Dr. Hunt of the appropriate paperwork for a workers' compensation benefit. Fortunately, I made a follow-up phone call with that individual to check on the status of that paperwork. In any case, the verbal denial from Blaster to the doctor's office was not received in a timely manner. Further, I personally never received a denial and proceeded with the pain program starting 08/24/1998. I also planned on reviewing the circumstances surrounding the pain program as a potential fraud item in that Nurse Jones prescribed and approved the pain program to me and at the same time informed the doctor's office that the pain program was denied.

I left a number of messages at your office to request your help with reporting fraud. In addition to the above, I believe there are other circumstances of fraud with my claim. I will assume that fraud is outside of your scope of audit and will move forward with fraud reporting unless I hear back from you within two weeks.

Later in your letter you indicated there were numerous contacts between me, Nurse Jones, and the third-party administrator during the course of this claim informing me of proper procedure in obtaining care and getting reimbursement. As you can see by the detailed notes that I attached to my complaint, the tactics used by Blaster and the third-party administrator were those of denying my claim as opposed to informing me of proper procedure in obtaining care and getting reimbursement. It appears that the files Blaster and the third-party administrator and the files I have are inconsistent. I would be interested in your conclusion with respect to that inconsistency.

You also noted that I had retained legal representation in this claim who should have provided me with information for pursuing a workers' compensation claim. Nurse Jones and my counsel were unable to work together. My legal representation warned me of Blaster "tactics." Upon my return to work in 05/1998, Blaster asked me to work directly with the company relative to any injury and workers' compensation claims, and I agreed. I told Blaster and Nurse Jones upon my return to work in 05/1998 that I no longer had legal representation, and I was going to rely completely on their help in processing the appropriate paperwork and getting the appropriate documentation for reimbursement of my claim.

Reviewing the amount of the outstanding bills and wage loss suggests that I have not been successful. It surprises me that the Bureau would find a self-insured employer in compliance when only a few hundred dollars of a claim have been paid against medical bills of $30,000 and substantial lost wages, especially when the claimant relied on the self-insured employer and worked as hard as I did to provide the documentation and paperwork. This is probably a policy issue I will need to address to the Administrator of Workers' Compensation.

Please note I have once again retained legal counsel because obviously I was not getting the support that I needed from Blaster or the third-party administrator in order to understand and appropriately process my claim. I have retained Attorney Cliff to help me with my claim. I believe it is unfortunate that injured employees must turn to legal counsel in order to understand and have their workers' compensation benefits explained and claims processed appropriately.

I look forward to your response to the above comments and I appreciate your help in this matter.

Sincerely,

Michael J. Werb
Address
City, State, Zip
Telephone
Enclosure

c: Attorney Cliff

Appendix 13

04/1999

Bureau of Workers' Compensation
Fraud Investigation
Address
City, State, Zip

Dear Sir/Madam:

Thank you for your help last Friday relative to reporting fraud to the Bureau of Workers' Compensation (BWC) for investigation. I have attached the documentation you requested and a couple other items I found during a review of my files. Please note that I have additional documentation and contemporaneous records of conversations I had with people at Blaster and their third-party administrator.

Attachment 1 is the notes I referred to in our conversation. We talked about the pain program and the investigation by the BWC auditor as two areas where fraud has occurred. I have noted a third area of "numerous documented deny tactics" as detailed in the attachment to the complaint I filed with the BWC 10/1998 (attachment 5).

With respect to the pain program, attachment 2 is the note I received from Blaster via Ms. Jones, the company nurse, to proceed with the pain program. Attachment 3 is the note I sent to Nurse Jones indicating I was going to process the pain program bills through workers' compensation insurance. This note documents that she was working with my doctor, Dr. Hunt, to get the appropriate forms for coverage through workers' compensation. Attachment 4 is another note dated 07/17/1998 addressed "To Whom It May Concern, c/o Nurse Jones," where I noted my doctor had prescribed a pain management program for my injury and that Nurse Jones is acquiring the information and forms needed for Blaster and workers' compensation insurance relative to this pain management program. The purpose of this letter was to provide documentation and understanding with respect to my physician of record. I also noted in this letter as a reminder to Nurse Jones that she had agreed to get the information and forms needed for Blaster and workers' compensation insurance relative to the pain management program. You and I discussed the 08/12/1998 note on attachment 3 that I talked to Angie at Dr. Hunt's office. Angie indicated to me that Nurse Jones had told her I was not processing the pain program through workers' compensation. This is where I believe the fraud occurred in that not only had Blaster prescribed the pain program and agreed to work directly with my doctor to process the appropriate paperwork for coverage under workers' compensation insurance, but Blaster (Nurse Jones) then told my doctor not to process the BWC paperwork. I attended the pain program and incurred the $16,000 in medical bills, and now the company is denying responsibility for these bills under workers' compensation.

The second area of fraud relates to the audit by the BWC relative to the complaint I filed in 10/1998, attachment 5. Attachment 6 is the appeal I filed 04/05/1999 with respect to complaint 8301 and the BWC auditor's findings. In the appeal I noted calculation of lost wages. Apparently Blaster told the auditor I had no lost wages. Attachment 7 is a copy of my pay stubs for that period of time that show the lost wages. Later I was paid vacation as the company insisted I use up my vacation pay to off set the lost wages during that period of time.

The appeal also covers the issue of my involuntary termination from the company at the end of 07/1998. Attachment 8 is the personnel announcement where my supervisor indicated I was relieved of my responsibility due to a medical condition that detrimentally affected my ability to do my job. As I mentioned in the BWC appeal, I was involuntarily terminated per the Blaster Employee Termination Policy. The Employee Termination Policy is fairly large. It can be reviewed at Blaster or I have a copy for your review.

You were also interested in Blaster's position with respect to providing me with alternative work at the company. I have attached a letter from Blaster to me dated 04/10/1998 from Mr. Seabert, the Director of Human Resources at Blaster, attachment 9. In the third paragraph, he indicates there are presently no other jobs available which fit my qualifications. Further, he says if you return to the controller position you will be expected to fulfill all the normal duties of that position. Please note in this letter from Mr. Seabert that he references a report from Dr. Blunder which concluded I did not have an impairment and could return to work. I provided the company with a marked up copy of the Dr. Blunder independent evaluation which showed there were over 30 errors, omissions, and misstatements in the doctor's evaluation all directed to support the conclusion to return to work (attachment 10). I told Blaster that this grossly inaccurate IME should not be used to determine my fitness to return to work. In fact, one week before this IME on 02/18/1998, my doctor had placed me on an eight-month medical leave. The IME was performed 02/24/1998. I was subsequently completely out of work for over eight months (I returned to work limited to part time in 02/1999). I later filed a complaint with the State Medical Review Board with concern over this grossly inaccurate independent medical evaluation from Dr. Blunder, as well as the company doctor's concurrence with Dr. Blunder even though at that point in time I never even met the company doctor.

You and I also discussed a conversation I had with my supervisor, Mr. Blair, about me working with an attorney to get help with workers' compensation. This conversation also covered a request I made to return to work part time earlier in the year. My notes indicate that conversation took place in a meeting 06/26/1998. A letter dated 06/24/1998 from Mr. Seabert said that neither Mr. Blair nor he recalled any conversations in which I offered to return to work part time and was flatly turned down. I asked my supervisor about this statement and indicated that I had notes covering the related conversation Mr. Blair and I had on 04/15/1998, as well as a similar conversation I had with Mr. Seabert on 04/09/1998. In our meeting of 06/26/1998, Mr. Blair remembered we had that conversation and that he had said no to me returning to work part time since he could not manage the process, he needed a full-time controller, etc. His position was that I return to work "all or nothing" as the controller. Later in that conversation Mr. Blair indicated I should work with the company directly, continue with the company doctor visits, and there shouldn't be a need for additional outside doctors, attorneys were not necessary, the company would help me through this process, etc. I indicated to Mr. Blair that I no longer had legal counsel and that I would work and was working directly with Nurse Jones for processing of bills and payment under workers' compensation insurance. I had earlier explained to Nurse Jones my need for the company's help with BWC administration as I no longer had legal help. When I returned to work 05/20/1998, I went to the medical office daily and frequently requested help from Nurse Jones with respect to my medical bills and BWC requirements and processing. You can see in the attachment 5 detail that I had worked very hard to understand the BWC paperwork and satisfy the requirements for reimbursement of medical bills and lost wages. I was not successful. The company has reimbursed only a few hundred dollars of $30,000 of medical bills and no reimbursement of lost wages.

I look forward to your conclusions with regard to your investigation.

Sincerely,

Michael J. Werb
Address
City, State, Zip
Telephone

Appendix 14

06/1999

Ms. Cathy Bronson
Country Garden Insurance Company
Address
City, State, Zip

Dear Cathy:

FYI, I have attached a copy of the fraud report I filed with the Ohio Bureau of Workers' Compensation (BWC). Attached to the report is documentation of tactics and fraud used by Blaster to deny my workers' compensation benefits.

I was disappointed but not surprised that Blaster lied again by saying to you that I have not filed a BWC claim. My BWC claim number is 55-555555. Please contact the Ohio BWC for claim verification. Please send me a copy of the letter you received from Blaster stating that I have not filed a claim.

I hope Country Garden is not going to stand behind the Blaster tactics and fraud to deny my claim for PIP no-fault benefits.

Further, note the extent of my wage loss and medical bills even if workers' compensation benefits had been paid.

(1)   Wage loss:
        Salary was: $7,800/month (excludes 17% bonus & benefits)
        Current salary: 1,000/month
        S/T lost wage: 6,800
        WC should
          pay (max):   2,100

S/T lost wage
  w/o BWC: 4,700
PIP @ 85%: $3,995 subject to max $500/week

Country Garden should pay lost wage of $500/week starting 08/01/1998.

(2)   Medical benefits: Workers' compensation is supposed to pay 70% of medical bills. Further, the BWC limits massage therapy to $1,030. My health insurance paid most bills (excluding massage therapy) at 90%. The 06/02/1999 summary I sent you for $5,719 was primarily deductibles and massage therapy, both exceeding the BWC guidelines. Country Garden should pay the $5,719 plus mileage of $1,232 (as noted on the individual medical bill sheets of $1,066 plus mileage for local doctor visits – 34 trips x 15 miles x .325 = $166). BWC does not pay mileage expense to and from medical providers.

Country Garden should pay $6,951 for medical bills to date.

Please process the above payments. Please also send me a full copy of my insurance policy in effect 04/30/1997. This is my third request to Country Garden for a copy of my policy.

I have hired a lawyer to help me with my BWC claim. I would appreciate any help possible from you and Country Garden Insurance Company relative to my PIP claim and the BWC claim issues. Thank you.

Sincerely,

Michael J. Werb
Address
City, State Zip
Telephone
Enclosures

Appendix 15

To: Attorney Landis
      c: Attorney Law
From: Mike Werb
Date: 03/01/2000

PREPARE FOR COUNSEL

Thanks for meeting with me yesterday. After reviewing the files provided by Blaster for discovery, I realized there was a lot of information not provided by Blaster. This oversight may be their desire to cast my unemployment as a choice and minimize my injury. They have asserted in my workers' compensation case that my departure from Blaster was a mutual decision and they could try to do the same for the personal injury case. The notes and letters show I agreed I could no longer do my job but tried hard to stay at the company. Further, Blaster obviously does not want this information to be made public. Please call me to discuss demanding this information from Blaster.

I also look forward to seeing a vocational rehab specialist to evaluate my employability when appropriate. The travel to Ohio is painful for my back, but important for my future.

The missing notes and memos to support my involuntary termination include meeting frequently with Mr. Blair (my supervisor and General Manager) and Mr. Seabert (Director of Human Resources) after the accident to explain my injury, medical care, and work impact. In addition to the following formal letters, they have notes (I have some too) of the more significant meetings. Some of their notes may be in their "day planners."

In 09/1997, I filed a workers' compensation claim form and met with Messrs. Seabert and Blair to discuss how the impairment was greater than the doctors thought, i.e., I was one of 10-20% of people with this type of injury who do not heal in a few months.

During the fall of 1997, Justine and I had Mr. Blair and his wife to our house for dinner. I explained the injury, pain, impact on me and my work, and the many medications I was trying and their effect on my business intuitiveness and motivation.

Even with slowing down at work, a week's vacation in 10/1997, November and December holidays, and vacation, the pain was worse. In 01/1998, I told Mr. Blair that I could not do FL and CA back-to-back business trips because of my injury, and I requested a lesser job in a warmer climate, if possible. We met with Mr. Seabert to discuss my injury and alternative employment.

In my 01/1998 performance review, Mr. Blair noted performance issues in the last half of the year (after the accident). I provided an attachment to my review to further detail the impact of the impairment on my work, as well as my job change request.

Mr. Seabert checked with Blaster Corporate headquarters and other divisions to request a different job for me. All replied that my injury was too risky to employ me or that no positions were available.

In 02/1998, when my medical leave from Dr. Lee started, I had to meet with Messrs. Blair and Seabert. They took many notes at this meeting.

The 03/1998 letter from Mr. Seabert explained medical leave benefits and FMLA. I called and asked to return to work part time as the leave and therapy helped me some. One week later, another letter removed all benefits because of the Dr. Blunder IME.

FYI, I caught Messrs. Blair and Seabert in a lie over my return to work request. Mr. Blair confessed but Mr. Seabert held firm.

In 03/1998, I had lunch with Mr. Blair about my medical leave, recovery, and return to work.

I wrote a letter dated 04/15/1998 to agree to another IME for a return to work decision and to explain my desire to return to work ASAP.

On 05/20/1998, I returned to work and met with Mr. Blair. He told me they would be watching my performance. I met with the company nurse and company doctor regularly. I reviewed a daily log with them of my pain, medication, activities, therapy, etc. The nurse wrote a note dated 07/15/1998 saying I took two pain pills that day and complained. In my daily log for early July, I was taking 4 or 5 Tylenol No. 3 and 4 or 5 Soma, together with alcohol, many days to handle the pain. In mid July, I was up to five or six of each. The nurse's notes minimized my situation. I could not read the doctor's notes in the file from Blaster. The company doctor eventually suggested I return to Dr. Hunt, who prescribed a pain program.

In June and July 1998, Mr. Seabert and I exchanged letters and had discussions about a potential ethics violation. Ted Sloan (Blaster Corporate) performed a review of my formal ethics report to Corporate. The ethics violation covers the Blunder IME, cut off of benefits, no special chair, spying at my home, doctor review promises, etc.

On 07/06/1998, I wrote a letter documenting the discussion I had with Mr. Blair about my job and my inability to meet its requirements, including that I needed more than the limitations imposed by the second IME. Mr. Blair and I talked about alternatives for attending the pain program, including medical leave benefits from Blaster (my desire) or severance (Blair's preference).

On 07/27-28/1998, I met with Messrs. Blair and Seabert at their request. I was told by Mr. Seabert that I was "involuntarily terminated." I had no choice. My stated preference all along was a lesser position at Blaster and/or employee medical leave benefits to allow me to heal.

In 07/1998, Messrs. Blair and Seabert must have worked with Blaster Corporate to involuntarily terminate my employment per the

Employee Termination Benefits Policy that says, "The plan provides (some) continuation of pay and benefits if you are involuntarily terminated without cause." The Employee Termination Benefits Policy is referenced in my severance agreement.

An 08/06/1998 announcement posted at Blaster from Mr. Blair: "Due to a medical condition which has detrimentally affected his ability to execute his job duties, Mike Werb and I have mutually agreed that he should be relieved of his current responsibilities." I agreed I could not do my job, and Blaster decided I should leave the company – involuntarily terminated.

Appendix 16

Michael J. Werb
Address
City, State, Zip
Telephone
Email address

04/26/2000

Ms. Cheryl Simpson
Country Garden Insurance Company
Address
City, State, Zip

Dear Ms. Simpson:

Enclosed is my promise of reimbursement to Country Garden Insurance that you requested for medical bills paid by workers' compensation.

As an alternative to the current approach where I first struggle with Blaster for reimbursement of my medical bills through workers' compensation then ask for reimbursement from Country Garden, I hereby request that Country Garden take over my claim for medical bills in its entirety. I propose I turn over my rights to workers' compensation medical bills to Country Garden for subsequent collection from Blaster. This approach is used in other insurance situations where the insured is reimbursed first, then Country Garden pursues recovery from other responsible or liable parties. Why not here? Country Garden has more resources and clout than I do to recover from a large company like Blaster.

I am also requesting that Country Garden reimburse Alto Health Insurance, my employee health plan, $14,492 for medical bills related to the car accident on 04/30/1997. I understand this is appropriate according to Minnesota law. You have the detailed billing information that I provided you 03/03/2000. If you would like to discuss this, please provide me with a copy of the Minnesota Statute that indicates workers' compensation is primary to automobile insurance whereas automobile insurance is primary to my employee health plan (Alto). Also provide me with the no-fault policy sections that cover the handling of claims with multiple sources of insurance benefits. You understand that I only want to be reimbursed once, but I definitely do want to be reimbursed for the medical bills related to a car accident where I was a passenger three years ago. Multiple insurance sources should not be an excuse to deny insurance coverage.

As you consider this request, please note the attached guarantee of reimbursement and other facts Country Garden has, including my many unsuccessful attempts at reimbursement from Blaster's workers' compensation over the last three years, even with the help of lawyers. I have also filed complaints and reported fraud to the Ohio Bureau of Workers' Compensation (BWC) relative to my workers' compensation claim and Blaster. And I have foregone medical care because I cannot afford it even though I have $40,000 of no-fault insurance coverage for the medical bills related to the car accident. Country Garden has obviously benefited from the denied workers' compensation benefits even though a large portion of my medical bills exceed the workers' compensation guidelines and should be covered immediately by no-fault insurance.

While you consider this request, I ask for immediate reimbursement of medical bills per Attachment I. I have discussed my workers' compensation claim with my workers' compensation lawyer in Ohio and another lawyer in Minnesota. I have also discussed my claim with Ellen Heart, J.D., with the Minnesota Department of Labor and Industry. The Ohio workers' compensation guidelines you requested are enclosed, along with the corresponding Minnesota guidelines

(Attachments II and III). With this background, I ask Country Garden to consider the physical therapy, massage therapy, acupuncture, and psychology bills per Attachment I for immediate reimbursement under no-fault insurance. Please also consider the pain program bills for payment that are included with the medical bills submitted to you on 03/03/2000.

Note further that Blaster has only paid some doctor bills and prescription co-pays to date (less than $1,000 of $25,000 in medical bills), with the remaining medical bills denied primarily because no pre-approvals were obtained. Blaster has never granted pre-approvals and probably never will. Physical therapy, massage therapy, acupuncture, and psychology all require pre-approvals. Further, my claim is three years old and because of delays, it was not recognized by the BWC until 04/02/1998. This initial one-year delay alone made it impossible to obtain benefits that required pre-approvals for the first eleven months after the accident. Nevertheless, if there is any subsequent reimbursement, Country Garden is protected by the attached promise of reimbursement.

It is inappropriate to use Ohio guidelines (Attachment III) as a reasonableness test for an insurance policy obtained in Minnesota and covered by Minnesota law. My Minnesota car insurance premiums and coverage were greater than in a comparable Ohio policy. The medical expenses on Attachment I are within the Minnesota workers' compensation guidelines (Attachment II). Further, significant differences between the Minnesota and Ohio workers' compensation guidelines have to do with pre-approvals required and the daily time allowed for massage therapy (MT). Minnesota requires no pre-approvals for the initial treatment duration, while Ohio requires pre-approval from the start for most medical care beyond the physician of record visits. Ohio also limits MT to two units, or $51.52 per day, whereas there are no limits to the number of units per day in Minnesota. FYI, at the time I had the MT, I consulted with my doctor and massage therapist about my work schedule, other medical treatment, and other commitments relative to the number of MT sessions I would take each week. They agreed that I should take MT once per week for 1½ hours rather than the massage therapist's initial suggestion of twice per week at one hour each. Note the overall MT expense and mileage savings by going for one session of 1½ hours rather than 2 sessions per week. Certainly reasonable overall, nonetheless, I will accept payment for MT reduced by the $1,030.40 Blaster and the BWC guidelines suggest as the limit for the life of the claim.

The total reimbursement for medical bills I am requesting at this time is $4,024.99 per Attachment I. This amount compares to almost $7,000 that I have paid out of my own pocket to date. The difference relates primarily to pain program expenses that I paid, which are included with the medical bills submitted to you on 03/03/2000.

I also ask Country Garden to propose a process for medical care and reimbursement under my no-fault insurance for the future. At a minimum, I request direct reimbursement of doctor referrals and tests, along with massage therapy, without first submitting to Blaster since this medical care requires pre-approval and/or is subject to limits already exceeded. If Country Garden assumed my claim in its entirety as proposed above, then the process for the future is not an issue as the expenses will be reimbursed by Country Garden up to my policy limits.

I look forward to your response, including alternatives to the above suggestions, to provide me the medical care and benefits I need under my Country Garden no-fault insurance policy.

Thank you for your help.

Sincerely,

Michael J. Werb
Attachment

04/14/2000

Country Garden Insurance Company
Attn: Cheryl Simpson
Address
City, State, Zip

RE: Workers' Compensation Insurance
      Country Garden Claims Numbers: 33-333-33 and 44-444-44
      Date of Loss: 04/30/1997

Dear Ms. Simpson:

As we discussed, if I am reimbursed for medical bills under workers' compensation that have already been paid by my Country Garden no-fault insurance, I agree to reimburse Country Garden Insurance Company for these items.

Sincerely,

Michael J. Werb   Attorney Law
Address   Address
City, State, Zip   City, State, Zip

Appendix 17

Review of Blaster Workers' Compensation Summary
Claimant: Michael Werb
Claim #55-555555
DOI: 04/30/1997

Questions and Comments:
Att. A (p. 1-17) Note:

1. Need Blaster comment for $162 (p. 1) and $15, $1.72, $23 (p. 2) denied – why?

2. P. 1, 2, 11, 15, 16, 17 total $618.79 denied for "not received prior to attachment to SI-28." Please explain what this means.

3. P. 2, 3, 4, 5, 6, 7, 8, 9, 13 "denied: not attending physician" for Lee, D.O. These charges are for physical therapy (Att 3a) – please process per guidelines, total $2,828.

    P. 16 "denied: lacking office notes." Dr. Hunt's office forwarded the office notes to Nurse Jones on 04/07/2000, total $1,932, for the physical therapy he ordered (Att 3b).

4. P. 9, 10, 11 has massage therapy "denied no prior authorization" – see Dr. Hunt authorization and process total $2,501.70.

    P. 13, 14 has massage therapy mislabeled as pharmacy reimbursement that was "denied no prior authorization" – see Dr. Hunt authorization and process. Total $510.

5. P. 16 Stoutle Hospital – x-rays, imaging $163, $134, $668 – on 03/29/2000, I requested Stoutle Hospital send the office notes directly to Nurse Jones.

6. P. 10, 14, 15, 16 is the doctor visits "denied lacking office notes." The notes and complete billings were sent by the doctor's office directly to Nurse Jones on 04/07/2000 for Dr. Hunt and on 04/06/1999 for Dr. Smith. Dr. Master's notes and billings are included as Att 6.

7. The summary does not include the pain program attended at Valley Hospital (VH) in 1998. I asked the hospital in 08/1998 and 06/1999 to send all bills to Blaster. On 06/21/1999, I sent a letter to Nurse Jones to process the VH bills. On 03/03/2000 and 03/17/2000, I again asked VH to verify that the bills totaling $14,420 were sent to Blaster, c/o Nurse Jones. Attached are the separate bills for Dr. Demeral for the pain program (Att 7a). Also attached are bills for acupuncture prescribed by Dr. Hunt for $356 (Att 7b). Please process per guidelines.

8. Mileage should be reconsidered, most denied because less than 51 miles – where is this constraint in the guidelines?

Appendix 18

Work Restrictions and Daily Pain Management Program
(10/2000 with Dr. Bell and Dr. Norton)

Work Restrictions
- Work time, responsibilities and environment must fit within daily pain management program
- Maximum 2 hours of work in low stress environment with minimal responsibilities and stress:

    Physical stress – ergonomic work environment, good body mechanics (squat, no bending, minimal lifting), regular breaks, 15-20 min to move around, alternate sit, stand, walking, and use of heating paid with high/flat back chair always available.

    Mental stress – relatively simple problems/assignments that are self-paced with minimal responsibilities, conflict, aggressive behavior, public speaking and/or deadlines

    Emotional stress – flexible, supportive, positive workplace that allows pain management and missing 3 or more days per month as needed

    Environmental stress – warm and quiet with pain management tools available

- Driving to and from work, medical care and other personal activities must be considered as work within the above restrictions

Daily Pain Management Program

7-8 a.m.	Stretching (S) of back, shoulder blades, neck; slow preparation for day; breakfast; take meds
8 a.m.	Tailored strengthening exercises; 15-30 min fast walk as pain permits
9 a.m.	30-min relax w/heating pad
9:30 a.m.	S; relax while prepare work site and plan activities
10-11 a.m.	Low-stress computer work; teaching; reading–S every 15-20 min; walk around or stand as needed
11 a.m.	30-min relax w/heating pad

11:30 a.m.	Lunch preparation; slow unwind walking around or standing
Noon	Lunch
12:30 p.m.	45-min meditation w/15-min to prep & conclude
1:30 p.m.	S; relax with heating pad, prepare work site and plan activities
2-3 p.m.	Low-stress computer work; teaching; reading-S every 15-20 min; walk around or stand as needed
3 p.m.	Spine stretch exercises on floor; S
3:30 p.m.	30-min relax w/heating pad
4 p.m.	S; 15-30 min walk as pain permits
4:30 p.m.	45-min meditation w/15-min to prep & conclude; muscle relaxer meds as needed
5:30 p.m.	Dinner preparation; slow unwind walking around or standing
6 p.m.	Dinner
6:30 p.m.	Heating pad; relax; meds
7-9:30 p.m.	S; sedentary, slow movements; off and on heating pad, muscle relaxer meds as needed
9:30 p.m.	S; bedtime; apply topical analgesics; light massage
Nighttime	S every 2-3 hours and apply heat as needed, add muscle relaxer if needed

The above represents good or normal days. On bad days (2-3 days every other week):

Alternate bed rest, sitting, lying, walking, standing as needed; add medication as needed

Continue stretching and meditation only, along with sedentary behavior, and stop all activities including strengthening exercises, walks, driving, work, etc.

Working more than 2 hours/day or without other restrictions increases the frequency of bad days and days off work

—————————————————
Doctor's Approval   Date

Appendix 19

Michael J. Werb
Address
City, State, Zip
Telephone
Email address

11/21/2000

Ms. Cheryl Simpson
Ms. Ann House
Country Garden Insurance Company
Address
City, State, Zip

Dear Ms. Simpson and Ms. House:

Here are additional expenses for reimbursement, along with the mileage log you requested.

Please also consider this letter a formal request for Country Garden's (CG) reimbursement of Alto for bills they paid related to the 04/30/1997 car accident as covered by my no-fault insurance policy with Country Garden. The bills Alto paid of $14.492 (excluding prescriptions not identified) are detailed in the letter from me to CG dated 03/03/2000.

Further, in the 03/03/2000 letter, I provided support and explanation of some of the Ohio Bureau of Workers' Compensation (BWC) guidelines. As noted, most medical expenses are subject to the self-insured's (Blaster) approval. Blaster has never approved any expense under this provision either for no reason or by saying the expense was not supported or some other excuse. In March and April of this year, I addressed all outstanding concerns that Blaster had with my claim yet received no additional reimbursements or clarification from the company or their third-party administrator for workers' compensation. Recently, my attorney suggested that recovery of outstanding medical bills is unlikely given these paperwork issues (real or contrived).

Blaster has also used fraud and other tactics as I reported to the State BWC and copied to CG. As we have discussed, I hope CG will not use Blaster's fraud and tactics as an excuse for not paying my medical bills. These bills were incurred as a result of medical care prescribed by my treating physicians at the time.

Now Ms. House indicated that CG will only pay medical expenses not statutorily covered by workers' compensation since workers' compensation is primary in Minnesota. Please send me a copy of the language in my insurance policy that indicates this is an appropriate position for CG to take. Please do not ignore my request for policy provisions as you have in the past.

In response to this argument, if Blaster does not provide pre-approvals of medical expenses, then the item is not covered (or directed) statutorily by the Ohio BWC and should be paid by CG. I have given you the website and phone number of the Ohio BWC guidelines and ask again that CG research these issues and pay the medical bills outstanding, including Alto and all of the recent medical bills submitted but not approved or paid by Blaster.

Upon reflection, I am disappointed with CG relative to the above and,

- CG lied to me in Ohio by saying I had no coverage
- my repeated request for written policy support from CG for your position were followed by long delays and some requests were ignored
- there was a long CG Minnesota/Ohio delay over which CG office was responsible

- CG required permission from my attorneys to work with me (the insured)
- there were many long reviews by CG attorneys
- CG demanded a legally certified promise of reimbursement if workers' compensation pays, yet CG also argued to not reimburse work-related expenses with even the remote possibility of being paid twice
- CG repeatedly changed the documentation requirements for reimbursement
- CG reneged on agreements over which expenses would be reimbursed
- CG changed personnel who were handling my claim without a reasonable transition
- CG demands a direct request from Alto for reimbursement of bills for the accident when I am the insured
- at the same time, CG refuses to work directly with Blaster on my workers' compensation requests.

Indeed, I understand CG's need for business processes to ensure that only appropriate covered claims are reimbursement. Unfortunately, the myopic, risk-free reimbursement process CG has taken with me suggests that CG is managing and even benefiting from these processes and tactics. Further, these processes result in their injured insured carrying these expenses while also delaying or not receiving much-needed medical treatment. Please consider changing the CG processes to provide for timely reimbursement to your insureds. There must be a way for CG to manage reimbursement risks for claims similar to your ability to manage customer risks related to promptly signing up new customers and insurance policies.

CG, with its talented cadre of lawyers and staff, could also support the injured's recovery of workers' compensation benefits rather than increasing its insured's suffering as a result of the added effort of asking for insurance benefits while delaying much-needed medical care. Helping your insured would financially make sense since workers' compensation would pay more and CG would pay less. Partnering could also include the insured and CG discussing providers and other cost reduction alternatives for medical care. Supporting your insured is the right thing to do for your business and the injured insured.

The above represents my thoughts and concerns over my insurance coverage that probably affects others injured and insured by CG. I ask that you reply to the above directly to me via mail or through my website, www.heywer.com, which was designed in part to support people with chronic illness who are adversely affected by insurance issues similar to mine.

Sincerely,

Michael J. Werb
Enclosures

Appendix 20

Michael J. Werb
HEYWER LLC
Address
City, State, Zip
Telephone
Email address

01/16/2001

Ms. Ann House
Ms. Cheryl Simpson
Country Garden Insurance
Address
City, State, Zip

Dear Ms. House and Ms. Simpson:

Thank you for your letters dated 12/04/2000 and 12/08/2000 in response to my letter of 11/21/2000. I would like to thank Country Garden Insurance (CG) for continuing to address my no-fault insurance concerns related to my injury from a car accident on 04/30/1997, almost four years ago when I was a passenger and your insured. In my 11/21/2000 letter, I identified significant concerns with my claim for insurance benefits from CG and asked that CG consider changes to their business practices in order to help me and other insureds by partnering with us to resolve outstanding issues. Even though my concerns with CG's business practices include potential fraud and other deny/delay tactics that you have not addressed, you replied that if I continue to disagree with CG, my "remedies in Minnesota are mandatory arbitration or district court." Before I consider these options or other alternatives with respect to my injury and permanent disability from the car accident, I ask that CG reply directly to me as your insured and customer for many years with regard to the following areas of concern. While I apologize for the length of this letter, I hope to have captured the essence of CG's unreasonable and inappropriate excuses for denying benefits that suggests CG has little or no interest in paying the benefits promised in the insurance policy I had contracted with CG for years. These concerns include looking at the facts ... potential fraud and other delay/deny tactics, inappropriate policy language you referenced for my claim, insurance laws of Ohio apply to my claim, a reasonable interpretation of Minnesota statute, my satisfaction of all the requirements for no-fault insurance, recovery of workers' compensation insurance benefits has been exhausted, the arbitration and court cases you sent to me do not apply, looking beyond questions of contracts and law at other issues of a more personal and heartfelt consideration, and benefits of partnering that can accrue to CG as well as the insured. Please seriously consider these concerns and recommendations not only for me, but more importantly, for so many other people who are unable to ask the questions and/or request satisfaction from their insurance providers for the benefits they were promised in the policies they purchased.

After careful consideration of your comment that CG has been fair and reasonable with my claim under no-fault insurance, please look at the facts and reconsider this conclusion. Since the car accident happened in Ohio and was work related, the insurance issues were somewhat more challenging but should not have been an excuse for denying and delaying benefits as much as CG has for my claim. Nonetheless, CG engaged in potential fraud and other delay/deny tactics when the company lied to me when I first asked about benefits, reneged on promises you made about benefit payments, changed documentation requirements, inappropriately demanded workers' compensation insurance pay instead of CG, and used other tactics listed in my 11/21/2000 letter to you. With almost $30,000 of medical bills alone, workers' compensation insurance through my former employer (Blaster) has paid only $1,000, while CG, under my no-fault insurance policy, has paid only $5,200 for medical bills that have been outstanding for several years related to a car accident and injury from almost four years ago. Further, CG took almost two years to pay wage loss benefits from the time that I notified my agent in Ohio of my loss, and she told me that I had no benefits due from CG. Then I had to repeatedly argue with CG for benefits until I was paid some benefits months and years later. Now CG demands litigation to resolve outstanding claims even though issues still exist over my policy contract and statutory law, along with other concerns that you have not adequately addressed or responded to at all.

Thank you for finally sending me a copy of my no-fault insurance policy. Upon review, I do not agree with your conclusion about the policy language you referenced for my claim for benefits to pay medical bills. The section in the policy you highlighted reads "income loss or survivor loss ... coverage is excess over other benefits paid or payable under a workers' compensation law." This policy provision you highlighted has to do with "income loss or survivor loss," not medical expenses. The policy is silent relative to medical bills and workers' compensation laws. Further, the appropriate statutory law explained below does not support your assertion about workers' compensation insurance. I am disappointed that you inappropriately referenced this contract language and position in your letter to Alto about their subrogation for $14,400 of medical bills that they paid related to my injury from the car accident. Please revise your letter to Alto clarifying this point ASAP. I have also asked CG repeatedly for a copy of the umbrella policy I purchased from CG that was in effect at the time of the accident. Please send this to me ASAP.

When I reviewed my situation and insurance claims with attorneys in both Ohio and Minnesota relative to workers' compensation insurance being primary, I did not get the same opinion that CG has been giving to me. At the time of the accident, I was in the process of moving from Minnesota to Ohio. Although my CG automobile insurance policy that was in effect on the day of the accident was purchased in Minnesota, because the car accident that caused my injury occurred in Ohio, the insurance laws of Ohio apply to my claims. Ohio law does not identify workers' compensation benefits as primary to automobile insurance economic loss (no-fault) benefits. Further, Ohio law states, "No insurance company issuing a policy of automobile or motor vehicle liability insurance shall be relieved of its contractual obligation to defend its insured against any claim on the basis of coverage for such claim being provided by any other policy ..." Further, per Ohio law, "Any disputes between insurers regarding the obligation to defend shall be settled without expense to the insured by agreement between the insurers involved ..." Therefore, under Ohio law, CG must pay my claim and pursue any recovery with workers' compensation insurance as CG deems appropriate. This has been my request to CG all along. In your 12/04/2000 letter and other correspondence, CG repeatedly indicates that workers' compensation "benefits are primary to basic economic loss benefits under the no-fault act," and CG also demands that I pursue my claim against workers' compensation insurance. CG demanding that I pursue workers' compensation benefits instead of no-fault benefits is clearly contrary to Ohio law. Demanding that I litigate or arbitrate with CG to settle my claim is asking me to incur expense, which again is a violation of Ohio law by CG. Your frequent declaration to me that workers' compensation insurance is primary in Minnesota and Ohio is incorrect. The above two paragraphs disprove your assertion that "[your] handling of [my] claim is consistent with the language in the policy contract [I] signed as well as the laws and statutes in both Minnesota and Ohio." You must know this with all the lengthy legal reviews CG has conducted with my claim over the last few years.

Even if Minnesota law applied to my situation, the appropriate reasonable interpretation of the Minnesota statute with respect to primary insurance is that once the medical bills are denied by workers' compensation, CG should pay all reasonable and necessary medical expenses under my no-fault insurance. Minnesota statutes do not say that the workers' compensation claim must be pursued through formal hearings and litigation before payment will be made by no-fault insurance, as you are demanding. No-fault benefits should be paid once a denial from workers' compensation insurance has been received subject, of course, to repayment of duplicate benefit payments should any occur with workers' compensation insurance. In your letter of 12/08/2000, you indicated that you are in receipt of medical bills from Medical Pain Specialty (MPS) for service dates 06/15, 06/28, 07/26 and 10/24/2000, and attached to these bills was a copy of an explanation of review from the third-party administrator for those dates that says no allowance has been recommended for these charges under workers' compensation insurance. At your request, Blaster's third-party administrator denied payment for these charges; therefore, my CG no-fault insurance should have immediately paid these bills since they were denied for payment. Yet you did not pay benefits, thereby reneging on another approach to my CG claim that I thought we had agreed to where you pay no-fault benefits and are later reimbursed for any duplicate payments from workers' compensation insurance. You even asked me to provide CG a formal legal promise of reimbursement for any benefits paid by CG that are later recovered under workers' compensation insurance. As a result of this request, I met with my attorney in Ohio and had him sign the promise as was earlier drafted by CG and me together. Yet now you will not pay no-fault benefits until I litigate workers' compensation insurance and/or no-fault insurance with CG. Why did you have me go through so much effort and expense to obtain a formal promise of reimbursement for CG? Ms. Simpson forwarded a copy of the MPS medical bills and the third-party administrator denial at my request by telephone. In the future, please forward a copy of all medical bills and workers' compensation insurance correspondence to me as I have repeatedly requested.

Even though the insurance process was onerous, my doctors or I, as appropriate, have assertively completed all forms and requirements, usually more than once, to satisfy all of the requirements for workers' compensation insurance and/or no-fault insurance. Further, I have only asked for reimbursement of medical care formally prescribed by reputable doctors, including doctors in my former employer's (Blaster's) health care plan through Alto while I lived in Ohio and once I returned to Minnesota (in 12/1999) by Dr. Bell or doctors

300

referred by Dr. Bell who are experts with my type of injury. My experience as a former business financial executive, contracts expert, and now part-time business professor has also ensured propriety for the benefits that I have requested as an insured.

Even if I consider CG's restrictive interpretation of my no-fault insurance benefits, the facts in my situation further indicate that recovery of workers' compensation insurance benefits has been exhausted. All of my medical bills have been submitted and disapproved by Blaster's workers' compensation administrator primarily due to the lack of pre-approvals or missing paperwork tactics. All paperwork needs have been met more than once, including Attachment I, where a comprehensive effort early last year accomplished all the paperwork requirements once again, yet no additional payments were made by Blaster's workers' compensation insurance. Further, as I have indicated to you previously, the requirement for pre-approvals is much greater within Ohio workers' compensation guidelines as compared to those in Minnesota. Blaster is self-insured for workers' compensation and has never given me a pre-approval directly or through their third-party administrator. The company uses this reason for denial in almost every situation. Consider last year, 2000, as an example. I held off medical care with Dr. Sun for more than six months and with (MPS) as long as possible while awaiting pre-approvals from Blaster. The pre-approvals did not come. Instead, Blaster formally rejected the medical care since it was not pre-approved even though requested months earlier. I had no choice but to accept the medical care and turn to my no-fault insurance for reimbursement. As we have discussed, medical care for work injuries in Ohio is not as clearly "intended for employers to be responsible" as you told me it is in Minnesota especially where an automobile accident is the cause of the injuries. Please review the Ohio and Minnesota BWC guidelines more carefully, including those I referenced in my earlier letters to CG.

My workers' compensation lawyer has indicated that recovery of my outstanding medical bills through Blaster's workers' compensation insurance is unlikely without the pre-approvals and given the paperwork issues, including potential fraud and other tactics that I formally reported about Blaster. The fraud report I filed with the Ohio authorities was provided to CG at your request, along with my comment that "I hope Country Garden will not use Blaster's tactics as an excuse for not paying my medical bills under my no-fault policy." Upon reflection, it appears you are doing exactly that, exacerbated by your own delays that have further complicated and aged the files thereby making the documentation concerns worse. My lawyer now has no desire to support me in the pursuit of workers' compensation medical benefits for the past where such contamination of a file exists. Therefore, I have concluded that hearings and litigation to collect from Blaster's workers' compensation insurance are futile. You have a copy of the fraud report and a copy of the Blaster status report of medical bills I sent you in 3/2000, along with other reports and correspondence about workers' compensation insurance that you received from me or directly from Blaster.

Finally, the arbitration and court cases you sent to me do not apply to my situation since my expenses are not excessive or unnecessary, they were formally prescribed by reputable doctors as noted above, and all bills were submitted and denied by workers' compensation insurance for reasons other than reasonableness or necessity. Further, according to Wolf copied in your letter, once "Country Garden received reasonable proof of [my] losses, the burden [is] on [CG] to establish [I] am not entitled to benefits." It seems that you keep asking me for proof, whereas case law says you must either disprove or pay benefits. Finally, any arbitration or litigation relative to my claim would have to occur in Ohio where "[a]ny disputes between insurers regarding the obligation to defend shall be settled without expense to the insured by agreement between the insurers involved or, if they fail to agree, by arbitration or a declaratory judgment proceeding."

With the above review of appropriate policy contract provisions and statutory reference with respect to my medical bills, I ask that you immediately pay $2,759 for the medical bills that I have paid and previously submitted to you (reference my 03/03/2000 and

302

04/26/2000 letters that show I directly paid $6,893 of medical bills related to the car accident. From that, subtract the $4,134 that CG reimbursed to me in 06/2000). Further, I ask that you immediately pay all medical bills that you received in 2000 and those that are forwarded to your office in the future whether or not denied by workers' compensation insurance. A current status of my CG claim is summarized in Attachment II for your immediate payment under my no-fault insurance policy.

With so much struggling over insurance benefits, when you <u>look beyond questions of contracts and law, there are other issues of a more personal and heartfelt consideration</u>. These issues not only have an impact for me but for many other people injured who need insurance benefits to help them heal but instead suffer more because of deny/delay tactics used by large companies like CG. Most other people are unable to ask the questions and/or request satisfaction from their insurance companies for the benefits they were promised in the policies they purchased. Please help me understand how you are being "fair and reasonable" in the context of the above and your aggressive position of arbitration or litigation before you pay the benefits promised in my no-fault insurance policy. Your demands to me to either arbitrate or litigate are very difficult alternatives for an injured and disabled person to pursue, and very expensive with respect to legal fees (also, in my situation, contrary to Ohio law as noted above). Further, more than once CG delayed paying me "no-fault" wage loss and medical benefits so your lawyers could review my claim for several weeks and months. Meanwhile I was forced to struggle with you during many argumentative phone calls while medical care was delayed and my pain exacerbated. Yet, as noted above, your legal position is incorrect even with all the legal reviews. Was this delay simply a tactic to discourage my claim or perhaps manage cash flow and improve profits at the expense of your insured? Indeed, I understand the need for companies to manage their expenses and cash flow, but how can CG do so on the backs of their injured and disabled insureds? Yes, you eventually paid my wage loss claim but took the cash flow benefit for your company at my expense, about $2,000 for each year the benefits were delayed.

The same is true for medical bills where the time value of the benefits you delayed was several hundred dollars. While there is little CG can do about the added suffering that your benefits process caused me as your injured insured, CG should at least pay me and other insureds for "interest" when your delays prove unnecessary in the end.

While I understand that many companies are not very open to other stakeholders of their company questioning their business practices, including their insureds or customers, I continue to ask that CG pursue an approach of partnering with their insureds. Note how the benefits of partnering can accrue to CG as well as the insured. For example, I pay cash for massage therapy, thereby saving 20 percent as a cash discount that I pass on to CG. I also question all medical care suggested by my health care providers to be sure we are considering the most cost-effective approach, including the medications chosen for ongoing pain management. I challenged my health care provider when she suggested medications with a cost of $200 per month and a long-term view for help with my symptoms. Without a guarantee or promise of resolving my symptoms, we opted for less expensive medications at a cost of about $50 per month. Indeed, CG could also save a lot of expense associated with internal legal reviews in pursuit of excuses to deny benefits. Why not use this money to pay for medical care for your injured insureds? There may be more CG and your insureds can do to work together to reduce medical expenses while, at the same time, your insureds receive the medical care they need in a timely manner.

The above only covers the no-fault portion of my insurance policy and claim with CG. You have yet to respond to my attorney's request related to my uninsured/underinsured motorist claim where a preliminary conservative evaluation by experts shows my loss of earning capacity, alone, calculated at $1.5 million. I have many other losses from this car accident to consider and resolve, along with ongoing medical expenses for my permanent disability. As you can imagine, I need the help of the insurance policies I purchased from CG. Yet, while I have been your customer and insured for almost fifteen years, you now respond to my first significant need for benefits by denying/delaying benefits and increasing my suffering, as I struggle over insurance benefits and delay much needed medical care. Many times I had no choice but to pay medical bills out of my retirement savings that CG should have paid. Further, CG demanding difficult and expensive arbitration or litigation for benefits promised to an individual suffering with an injury and disability is untenable in my opinion. And, even though I have been diagnosed with a permanent disability, CG continues to hold a further threat of denial for the minimal benefits that you are paying with comments like "we will continue to pay your prescription charges until we determine these ongoing prescriptions are not necessary for the injuries suffered in this motor vehicle accident." What tactic will be next and when? Is not insurance supposed to provide for some level of security as a safety net when the insured is injured and/or disabled? Unfortunately, the opposite is many times the case and now seems true for my claim for CG no-fault insurance benefits.

I look forward to your response to this letter that will help me decide my next steps and if my protection for the future with CG is acceptable to me, as well as the story that I will share with others as a responsible and cautionary notice about your insurance company.

Sincerely,

Michael J. Werb
HEYWER LLC
Enclosures

c: Attorney Law
c: Attorney Land

Appendix 21

Michael J. Werb
Address
City, State, Zip
Telephone
Email address

07/13/2001

Minnesota Attorney General
Address
City, State, Zip

RE: Country Garden Insurance
        File No: 5555555555

Dear Sir/Madam:

Thank you for your letter dated 07/12/2001, regarding my complaint with respect to Country Garden Insurance. I have reviewed Country Garden's response and would like to offer the following comments and ask for your continued support of my complaint.

In general, I believe the business practices used by Country Garden are as bad or possibly worse than those the Attorney General office has recently investigated and publicized. I have more than twenty years experience as a business manager, and finance and contracts expert including as a former board member of the National Contracts Management Association and member of the Financial Executives Institute. Contract law and ethical business practices were a key responsibility of these professional organizations. Now I work as a part time professor of business management at St. Cloud State

University. During this entire time, I have experience with companies like Country Garden with similar disregard for their contract commitments, the law, reasonable business practices, and basic human compassion. Once discovered, they were required to make substantive changes to their business practices. I hope that you will consider my situation worthy of your detailed review of my records and those of Country Garden in order to draw a reasonable conclusion with respect to my complaint about Country Garden.

More specifically, with regard to the Country Garden's comments in the same order as in their letter dated 07/02/2001 to you, Country Garden indicated "in May 1999 that [I] turned to [Country Garden] and demanded [they] step into the shoes of [my] Workers' Compensation carrier and satisfy all unpaid and disputed charges." This was two years after the car accident when workers' compensation and Country Garden had each paid about $200 of approximately $25,000 of medical bills for this accident. They had both taken the position that the other was responsible for my medical bills. I pleaded, not demanded as noted in the Country Garden letter, with Country Garden to work with Blaster, my former employer, who is self-insured for workers' compensation insurance, to determine who was responsible for my medical bills. This request is in concert with Ohio statutory law with regard to multiple insurance sources for an injury where the insurers, not the insured, has the responsibility to sort out these issues. My plea was a reasonable request for someone suffering with a permanent and total disability, significant medical bills, and very little source of income.

After I proved I had coverage with Country Garden, despite their initial assertion that I did not, I worked diligently with an individual at Country Garden to recover benefits. He seemed to be struggling with the Country Garden requirements and practices of long legal reviews and overwhelming documentation just as I was. A year later, Country Garden paid over $4,000 of my medical bills with a commitment to review the other outstanding medical bills and pay for my medical bills in the future. This individual at Country Garden was replaced by another who then took the position that "the

Minnesota No-Fault plan ... does not allow [Country Garden] to substitute benefits payable under the Workers' Compensation system." Please note in Country Garden's response that they continue to also hold a position that Minnesota law is applicable for no-fault insurance benefits whereas Ohio law is applicable for my underinsured and uninsured motorist claim. Country Garden appears to be inappropriately applying Minnesota law to my no-fault claim which, when compared to the workers' compensation system in Ohio, results in neither Country Garden or Blaster being responsible for my medical bills. A key provision in the Ohio workers' compensation system is the option for employers to grant approvals for medical care. Without these approvals, the employer is not required to pay benefits. Blaster has never approved any of my medical care. This is their standard practice for Workers' Compensation claims. Country Garden has continued to assert their position while no longer considering other medical bills of the past and many of my current medical bills except for prescriptions and massage therapy. Because of the lack of benefits from these insurance sources, I have paid many medical bills on my own and continue to forego much needed medical treatment that could possibly permit me to work more than my current limit of ten hours a week.

In their letter, Country Garden also made reference to a one million dollar umbrella policy that I had in effect at the time of the accident. First note that I have in writing that Country Garden denied that I even had an umbrella policy in effect until just recently. This was one more of several lies that I have had to disprove. Country Garden now claims that additional "coverage for underinsured and uninsured coverages" was declined at the inception of this policy. This is true when I signed up for the policy in 1994. Yet I am fairly certain that I changed this coverage prior to the accident. Unfortunately, many of my records were lost when I moved to Ohio, which was coincidentally in the same month as the car accident. I have seriously regretted my loss of records, yet it has generally highlighted the lengths that Country Garden will go to in order to avoid their responsibility to me as their insured. To adequately address the umbrella policy coverage issue, I have asked for Country Garden to tie out the premiums I paid in 04/1997 that were taken out of my checking account to the premiums for each of the policies I had in effect at that time. We can then look at the policies and determine exactly what coverage I had at the time of the accident. Country Garden did not mention this request in their response, which leaves me suspicious. As a former business executive disabled from the car accident with needs for ongoing medical care, my loss from the car accident was conservatively estimated by experts at more than $1.5 million. Country Garden indicated they are working directly with my attorney to resolve the umbrella policy coverage issue. This is unacceptable to me yet I have no other choice since they refuse to tie out the premiums I paid with the policies I had purchased from them at the time of the accident. The need for a third party to tie out the premiums I paid with my policies in effect at the time of the accident was one of the requests I made of the Attorney General's office in my complaint. Please consider again my request for you to audit the records of Country Garden in this regard.

I was Country Garden's insured for more than a dozen years for several insurance policies where I paid my premiums on time. I expected that if I ever experienced a tragedy like the accident on 04/30/1997 that the insurance benefits would be there to pay my medical bills and help me with my lost wages as I recovered. Country Garden has not honored their end of the agreement by engaging in fraudulent and deceitful tactics, as well as long legal reviews and other excuses. I had no choice but to file a claim in court. The money spent on lawyers and litigation could be better spent paying benefits to their insureds, including me. Please seriously consider all the issues identified in my complaint and this letter and request Country Garden make substantive improvements to their business practices.

A recent example, on 07/06/2001, I was deposed by Country Garden and two other insurance companies with respect to my underinsured and uninsured claim. I was previously deposed for six hours when my entire life was reviewed in detail and documented for these lawyers to review. Their agreement going into the deposition on

07/06/2001 was to focus on the circumstances specific to the car accident itself and avoid wasting time by again reviewing the details of my background. Unfortunately, the Country Garden attorney chose to review the background details, which turned an estimated one-hour deposition into two and a half hours. As a result, I experienced intense pain and other symptoms of my injury that was not only unnecessary but made it very difficult for me to respond to questions with clarity and precision. This legal tactic was absolutely unnecessary. It disappoints me that the insurance company with whom I entrusted so much of my safety net for so many years would do such a thing.

As you can see from the above, I am not satisfied with the Country Garden response to my complaint to the Attorney General. Please continue to support me in any way you can to not only request the benefits that I was promised in my insurance policy with Country Garden but also to request Country Garden review and improve their business practices for all their insureds of today and into the future for all their insureds. Thank you.

Sincerely,

Michael J. Werb

Appendix 22

Michael J. Werb
Address
City, State, Zip
Telephone
Email address

01/19/2001

Dr. Norton
Address
City, State, Zip

Dear Dr. Norton:

Thank you for your help with both my medical care and the paperwork for insurance benefits. Since my injury was caused by a work-related automobile accident, there are paperwork requirements needed for both sources of insurance benefits. Unfortunately, each has suggested the other is responsible with Country Garden Insurance (CG) paying $5,200 and Blaster workers' compensation insurance (WCI) paying $1,000 of about $30,000 of medical bills. Fortunately, my health care insurance has paid most of the balance and I have paid the rest, which I hope to recover from CG or WCI.

I would like to continue under your medical care and for you to become my "physician of record" for workers' compensation insurance replacing Dr. Bell. This will increase the probability of WCI paying your bills. If you agree, please sign and return the enclosed approval of "Work Restrictions and Daily Pain Management Program" that Dr. Bell signed on 11/01/2000, and your nurse practitioner reviewed and initialed in 10/2000.

Pending your reply, I will bring the additional WCI forms for your review and completion at my next MPS office visit.

According to MPS', Dr. Bell's, and Dr. Sun's recommendations for medical care, I plan to continue with the attached pain management program, medications from MPS, massage therapy weekly, and facet injections from MPS this summer. I have delayed the facet injections in order to complete the paperwork and get the approvals for insurance recovery. More importantly, my work and pain management is a delicate balance. Added medical procedures, like the trigger point injections and change in medications last summer with MPS, result in a high-risk inability to function that could jeopardize my part-time employment at the university. So I will wait for summer break from school to have the injections.

Please also note that I have a personal injury lawsuit that may come to trial this spring and I will ask for your support there too.

Thank you.

Sincerely,

Michael J. Werb
Enclosure

Appendix 23

HEARING RESPONSE

Thank you for letting me read these comments. The travel to get here and time of day makes the pain worse and difficult for me to answer questions completely. The following covers the last four years since my injury and some comparison to before the injury to help everyone understand my situation better **and address concerns raised at the 03/2001 hearing**.

The issues for denial were: "The District Hearing Officer does not find sufficient medical evidence to indicate that the claimant's diminishment in wages is a direct result of physical restrictions caused by the injury ... The claimant resumed his former position of employment for approximately ten months after his injury. He was terminated from his employment with the employer on 07/30/1998. From the affidavit prepared by the claimant and approved by his doctor, the claimant appears to be limited in his capacity for employment due to non-allowed psychological conditions in this claim, per the notarized affidavit by the claimant and approved by Dr. Bell on 11/01/2000."

1) About the comment that "the claimant resumed his former position of employment for approximately ten months after his injury:"

I returned to work the day after the accident and was helped with my job by people at Blaster and the activities I was engaged in dropped off dramatically. The five months in Ohio prior to the accident, there was the usual overtime along with a number of special projects, including a strategic plan, an offsite management conference where I gave a presentation on cash flow management, a complete rebudgeting for the division, year-end closing, separate corporate operations and financial reviews, interviews for staffing, frequent travel, and more. After the accident, I was helped a lot by people at Blaster and the projects dropped off significantly. Other than a rebudget in the fall and year-end closing, there were no significant projects, special projects,

313

and/or much travel during the next 9½ months until I was put on a medical leave by my doctor 02/18/1998.

I reviewed my large stack of medical bills along with my 1997 and 1998 calendars for the 9½-month period. A significant amount of time in the mornings and afternoons was spent either with doctor visits or in physical therapy. I also went home most days at lunch so I could apply heat and/or ice to my back depending upon the approach that was suggested by my medical care providers. I usually left work by 11:30 a.m. and tried to return to work by 1 p.m. Looking at my medical records, I went to see Dr. Smith several times, I went for a CT scan in May, I saw Dr. Hunt or his partner numerous times, and I had physical therapy a couple of times a week in the afternoons under Dr. Hunt's supervision during the months of July and August of 1997. In November, I started to see Dr. Lee for chiropractic-type adjustments suggested by Dr. Hunt while also going to Dr. Hunt for emergency trigger point injections. Approximately once a week for a couple of months, I went for physical therapy in Dr. Lee's office and adjustments. I went to see a psychologist in January and February of 1998 three times. For massage therapy, I generally went right after work, usually leaving a few minutes early at least once a week for a number of months. All this time, the medication that I was taking left me in a drug stupor.

The time I spent at work dropped off significantly. How was that possible? I frequently reviewed with my supervisor, a VP General Manager, that my time available for work, energy level and intuition were much less because of the pain, medications, and medical care so I was unable to get involved in as many issues as I had prior to the accident. He was helpful by accommodating the number of doctors' appointments and my going home every day at lunch. The other controller at the location was a long-term Blaster employee who also picked up some of my responsibilities. Soon after I started working in Ohio, I had hired a very talented senior accountant to assist me and since she was up to speed, she was able to take on many of the responsibilities that I had done. And I hired another person shortly after my injury, in about the May/June time frame, and he was also able to pick up some of the lower level accounting

responsibilities within the group. **A weeks vacation in June and in October 1997, along with time off for the holidays when I did very little other than the medical treatment and relax, also helped but seemed to only buy a little more time.** In my 01/1998 performance review, my boss indicated that my performance prior to the accident was significantly better than my performance after the accident. We also spent quite a bit of time talking together and with Human Resources about finding alternative employment with lesser responsibility. Unfortunately, none was found. All along, Blaster was supportive and allowed me the time I needed to go to doctors' appointments and physical therapy, go home for rest, as well as do what I had to do at work in order to accommodate my condition. **During the 9½ months prior to my medical leave, I would estimate that on average I was working between 25 and 35 hours a week.**

Prior to the accident, I was intensely active. I lifted weights, ran every day, ran many races and marathons, traveled, socialized, "worked hard, played hard"... everything was very positive, high intensity up until the day of the accident. **Immediately after the accident, most of my personal activities stopped**. I reduced the amount of work as well as time at work, I was tired, running stopped, I tried to run slow a couple times (Hunt 07/08/1997) but couldn't continue, **and I tried to focus as much as I could on my work but the pain increased over time** while more medical care and drugs were tried as each was or became ineffective. The medical literature I have studied recently suggests that you should stop all activities until the trigger points are fully addressed, but I didn't for quite some time. That probably just hurt my recovery. There were many times when I did not work while I was at work. I usually took hour-and-a-half lunch breaks. The physical therapy helped and trigger point injections helped. But they were not long-term solutions. As the pain increased more and more, **the effectiveness of the medical care and medications was becoming less and less, until there came a point when my doctors would no longer support additional trigger point injections or other medications or medical care**. **It all came to a head when the pain increased to an unbearable level and 02/18/1998 my doctor put me on a medical leave for more aggressive therapy and medical care.**

During the period of my medical leave from 02/19/1998 through 05/19/1998, no one was hired to come in and do my job. Only one individual from corporate in Akron, Ohio, came to Troy a couple of times for a couple days during the two months to help with my job. Most of my job duties had been covered since shortly after the accident. I returned to work on 05/20/1998 as a result of Blaster's second IME who said I should "return to 40 hours a week for at least several months." The first IME by Dr. Blunder was filled with errors so Blaster hired a second IME. The Dr. Blunder IME was reviewed by Blaster Corporate Audit as part of an ethics review of the Blaster injured employee process. When I went back to work, I explained to my boss that I was concerned about returning to my job and having all the responsibilities come back to me, from him, the other controller, and the people who worked for me. He replied that I would have now to do my complete job just as Blaster had said in a letter to me. I was seeing some improvement during my doctor's eight-month medical leave, but it was cut short after only two months. I wanted to try the 40 hours a week but was concerned that I was not recovered enough to handle the required 50 to 70 hours a week to do my job.

During the two-month period that I returned to work, I tried but again did not work a 40-hour week. I was at the plant for most of the 40 hours but during lunch I went to the company exercise room to do my tailored exercises and to the nurse's office to apply heat to my back. I returned to work where many times, because of the pain and/or medication, I would close my office door, stare off into space, or sometimes lay on the floor and meditate to try to get through the pain as it continued to build and build. Sometimes I returned to the nurse's office for more heat. I saw the company nurse almost daily and the company doctor frequently. After a few weeks, the nurse suggested I attend a pain program and other treatment while the company doctor said I should reduce my hours to 30 per week. The medications that I was taking had increased to five or six Tylenol No. 3 and five or six Soma per day to a level that later the staff at the pain program said I had risked going into a coma or other physical problems from taking so much medication. I reviewed this with my boss and he said I had to do my regular job. I told him I could not but would do my best. **At the end of July, I was involuntarily terminated because of my injury. Blaster not only helped me a lot while at work, but when I was involuntarily terminated because of my injury, they helped me with severance pay. And in the severance agreement, they agreed that I could pursue workers' compensation benefits.**

After I was terminated, I attended the pain program at Valley Hospital in Dayton, Ohio, from August until mid 09/1998. After I attended the pain program, I had one interview for a part-time job but did not get hired. **I continued to look for work and finally was hired at the vocational school in Piqua in 02/1999 where I worked four hours a day, four days a week (16 hours a week). The symptoms of muscle tightness and pain increased so I had to take more medication**. To help my situation, I **took a week off after working for a month and a half and another week off a couple months later. In May, I went to see Dr. Hunt and explained how even that wasn't working and he said** that **16 hours a week was my maximum and supported my move to a warmer climate in a note he wrote**. We knew that **even 16 hours a week would require more medical care or warm weather or both**. I hoped that by moving to Florida I would be able to achieve 16 hours a week and more. About the same time, Dr. Hunt put a note in the work comp file that I could work 20 hours a week. I never did understand the inconsistency.

I took several weeks off that summer while waiting for the apartment in Florida available 09/10/1999. **My significant other packed us; we hired a mover and moved to Florida. We looked hard for jobs, but neither of us found one**. Then when I called about my COBRA health insurance running out, I found that because of the accident and my injury that I was uninsurable in Florida for health insurance. The **combination of no jobs or health insurance, along with the chance to get help from our family, said that we should move back to Minnesota**. I'm now in a health insurance risk pool because as the insurance agent explained, the life expectancy for people with injuries like mine is less, because they often develop heart conditions, blood pressure, or any number of problems related to the injury that shorten our life span. My health insurance is now $180 per month with a $1,000 deductible and the massage therapy that I need is not covered. A few thousand dollars of medical bills a year adds up.

After returning to Minnesota, I continued to aggressively search for employment. I found that I couldn't even get an interview for a part-time job so I looked at full-time employment hoping to get my foot in the door and convince them to hire me. It worked and **I was hired and taught two courses at St. Cloud State University in the fall of 2000. I quickly found that the 20 hours a week required for two courses was too much pain.** I turned to my boss at the University and we did a number of things. He and the other professors helped me out with my classes by providing me with class projects to give to the students. The students helped me with grading and other work in the classroom. I had the students do more presentations while graduate assistants proctored tests, guest speakers covered classes – anything to get through the semester. **Even with all their help, I was working about 15 hours a week and that was too much. In the spring quarter, I dropped down to one course averaging 10 hours per week and found that this works. The pain is still greater but is manageable by using the pain management and work restrictions approved by my doctors and Blaster's fifth IME.**

The try at two courses (15 to 20 hours per week) convinced my doctors and I that one course or 10 hours a week was enough. **Dr. Bell and I talked about other jobs like being a receptionist or security guard where maybe I could work more than 10 hours per week, but the flexibility of any job and body mechanics is always a concern**. **And a few more hours at the lower pay would not financially justify the change from teaching at about $20 per hour. Teaching is flexible and also keeps me close to the business world where hopefully I can eventually increase my hours over time and/or find consulting work that pays more.**

Now I have achieved a balance in my life where I work 10 hours a week, the medications are not a danger, and massage therapy helps with the symptoms. Some weeks I may work up to 12 or 13 hours, but then I have to pull back even more as the real bad pain days come as a result. **Why only 10 hours average compared to maybe 30 hours average during the 9½ months after the accident? The muscle tension and pain builds until more invasive medical care is required such as trigger point injections and medications that is an approach with health risks and only feasible in the short term**. I've tried everything suggested by my doctors, and even the Blaster IME doctors, but I keep coming back to a slow-paced recovery process.

I need financial help from workers' compensation insurance. I'm earning $5,000 to $7,000 a year now compared to over $100,000 as a controller. Of almost $30,000 in medical bills, Blaster has paid only $919 because of paperwork issues and no lost wages. Note attachment I from last year where I addressed all outstanding issues but no additional bills were paid by Blaster. Certainly the money is one thing, but I enjoyed the career and work tremendously and would love to return to it. As you can see by my job search, I tried to find similar work as an employee or consultant to work as much as possible and earn as much as I could. **I will continue to look for more recovery and work. This summer I hope to get facet pain blocks and see if that will help and try once again to increase my work** "activities."

2) In response to the non-allowed psychological conditions:

I understand the concern over psychological versus physiological. I had it too after the medical care did not work. I've researched the issue and consulted with all the doctors, medical care providers, IMEs, and others. **I've counseled with psychologists**, first on my own in 01/1998 before I went on a medical leave. The psychologist quickly **determined that it was not a psychological problem but that it was a pain issue** so she began training me on pain management techniques, including meditation and imagery. The same was true at the Valley Hospital pain management program where the interviews for the pain program include weeding out people with psychological problems to ensure success for all patients. A psychologist was on the staff to focus on pain management exclusive of psychological problems. My daily pain

319

management program was first learned when I attended the Valley Hospital pain program in August and September 1998 and was modified over time. The recent treatment plan by Dr. Bell includes medication, massage therapy, and facet blocks along with reference to the modified daily pain management program and work restrictions that he approved as appropriate for my injury.

It is not unusual for people to conclude the possibility of psychological conditions for an injury like mine. The medical information I recently received from my doctors to help me understand my disability refers to a number of other studies that span the last 40+ years. Medical research for soft tissue neck injuries, also called **cervical strain/cervical sprain**, concludes that, "the **resulting syndrome is due to damage to cervical muscles, ligament discs, blood vessels, and nerves ...** The symptom complex resulting from these injuries is often so confusing both to the physician and his patient that the specter of psychosomatic illness and secondary gain is considered." Experiments "found muscle hemorrhages and tears, ruptures of the anterior longitudinal segment, intervertebral disc disruptions ... most patients are not aware of significant injury at that moment ... a feeling of increasing tightness and stiffness gradually ensues most noticeable in the early post-injury days ... **The soft tissue injury syndrome is complicated by a wide variety of bizarre symptoms ... These include headache, ... pain in the interscapular area ... long-term follow-up studies found that complaints of interscapular pain ... carried a poor prognosis ... the injury had started the slow process of disc degeneration ..." My primary symptom, all along, mid-back pain between the shoulder blades, is referred to as the interscapular area or thoracic area where the neck muscles end.** Treatment includes "exercises to stretch muscles and increase neck motion are generally encouraged within limits of comfort ... Various forms of physical therapy are frequently used, including heat, massage, and traction ... Medication can be quite helpful ... use physical measures such as rest, support, and heat for pain relief ..." (Mason Hohl: Soft tissue Neck Injuries, 2001, Abbott-Northwestern Hospital, Mpls., MN).

"Myofascial (my-oh-fass-shall) pain syndrome (MPS) is a neuromuscular chronic pain condition with trigger points (TrPs) that can cause incapacitating, intolerable pain ... If you overextend your limits, you often have extra pain for days or weeks ... Symptoms can be severe, yet blood tests, X-ray and other common diagnostic tests do not show ... MPS. Chronic pain from a nonmalignant cause is often treated less vigorously than cancer pain, although the level of pain may be equal or worse ... Maintenance with mild narcotics ... for nonmalignant (noncancerous) chronic pain conditions is a logical, humane alternative ... (with) a program of gentle stretching and moderate exercise ... (while) no longer able to practice your profession." (*Fibromyalgia and Chronic Myofascial Pain Syndrome: A Survival Manual* by Devin J. Starlanyl, M.D. 1996.)

In direct response to the hearing officer's comment:

1) What non-allowed psychological conditions were identified in the affidavit approved by Dr. Bell? The **"tension myalgia HA" referred to in his treatment plan is muscle tension headaches that often accompany a cervical strain/cervical sprain. Dr. Bell prepared the plan in 09/2000 when I saw him and was struggling with teaching two courses at the University.**

2) In the last four years, I have been under incredible scrutiny by my doctors and Blaster's five IME doctors, lawyers and third-party administrator (who spied on me). No one has identified any behaviors and/or psychological conditions that would suggest anything other than those that were caused by the car accident.

Appendix 24

Michael J. Werb
Address
City, State, Zip
Telephone

07/12/2001

Alto Health
Address
City, State, Zip

Dear Sir/Madam:

This letter is in reference to Alto Health's file 66666666666, your summary of 12/20/1999 sent to my attorney, and all medical bills Alto Health paid on my behalf for a work-related car accident on 04/30/1997. My attorneys have advised me to write to Alto Health with the following notice:

Your rights to recovery should be against my former employer, Blaster, who is self-insured for workers' compensation insurance claims.

Please contact me if you have any questions.

Sincerely,

Michael J. Werb

c: Attorneys Law and Land

Appendix 25

01/25/2002

Ms. Mary Hagen
Third-Party Recovery Specialist
BlueCross BlueShield
Address
City, State, Zip

Subscriber I.D. Number: (Social Security Number)
Patient Name: Michael
Claim Number: 032XXXXX, 032XXXXX
Date(s) of Service: 06/15/2000 & 06/28/2000 (& 07/26/2000)
Provider Name: Medical Pain Specialists

Dear Ms. Hagen:

The above service dates were for medical care from the Medical Pain Specialists (MPS). They treated an old work injury from 04/1997 when I worked for Blaster in Troy, Ohio, who was self-insured for workers' compensation insurance. The injury was a sprain/strain of the neck and thoracic (codes 847.0 and 847.1). Blaster paid MPS for these services. MPS then informed you.

MPS is also treating me for cervicalgia (code 723.1), which is not my work injury.

Please direct any further questions to Mark Pain or Nancy Roster at MPS who has handled the insurance approvals and documentation for my medical care.

I am currently employed part time as an adjunct professor at St. Cloud State University. I receive no benefits as a part-time employee. I pay my health insurance premiums directly.

Sincerely,

Michael J. Werb
Address
City, State, Zip
Telephone

c: Mark Pain and Nancy Roster
c: Attorney Law and Land

INDEX

326

About the Author

Michael Werb and his partner, Jann Heyen, formed Heywer to be a voice and advocate for people with chronic pain. Heywer's goal is to understand and communicate survival alternatives to others in similar situations. Heartfelt stories and interviews of medical, legal, and other professionals, along with detailed research, are summarized and presented in brochures and books, on the Internet, and in public forums. Heywer addresses issues of adequate medical care, alternative medicine, lost insurance and employment benefits, future insurance protection, lost jobs, future employment alternatives, legal struggles, dignity, compassion, and more.

The key to surviving chronic pain is understanding and managing the condition, medical care, and life changes. Assertive management using a proven process holds the greatest promise for success. The author is a partner in Heywer, an adjunct professor of management at St. Cloud State University, and a management consultant. He is a former business executive and contracts expert at Honeywell, Emerson Electric, and B.F. Goodrich. He gained expertise with Total Quality Management and empowering people. He is a former board member of the National Contracts Management Association and a former member of the Financial Executives Institute and University of Minnesota Contracts Committee. In addition to his wealth of business and management experience, the author holds a Master's Degree in Business Administration. His vision and leadership, along with skills of strategy, analysis, and interpersonal relationships, were inspired by his wealth of life experience and challenges successfully met. This management talent and skill along with his accomplished chronic pain experience promises success helping others survive their own chronic pain experience.

HEYWER BOOKS AND PUBLICATIONS TO: "SURVIVE AND THRIVE," "IMPROVE YOUR ENTIRE LIFE AND LIFESTYLE," "GREATER RECOVERY," "FEEL MORE AT PEACE ... HELP MILLIONS OF PEOPLE"

____ SURVIVING THE CHRONIC PAIN EXPERIENCE: Understand and Manage Medical Care and Life Changes $15.00

____ SURVIVING THE CHRONIC PAIN EXPERIENCE: Successfully Recover Insurance Benefits and Other Promises $25.00

____ SURVIVING THE CHRONIC PAIN EXPERIENCE: The Complete Journey; Understand, Recovery, and Spirituality $50.00

____ SURVIVING THE CHRONIC PAIN EXPERIENCE: Appendixes for Recover Insurance... $8.00 (specify on paper, CD, or floppy disc)

____ Heywer Contributions (tax deductible contributions to Heywer NP) $_____ (your choice)

____ Free ... current list of Heywer books and publications

Order at www.survivingpain.com, www.heywer.com, your local bookstore (books only), or mail this form to Heywer, 11366-42nd Street, Clear Lake, MN 55319.

Please send me the above items. I am enclosing $___. (Please add $4.00 per order for shipping and handling.) Send check, money order, or credit card information (credit card name and number, name on card, expiration date month and year).

Ms./Mrs./Mr._____

Address_____

City/State/Zip_____

Prices and availability subject to change without notice. Please allow three weeks for delivery.